CHATEAUX & HOTELS DE FRANCE®

www.chateauxhotels.com

Reservation centre: 33 (0) 1 40 07 00 20

12 rue Auber 75009 Paris

Guide 2002

523 Castles, Hotels and restaurants
135 Bonnes & Grandes Tables

Bracelets Agrafe - 01 42 18 43 83

CHATEAUX & HOTELS
DE FRANCE®

Portrait d'Alain Ducasse par Vanessa Von Zitzewitz©

An enthusiasm to share

Enthusiasm, authenticity and sharing...these are the three key words that Châteaux & Hôtels de France will be enphazising in 2002. The desire to receive guests as if they were friends. The authentic style of a house and its cuisine, which is in complete harmony with the traditions of its region. Sharing a cultural heritage and a certain art de vivre that is unique to each province.

The new establishments that are featured this year share our philosophy which prizes the quality of welcome and comfort, the well-being of our guests and the exquisite food.

Our mission is to satisfy our customers and make their stay with us a really pleasurable occasion.

Once again, choosing will not be easy this year. To help you find us in the heart of the French countryside, a team of advisors at the reservations centre and an up-to-date website will be invaluable assets.

We hope to see you soon.

Alain DUCASSE
Président

Informations

Régions

Private Castles

Informations

661 *How to book!*

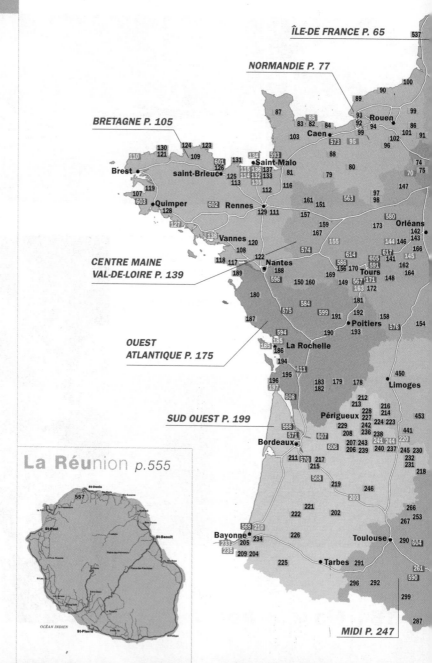

ÎLE-DE FRANCE P. 65
537

NORMANDIE P. 77

100
90
89
99
87 93 Rouen
83 82 84 85 92 94 86
103 Caen 99 101 91
102
573 95 96

BRETAGNE P. 105

130 124 123
121 109 88 80 74
110 131 134 Saint-Malo 70 75
601 115 136 137 81 79
Brest 126 114 132 133 147
saint-Brieuc 125 135 116 97 563
113 98
119 112
107 161 151
603 Quimper 602 Rennes 157
128 129 111 159 173 Orléans
127 167 142
155 143
138 Vannes 120 144 146 166
108 574 614 605 617 145
CENTRE MAINE 122 Nantes 156 170 586 591 141 162
VAL-DE-LOIRE P. 139 118 117 188 169 567 171 Tours 164
189 596 150 160 149 163 172 148
180 181
575 584 192
OUEST 187 599 191 158
ATLANTIQUE P. 175 190 193 Poitiers 154
576
594 185 La Rochelle
185 186
194 450
611 Limoges
196 195 183 179 178
197 608 182
212
213 216
228 214
Périgueux 227 224 223 453
229 242 441
SUD OUEST P. 199 566 607 208 236 238 241 244 220
571 206 207 243 240 237 245 230
Bordeaux 606 239 232
231
211 570 217 218
215
568
219
203 246
266
221 267 253
222 202
La Réunion p.555 569 210 218
Bayonne 233 205 234 226 Toulouse 290 604
557 235 209 204 290
225 Tarbes 291 261
590
296 292
299
287

MIDI P. 247

OCÉAN INDIEN

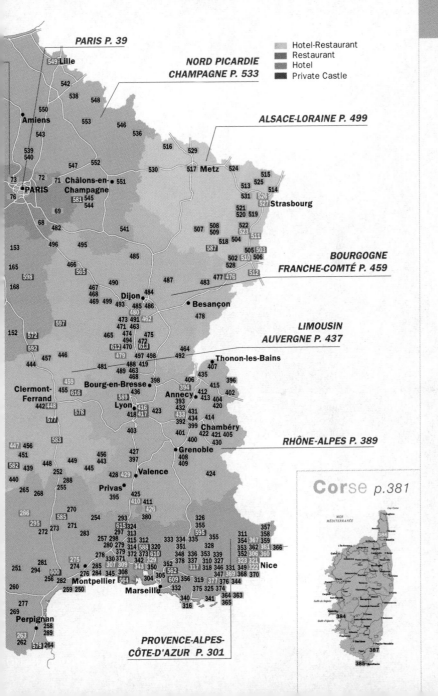

PARIS P. 39

NORD PICARDIE
CHAMPAGNE P. 533

Hotel-Restaurant
Restaurant
Hotel
Private Castle

549 Lille

542
538
548

550
Amiens
543
553   546
536

ALSACE-LORAINE P. 499

516   529

539
540
547   552
530   517 Metz   524
515
525
513   514
531 526
521 Strasbourg
521 520 519

73   72   71 Châlons-en-   551
76   PARIS   Champagne
581 545
544

507   508
509
522
523 511
518 504
587   505 503
502 510 506
528

BOURGOGNE
FRANCHE-COMTÉ P. 459

69
68
482

541
487   483   477 476
512

153
496   495
485

165
466
598   565   490

168
467   484
468   Dijon
469 499 493   485 486
480

152
572
597
467 468
469 499 493

592
465   473 491 462
471 463
474 475
494 472
612 470 613
479   497 498

464
492

Thonon-les-Bains
407

LIMOUSIN
AUVERGNE P. 437

444   457   446
481   488 419
489 463
468   435   406   396
394   412   415
393   413 404   402
420

Clermont-
Ferrand
442 448
459   455 616
Bourg-en-Bresse
436   398
589
Lyon 616
418 417   423
431   414
433 434
399 Chambéry
392   422 421 405
430

577
578

403

401   400

RHÔNE-ALPES P. 389

447 456
451   593
582 439
448   449   427   Grenoble
252 288   456   397   408
255   443   409
440   445
265   268   428 429 Valence
424

270
286   293
295 585   254   324
272 273 271   297 313
283   257 298
280 279   314 588 320
278   379 372 373 610
330 371   342 329
281   285 307 309   343 350
251   294   274 276 284 345 308   304
256 282
260   259 250   Montpellier   564
277   Marseille
269
258
Perpignan   289
263
262 575 264

326
355
595   355
333 334 335   311   357
351   328   354 387 358 359
348 336 353 339   353 362 361 366
378 310 327   306 360
352   317 318 346 331 349   323 321
562   609 356 319   347 369 368 370   Nice
332   377 376 344
375 325 374
340   341   364 363
316   365

Corse p.381

MER
MÉDITERRANÉE

386

384

387

385 Bonifacio

PROVENCE-ALPES-
CÔTE-D'AZUR P. 301

La quintessence du style Lanson

CHAMPAGNE
NOBLE CUVÉE
DE
Lanson
BRUT 1989

Charm and hospitality

From the authentic simplicity and friendliness of two helmet accommodation to outstanding places to stay, Chateaux & Hotels de France offers you the opportunity to discover some unique places at reasonable prices.

Selected according to precise and strict criteria, each establishment agrees to comply with our charter of quality :

> Attractive surroundings
> Buildings of character
> A friendly welcome
> Flawless comfort
> Authentic good food

servicequalite@chateauxhotels.com

LA PEUGEOT 607 EST

ET VOILÀ

www.607.peugeot.fr

DOTÉE D'UN FILTRE À POLLENS, À POUSSIÈRES ET À ODEURS.
QUE L'AIR VOUS PARAÎT PRESQUE PARFUMÉ.

607 PEUGEOT

LACOSTE

BECOME WHAT YOU ARE

Welcome

For the first time, Chateaux & Hotels de France steps overseas and includes an establishment on the Island of La Reunion.

And then again, if you dream of escaping to Corsica, we have gathered together our four addresses in a new chapter.

Restaurant, hotel or hotel-restaurant, here are 33 new establishments which we have selected for your pleasure, all of which strictly comply with the conditions of our charter.

NB : restaurant only

L'une des plus belles voitures au monde est un Break.

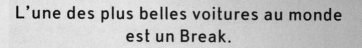

Rover 75 Tourer
À partir de 167 269,04 F / 25 500 € [1]

Modèle présenté : Rover 75 Tourer 2.0 CDT Pack avec peinture métallisée et jantes alliage Météor 17" : 191 867,43 F / 29 250 € [2]

Une nouvelle dimension du plaisir automobile vient de naître. Bénéficiant de la distinction naturelle de la berline, la Rover 75 Tourer s'impose comme l'un des plus beaux Breaks. Proposée en 3 niveaux de finition et 4 motorisations, elle allie style et praticité.

Toutes les Rover bénéficient d'une garantie de 3 ans ou 100 000 km [3].

ROVER

A CLASS OF ITS OWN°

Rover conseille

Pour connaître votre concessionnaire Rover le plus proche : www.rover.fr

(1) Prix de la Rover 75 Tourer 1.8 au 01/09/2001. (2) Tarif au 01/09/2001. (3) Garantie 3 ans ou 100 000 km au premier des termes échu . Voir conditions générales chez votre concessionnaire Rover. Taux de conversion : 1 € = 6,55957 F. *Une classe à part.

Unforgettable!

Here surroundings, welcome, decor, service and the food all reach the summit of perfection. With the exquisite taste that makes unforgettable memories.

45	Hôtel Westminster	Paris 75002
60	Saint-James Paris	Paris 75016
120	La Bretesche	Missillac
218	Château du Viguier du Roy	Figeac
211	Les Sources de Caudalie	Bordeaux-Martillac
384	Le Maquis	Ajaccio (Porticcio)
311	La Vignette Haute	Auribeau-sur-Siagne
314	La Mirande	Avignon
358	Château Eza	Nice
366	Monte Carlo Beach Hôtel	Roquebrune-Cap-Martin
418	La Tour Rose	Lyon
467	Château de Vault-de-Lugny	Avallon

The Molteni legend.

Since 1923, year after year, Molteni has been creating the best professional stoves—the dream of every great chef. A legend born of extreme attention to detail, in the tradition of ancient craftsmen, melding with the quest for strong, noble materials. The workmanship, always geared to maximum durability, combines with state of the art technology for the best results in every kind of food preparation.

This is the only way to create a high-performance, harmonic ensemble. Performance exalted by design, studied according to the latest innovations in ergonomics—taking advantage of space to maximize control and facilitate action in the kitchen. This is why Molteni stoves are the best-known among the world's greatest chefs. Dreamed of, sought after and loved, they have become a legend.

MOLTENI

France, depuis 1923

From the Electrolux Group. The world's No.1 choice.

Electrolux Professionnel SAS   43, Avenue Félix Louat   60300 Senlis   Tel. 0033 (0)3 44 62 26 25
Usine: Z.I.   9, Avenue Marc Seguin   26241 Saint-Vallier Cédex   Tel. 0033 (0)4 75 23 05 00
http://www.molteni-france.com

These talented chefs, whether for a restaurant or hotel, are masters of a ceremony in which the art of cooking is destined to delight the senses, and their vocation is to share their passion for good food with you, and to leave you with fond memories of dining at their table.

Bonnes Tables

The 120 establishments which display the Bonne Table label delightfully bring together the best fresh local produce, creating a generous cuisine. They skillfully defend our country's gourmet heritage.

Grandes Tables

Here, cooking is elevated to the highest art form and the chef, with his creative skills, knows how to create sublime dishes from rigorously selected fresh produce. The pride of the French gastronomic tradition, these Grandes Tables combine unique cuisine, atmosphere and service.

Guy Degrenne

www.guydegrenne.fr

SD-One porcelain

1 - Tahoé flatware

2 - Sundeck holloware

3 - Gastronome kitchen equipment

4 - Voltige glassware

Guy Degrenne - route d'Aunay - BP 69 VIRE cedex
tel: 00 33 2 31 66 44 00
fax: 00 33 2 31 67 78 07

Division Hotel
tel: 00 33 2 31 66 44 36
fax: 00 33 2 31 66 44 40
e-mail: exporthotel@guydegrenne.fr

Regional Classification

NB : restaurant only

Regional Classification

NB : restaurant only

Extrêmement Christofle

Christofle

CHRISTOFLE FRANCE, DIVISION ENTREPRISES
9, RUE ROYALE 75008 PARIS TEL : 01 49 33 43 75 FAX : 01 49 33 43 90

Travel - Gourmet style!

The "Promenades Gourmandes" guide* proposes 117 favorite places to visit which serve traditional French cuisine, created by talented men and women who respect the produce which is enhanced by their culinary expertise. The double page illustrating each property with photos of: the establishment, the chef, the style of cuisine and a receipe which has been especially selected for you.

This guide is intended as a culinary tour of France and is a living proof of the immense wealth of the French gastronomic heritage.

How to order this book ?

- Through the internet: www.chateauxhotels.com
- By writing to CHF, 12,rue Auber, 75009 Paris
- Price: 19.67 euros

*Only french version avaible

Ephémère depuis 1743

MOËT & CHANDON
Fondé en 1743

L'ABUS D'ALCOOL EST DANGEREUX POUR LA SANTE, CONSOMMEZ AVEC MODERATION.

A simple wish to treat yourself?
We have you in mind

Freedom to roam, desire to explore, time to dream - nothing could be easier. We have created for you a range of packages that will suit all budgets. They are readily available in most of Châteaux & Hôtels de France properties.

These packages are valid for one year, during the week or at the weekend, they offer the advantage of organizing a whole leisure program by making one single call.

For further information and to book your package:
- www.chateauxhotels.com
- Reservation Centre:
  Tél: 00 33 (0) 1 40 07 00 20
  Fax: 00 33 (0) 1 40 07 00 30
- resa@chateauxhotels.com

An original present

Easy to use, a gift voucher enables you to offer the person of your choice an original present to be used in any one of the 523 Châteaux & Hôtels de France establishments. The gift voucher can be used to pay for a meal or a full stay. The validity is for one year and transportation fees are not included in the packages.

You can choose the amount:

- **40 euros**
- **100 euros**
- **150 euros**

How to order your gift vouchers:
- www.chateauxhotels.com
- Reservation Centre:
  Tél: 00 33 (0) 1 40 07 00 20
  Fax: 00 33 (0) 1 40 07 00 30
- resa@chateauxhotels.com

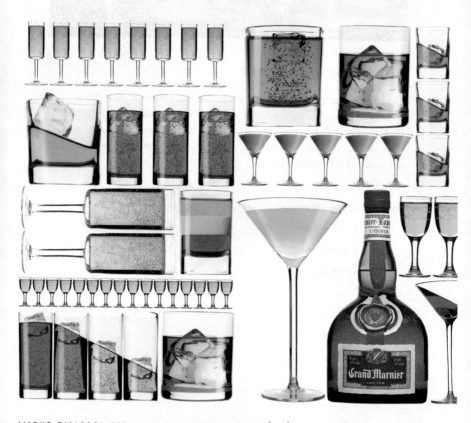

Enjoy your work in a serene and unique environment.

Certain Châteaux & hôtels de France establishments are equipped to welcome you in a unique environment which combines work and relaxation, whilst ensuring the highest quality of service that may be demanded for specific meetings.

Our business service will be able to advise you in your search according to your needs.

You can also consult the business column on our website.

How to organise your business meeting:

Business service:

- www.chateauxhotels.com
- Reservation Centre:
  Tél: 00 33 (0) 1 40 07 00 20
  Fax: 00 33 (0) 1 40 07 00 30
- resa@chateauxhotels.com

L'élégance.
La fraîcheur.
L'eau.

**L'Eau de Cologne Jean-Marie Farina
Extra-Vieille**

Incomparable Eau de Cologne
Accord originel
d'essences naturelles d'agrumes
Notes pétillantes et ensoleillées des épices
L'élégance selon Jean-Marie Farina.

DISPONIBLE DANS LES PHARMACIES,
PARFUMERIES ET GRANDS MAGASINS AGRÉÉS.

ROGER&GALLET
PARIS

SAISONS

How to chose? *www.chateauxhotels.com*

523 properties available for booking seven days a week and 24 hours a day.

With our reliable, quick and friendly website , you can :

- Use the multiple search function
- Browse the detailed introduction to each establishment
- Visualise your itinerary
- Book in real time in total security
- At any time, look at our selection of special offers

*In 2001, the website www.chateauxhotels.com was awarded the Hermes Trophy by the Hotel Industry in France.

Pouvez-vous seulement imaginer ce que peuvent vous apporter ces 46 cm^2 ?

Signe intérieur de richesse

Découvrez les avantages de la carte Diners Club

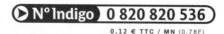
N° Indigo 0 820 820 536

0,12 € TTC / MN (0,78F)

2002, year of monetary revolution

All our prices are given in Euros as, after 18th of February 2002, all payments will be made in Euros

To help you, here below is a conversion chart:

Conversion memo:

France :	1 Euro = 6,55957 FF
Germany :	1 Euro = 1,95583 DEM
Austria :	1 Euro ≈ 13,7603 ATS
Belgium :	1 Euro = 40,3399 BEF
Spain :	1 Euro = 166,386 ESP
Finland :	1 Euro = 5,94573 FIM
Greece :	1 Euro = 340,75 GRD
Irland :	1 Euro = 0,787564 IEP
Italy :	1 Euro = 1936,27 ITL
Luxemburg :	1 Euro = 40,3399 LUF
Holland :	1 Euro = 2,20371 NLG
Portugal :	1 Euro = 200,482 PTE
United Kingdom :	1 Euro = 1,45 GBL
USA :	1 Euro = 0,89 USD
Japan :	1 Euro = 131,50 YEN

Exchange rate at 01/01/2002

Nestlé Noir. Intensément.

Hotel-Restaurant • **Hotel** • **Restaurant** • **Private castle**

Classification

Charming and friendly service

Elegance in Superior accommodation

Discretion and well being in Deluxe properties

DEMEURE D'EXCEPTION

Crowned deluxe properties, distinguished for their outstanding quality of service

Bonnes Tables

Simple but creative cuisine rooted in French tradition.

Grandes Tables

French fine dining in sumptous surroundings. This cuisine fully honors the produce and creates gastronomic gems.

Pictograms

Air-conditioning — Car park

Activities for children — Garage / Indoor car-park

Disabled access — Swimming-pool

Dogs accepted* — Tennis

Conferences — Golf

*Sometimes a charge may apply.
• Prices vary according to the type of room and the season.
• Half-board prices are per day and per person for a double room with two people and for a minimum stay of 3 days.

Toujours au sommet de son art,
Miele sublime l'encastrable.

Miele

Miele – Z.I. du Coudray – 9, av. Albert Einstein 93151 Le Blanc-Mesnil. Service Consommateurs : 0 810 233 600*.
Espace Encastrables – 55, bd Malesherbes 75008 Paris – Tél. : 01 44 90 90 00

Make life easy!

If you want a last-minute break
If you want to personnalise your trip and book each stay
If you want to find the best spot for a weekend just for two

Our reservation service benefits from a highly up-to-date IT system, even providing information on services, prices and availability of our hotels.

The reservation service can help you in your search according to your requirements, and can book your choice of hotel for you.

The reservations centre CHF is accessible from Monday to Friday between 8:30 am and 7:00 pm.

> *Reservations Centre:*
>
> - Tél : 00 33 (0) 1 40 07 00 20
> - Fax : 00 33 (0) 1 40 07 00 30
> - resa@chateauxhotels.com

for USA, UK and Germany see last page for direct number of our correspondents.

Paris New York Tokyo

Paris

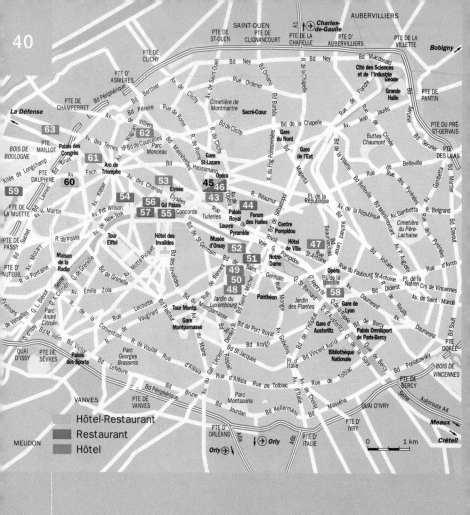

UNOPIU'

www.unopiu.fr

ESPACE UNOPIU'

PARIS PLACE DU MARCHÉ ST. HONORÉ - 75001 PARIS

EXPOSITIONS UNOPIÙ EN FRANCE:

ILE DE FRANCE 8, RUE L. DA VINCI - 78704 CONFLANS-STE. HONORINE (PARIS)

PROVENCE 286, AVENUE DU MILLET - 13782 AUBAGNE - CEDEX (MARSEILLE)

AQUITAINE 55, RUE DE TOULEYRE, R.N. 113 - 33140 CADAUJAC (BORDEAUX)

FRANKFURT · MÜNCHEN · BARCELONA · MILANO · TORINO · ALESSANDRIA · VICENZA · BOLOGNA · FIRENZE · VITERBO · TREVISO

PARTENAIRE DE TOUS VOS INSTANTS.

10, rue St-Hyacinthe 75001 Paris
Tel.: 33 (0) 1.42.61.04.17 – Fax: 33 (0) 1.49.27.91.56
tuileries@chateauxhotels.com
Jean-Jacques VIDAL
26 rooms: 120,43 € / 213,43 €
6 flats: 259,16 € / 335,39 €
Breakfast: 11,43 €

Between the Tuileries Gardens, the Louvre, the Orsay museum and Place Vendôme, an original 18th century residence. A dream comes true hotel. Exceptional situation in a peaceful little street. The former property of Marie-Antoinette's first Lady-in-Waiting. Louis XVI stayed here with the queen.

Open all year
equipments
lift, telephone, internet, T.V. Satellite, minibar, safe, baby-sitting
environment
architecture 18e, view, total calm
leisure, relaxation
jacuzzi

Visa ● Diners ● JCB ● MASTER CARD

Road map p. 619

Right Bank, dir. Place Vendôme

Orly/Charles-de-Gaulle: 35 km

Drouant
Paris

18, rue Gaillon 75002 Paris
Tel.: 33 (0) 1.42.65.15.16 – Fax: 33 (0) 1.49.24.02.15
drouant@chateauxhotels.com
Louis GRONDARD
Menu(s): 53 € / 104 € - **Carte:** 84 €

restaurant annual closing
27/07 > 25/08
equipments
lift
environment
architecture

Renoir, Rodin, Monet, Colette and Cocteau had made the renown of this old pub that became, since 1914, the sacred temple of the Goncourt Prize. The unbelievable luxuriousness of the decorations and the refined cuisine are in keeping with the image of the place: Unique!

Visa ● Diners ● JCB ● MASTER CARD

Road map p. 619

Right bank,dir. Opéra

 Orly/Charles-de-Gaulle: 25 km

13, rue de la Paix 75002 Paris

Tel.: 33 (0) 1.42.61.57.46 – Fax: 33 (0) 1.42.60.30.66
westminster@chateauxhotels.com
Volker ZACH

80 rooms: 390 € / 500 €
22 suites: 650 € / 1200 €
Breakfast: 20 €
Menu(s): 44 € / 57 € - **Carte:** 60 €

In Rue de la Paix, in the midst of the world's great names in jewellery, this luxury hotel is a fitting echo to their art. Guestrooms and suites where period furniture elegantly sets off the refined modern décor. A prestigious address when visiting Paris. Member of Warwick International Hotels.

Open all year
equipments
lift, telephone, internet, T.V. Canal+, minibar, safe, baby-sitting, valet parking, room service 24h/24
environment
architecture 19e, total calm
leisure, relaxation
beauty salon, sauna, hammam, fitness

Visa ● Diners ● JCB ● MASTER CARD

Road map p. 619

Right bank, between Opera and Vendôme place

Roissy/Charles-de-Gaulle: 25 km

Le Céladon
Paris
www.chateauxhotels.com/celadon | reservation service: 33 (0) 1.40.07.00.20

15, rue Daunou 75002 Paris
Tel.: 33 (0) 1.47.03.40.42 – Fax: 33 (0) 1.42.61.33.78
celadon@chateauxhotels.com
Alain FRANCHESQUINI
Menu(s): 44 € / 57 € - **Carte:** 60 €

restaurant annual closing
01/08 > 31/08
equipments
valet parking
environment
architecture 19e

Near the Opéra, the Céladon is the epitome of art de vivre as only the French know it. The fine food is subtly perfected by the talent of Christophe Moisand and his team. The Regency style décor, set off with Eastern touches, offers a plush charm and warm atmosphere.

Visa ● Diners ● JCB ● MASTER CARD

Road map p. 619

Right bank, between Opéra and Vendôme place

 Orly/Charles-de-Gaulle:
15 km

28, Place des Vosges 75003 Paris

Tel.: 33 (0) 1.40.29.19.19 – Fax: 33 (0) 1.40.29.19.20

reine@chateauxhotels.com

Véronique ELLINGER

33 rooms: 330 € / 385 €
22 suites: 495 € / 700 €
Breakfast: 20 €

Close to the Bastille Opera and the Picasso museum, in the heart of the historic Marais district, this elegant home, combining luxury and discretion, is found behind the arcades of the Place des Vosges. You are immediately seduced by the warmth of the atmosphere. It is a real romantic stop-over.

Open all year

equipments
lift, telephone, internet, T.V. Satellite/Canal+, minibar, safe, baby-sitting, valet parking

environment
architecture 17ᵉ, furniture 17ᵉ, garden

leisure, relaxation
tennis 2 km

Visa ● Diners ● JCB ● MASTER CARD

Road map p. 619

Right bank, Marais district

 Orly/Charles-de-Gaulle:
45 km

i Paris

Hôtel Luxembourg

Paris

www.chateauxhotels.com/luxembourg | reservation service: 33 (0) 1.40.07.00.20

4, rue de Vaugirard 75006 Paris
Tel.: 33 (0) 1.43.25.35.90 – Fax: 33 (0) 1.43.25.17.18
luxembourg@chateauxhotels.com
M. & Mme. J. MANDIN
33 rooms: 128 € / 168 €
1 flat: 228 €

Open all year
equipments
lift, telephone, internet, T.V.
Satellite, minibar, safe
environment
architecture 17e, terrace 30 m²

Located next to the Luxembourg garden, this splendid 17th century hotel has preserved the elegance of its glorious past and charm. In this former Verlaine's home, the hotel rooms are decorated with talent and make you feel the nostalgy of the legendary Paris.

Visa ● Diners ● MASTER CARD

Road map p. 619

Ring road exit "Porte d'Orléans", dir. Paris-centre

Orly/Charles-de-Gaulle:
25 km

143, Bd St Germain 75006 Paris
Tel.: 33 (0) 1.40.51.60.00 – Fax: 33 (0) 1.40.51.60.01
madison@chateauxhotels.com
Maryse BURKARD
53 rooms: 150 € / 305 €
1 suite: 380 € / 395 €

The view upon the St Germain des Près church is unique. In the heart of the Latin Quarter is a residence with living space decorated with furnishings and old paintings. The convivial atmosphere of the deliciously and joyful rooms and the warmth of the welcome illustrate all of the Parisian charm.

Open all year

equipments
lift, telephone, internet, T.V. Satellite, minibar, safe, baby-sitting

environment
architecture 19ᵉ, furniture 19ᵉ, view

leisure, relaxation
heated pool/covered, golf course 20 km, beauty salon, hammam, fitness

Visa ● Diners ● JCB ● MASTER CARD

PARIS 6ᴱ

Road map p. 619

Left bank, dir. Saint-Germain-des-Près

 Orly/Charles-de-Gaulle: 25 km

Paris

Le Clos Médicis

Paris

www.chateauxhotels.com/closmedicis | reservation service: 33 (0) 1.40.07.00.20

56, rue Monsieur-Le-Prince 75006 Paris
Tel.: 33 (0) 1.43.29.10.80 – Fax: 33 (0) 1.43.54.26.90
closmedicis@chateauxhotels.com
Olivier MEALLET
38 rooms: 125 € / 220 €
Breakfast: 10 €

Open all year
equipments
lift, telephone, internet, T.V.
Satellite, minibar, safe
environment
architecture 18e, garden,
terrace

In the heart of the Latin Quarter, a short walk from the Luxembourg gardens, the Clos was built by the Medicis in 1773. Today it is a splendid residence where Provençal-style warmth is combined with stylish contemporary design. Interior garden and lounge bar salon featuring antiques and fireplace.

Visa ● Diners ● JCB ● MASTER CARD

Road map p. 619

Ring road exit Porte d'Orléans, dir. Luxembourg

Orly/Charles-de-Gaulle: 20 km

13, rue de l'Ancienne Comédie 75006 Paris
Tel.: 33 (0) 1.40.46.79.00 – Fax: 33 (0) 1.40.46.79.09
procope@chateauxhotels.com
Gilles GRANDJEAN
Menu(s): 22 € / 28 € - **Carte:** 45 €

Right in the heart of Saint-Germain-des-Prés, at the Carrefour de l'Odéon, Le Procope, founded in 1686, is the oldest bar/restaurant in Paris. An authentic setting covering three centuries of France's history. Its 8 air-conditioned rooms are absolutely ideal for working and recreational functions.

Open all year
environment
architecture 17e, terrace

Visa • Diners • MASTER CARD

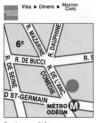

Road map p. 619

Left bank, dir. Saint-Germain-Des-Prés

Orly/Charles-de-Gaulle:
25 km

Relais Christine

Paris

www.chateauxhotels.com/christine | reservation service: 33 (0) 1.40.07.00.20

3, rue Christine 75006 Paris
Tel.: 33 (0) 1.40.51.60.80 – Fax: 33 (0) 1.40.51.60.81
christine@chateauxhotels.com
Yves MONNIN

34 rooms: 315 € / 365 €
2 flats: 700 € - **15 suites:** 490 € / 625 €
Breakfast: 20 €

Open all year
equipments
lift, telephone, internet, T.V.
Satellite/Canal+, minibar, safe,
baby-sitting, valet parking
environment
architecture 16°, furniture 17°,
garden
leisure, relaxation
tennis 2 km

In the heart of the legendary
Saint-Germain des Prés district, near the Louvre and
Notre-Dame, this superb residence retains the charm of
history. Cosy elegant guest
rooms are all individually
decorated. This is a haven of
peace set off by a beautiful
flowered garden.

Road map p. 619

Left Bank, dir. St-Germain-des-Prés

Orly/Charles-de-Gaulle:
45 km

3, rue de Ponthieu 75008 Paris
Tel.: 33 (0) 1.42.25.73.01 – Fax: 33 (0) 1.42.56.01.39
elyseesmatignon@chateauxhotels.com
Jean-François CORNILLOT – Alain MICHAUD
23 rooms: 105,2 € / 151 €
Breakfast: 9,15 €

Located in the neighbourhood of the Champs-Elysées, this magnificent Art-Deco style hotel is eminently Parisian. All rooms fully equipped with amenities are redolent of the extravagant 1920s. An inviting and dream-like spot for your next stay in the City of Light. the fashionable bar would welcome you at night.

Open all year
equipments
lift, telephone, internet, T.V. Satellite, minibar, safe
environment
architecture
leisure, relaxation
, shopping, fashion

Visa ● Diners ● JCB ● MASTER CARD

Road map p. 619
Right bank, dir. Etoile, Champs-Elysées, Concorde

 Orly/Charles-de-Gaulle:
25 km

| Paris

La Fermette Marbeuf 1900
Paris

5, rue Marbeuf 75008 Paris
Tel.: 33 (0) 1.53.23.08.00 – Fax: 33 (0) 1.53.23.08.09
marbeuf@chateauxhotels.com
M. CHEREAU
Menu(s): 23,20 € / 27,90 €

Open all year
environment
architecture 19e, terrace

Authentic turn-of-the-century restaurant, designed in 1898, included in the list of historic monuments. Sample Gilbert Isaac's cuisine: rib of veal and mushrooms simmered in a casserole, and nice Bordeaux wine list.

Visa ● Diners ● Master Card

Road map p. 619
Right rank, dir. Champs Elysées

Orly/Charles-de-Gaulle:
25 km

1, avenue Dutuit 75008 Paris
Tel.: 33 (0) 1.53.05.10.01 – Fax: 33 (0) 1.47.42.55.01
ledoyen@chateauxhotels.com
Philippe LANGLOIS
Menu(s): 57,93 € / 118,91 € - **Carte:** 129,58 €

Beneath the panelling of this magnificent Napoleonic vessel secured to the Champs Élysées, Christian Le Squer executes a cuisine in all freshness and elegance, a cuisine that lacks not spirit nor body. It is excellent indeed! The cellar is staggering and the service is impeccable.

restaurant annual closing
27/07 > 31/08
environment
architecture 19e, garden, view

Road map p. 619

In the Champs Elysées centre

 Orly/Charles-de-Gaulle:
25 km

Restaurant Lasserre
Paris
www.chateauxhotels.com/lasserre | reservation service: 33 (0) 1.40.07.00.20

17, avenue Franklin D. Roosevelt 75008 Paris
Tel.: 33 (0) 1.43.59.53.43 – Fax: 33 (0) 1.45.63.72.23
lasserre@chateauxhotels.com
Jean-Louis NOMICOS – Monsieur LOUIS
Menu(s): 55 € - **Carte:** 98 €

restaurant annual closing
04/08 > 02/09
equipments
lift, valet parking
environment
architecture 19ᵉ, furniture 19ᵉ,
view
leisure, relaxation
, musical entertainment every
evening, opening roof, near the
"Champs Elysées"

Lasserre is undoubtedly the
8th wonder of the world. For
60 years, Rene Lasserre delights his guests in aesthetically pleasing ways - from the
roof that opens on to the stars
to the supremely exquisite cuisine. One of the gastronomic
hot-spots in Paris. Exceptionally good wine-cellar.

Visa ● Diners ● JCB ● MASTER CARD

Road map p. 619

Round about Champs Elysées avenue

Orly / Charles-de-Gaulle:
25 km

25, avenue Montaigne 75008 Paris
Tel.: 33 (0) 1.53.67.65.00 – Fax: 33 (0) 1.53.67.65.12
adpa@chateauxhotels.com
Alain DUCASSE
Menu(s): 190 € / 250 €
Carte : 185 €

When Alain Ducasse moved his restaurant to the Hotel Plaza Athénée, he chose a place which would blend perfectly with the spirit of his cuisine. In tune with the rythm of the seasons, the stage is set for an array of dishes featuring first class french products combining tradition, change and modernity.

restaurant annual closing
12/07 > 20/08●20/12 > 31/12
restaurant weekly closing
mon(lun), tue(lun), wen(lun), sat, sun
environment
architecture 18e

Visa ● Diners ● JCB ● MASTER CARD

Road map p. 619

Right bank dir. Champs-Elysées roundabout or place de l'Alma

 Orly/Charles-de-Gaulle:
25 km

Pavillon Bastille
Paris
www.chateauxhotels.com/bastille | reservation service: 33 (0) 1.40.07.00.20

65, rue de Lyon 75012 Paris
Tel.: 33 (0) 1.43.43.65.65 – Fax: 33 (0) 1.43.43.96.52
bastille@chateauxhotels.com
Jean-louis CORRUBLE
24 rooms: 130 € / 130 €
1 suite: 213 €
Breakfast: 12 €

Open all year
equipments
lift, telephone, internet, T.V.
Satellite/Canal+, minibar, safe
environment
furniture contemporain

Near the Marais, facing the Bastille Opera, in a flower-filled courtyard, in the heart of the new fashionable Paris, a former town-house restored in a contemporary spirit. A court-yard full of history, warm wel-come, personalized service creating the atmosphere of a private residence.

Visa • Diners • JCB • Master Card

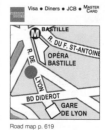

Road map p. 619
Right bank, dir. Bastille

Orly/Charles-de-Gaulle:
45 km

**Allée de Longchamp Bois de Boulogne
75016 Paris**
Tel.: 33 (0) 1.45.27.33.51 – Fax: 33 (0) 1.42.88.99.06
cascade@chateauxhotels.com
Georges MENUT
Menu(s): 54 € / 130 € - **Carte:** 95 €

*Parisians are justified in being
proud of this majestic great
waterfall so evocative of the
Belle Epoque. Richard Me-
bkhout bases his unique cuisine around matching natural
produce with harmonising flavours. Sumptuous food with
the taste of the sunny south.*

restaurant annual closing
18/02 > 18/03
equipments
valet parking
environment
architecture 19e, furniture 19e,
garden, terrace, view, total
calm

Visa ● Diners ● JCB ● MASTER CARD

Road map p. 619

Ring road exit Porte Maillot, dir. Bois
de Boulogne then Pont de Suresnes

Orly/Charles-de-Gaulle:
15 km

Saint-James Paris

Paris

www.chateauxhotels.com/saintjames | reservation service: 33 (0) 1.40.07.00.20

43, avenue Bugeaud 75116 Paris
Tel.: 33 (0) 1.44.05.81.81 – Fax: 33 (0) 1.44.05.81.82
saintjames@chateauxhotels.com
Tim GODDARD

20 rooms: 335 € / 420 €
28 suites: 550 € / 770 €
Breakfast: 20 €
Menu(s): 46 € - **Carte:** 58 €

Open all year
equipments
lift, telephone, internet, T.V.
Satellite/Canal+, minibar, safe,
baby-sitting, valet parking
environment
architecture 19°, furniture
contemporain, garden, terrace
50 m²
leisure, relaxation
tennis 1 km, sauna, solarium,
fitness, jacuzzi

*Close to the Champs-Elysées
and the Eiffel Tower, this magnificent hundred year old château invites you to indulge in
its club atmosphere. Set in a
courtyard garden, the rooms
offer calm and comfort as well
as space and light. The terrace in summer is as intimate
and warm as the library-bar in
winter.*

Visa ● Diners ● JCB ● MASTER CARD

Road map p. 619

Ring road, exit "Porte Dauphine"

Orly/Charles-de-Gaulle:
45 km

6, rue des Acacias 75017 Paris
Tel.: 33 (0) 1.58.05.10.00 – Fax: 33 (0) 1.47.54.93.43
villeetoile@chateauxhotels.com
Alain MICHAUD
15 rooms: 105,20 € / 151 €
Breakfast: 9,15 €

Charming hotel in the Etoile district, close to the Champs-Elysées. Near to everything you could wish to see in Paris, elegant setting, Art-Deco style, where hospitality rhymes with sincerity. Rooms with Minitel, cable TV, air-conditioning. Entertainment and transport bookings made, car rentals.

Open all year
equipments
lift, telephone, internet, T.V. Satellite, minibar, safe, baby-sitting
environment
architecture contemporaine, furniture contemporain, terrace

Visa ● Diners ● MASTER CARD

Road map p. 619

Right bank, dir. Etoile - Champs Elysées, Porte Maillot/Palais des Congrés

Orly/Charles-de-Gaulle: 20 km

Hôtel Eber Monceau

Paris

www.chateauxhotels.com/ebermonceau | reservation service: 33 (0) 1.40.07.00.20

18, rue Léon Jost 75017 Paris
Tel.: 33 (0) 1.46.22.12.12 – Fax: 33 (0) 1.47.63.01.01
ebermonceau@chateauxhotels.com
Martin DUPREZ – Jean-Marc EBER

13 rooms: 115 € / 140 €
5 suites: 205 € / 240 €
Breakfast: 12 €

Open all year
equipments
lift, telephone, internet, T.V.
Satellite, minibar, safe,
baby-sitting
environment
architecture 19°, total calm

A small charming hotel only two steps from the Parc Monceau and the Champs-Elysées, in a very quiet street. Comfortable rooms with cable TV and mini-bar, and large double bed. Refined breakfasts served on the patio in summer. Bar and small lounge. Paying car park 200 m away.

Visa ● Diners ● MASTER CARD

Road map p. 619

Ring road exit "Porte d'Asnières"

Orly/Charles-de-Gaulle:
20 km

5 rue Paul Deroulede 92200 Neuilly-sur-Seine
Tel.: 33 (0) 1.46.24.51.62 – Fax: 33 (0) 1.46.37.14.60
jardinneuilly@chateauxhotels.com
Danièle ROUAH
22 rooms: 114,35 € / 152,45 €
8 suites: 213,43 €
Breakfast: 14,5 €

This luxuriously renovated XIXth century mansion is synonym with elegance and originality. A short distance from the Porte Maillot and the Champs Élysées, it offers the tranquillity of its interior garden and the comfort of its antique-furnished rooms. Sumptuous breakfast served under a glassed veranda.

Visa • Diners • MASTER CARD

Road map p. 619

West ring road exit Porte Maillot (Underground "Porte Maillot" or "Sablons")

 Orly/Charles-de-Gaulle:
20 km

Open all year

equipments
lift, telephone, internet, T.V. Satellite, minibar, safe, baby-sitting

environment
architecture 19e, furniture 19e, park 3 ha, garden, terrace 30 m^2, view, total calm

leisure, relaxation
heated pool/covered, tennis 2 km, golf course 3 km, horse-riding 2 km, beauty salon, thalassotherapy, balneo, sauna, solarium, fitness, jogging (at 50 yds) in the Bois de Boulogne

68 Le Cheval Noir
69 Domaine de Fontenailles
70 Château des Berchères
71 Château des Bondons
72 Manoir de Gressy
73 Moulin d'Orgeval
74 Château de Villiers-le-Mahieu
75 Domaine du Verbois
76 Relais de Courlande

McCann

* Glenfiddich est servi au "Stag's Head"(Le Cerf), Edimbourg, Ecosse.

Glenfiddich

SINGLE MALT
SCOTCH WHISKY

La Vallée des Cerfs commence là où l'on trouve Glenfiddich.

Le Cheval Noir

Fontainebleau **I** Moret-sur-Loing
www.chateauxhotels.com/chevalnoir | reservation service: 33 (0) 1.40.07.00.20

47, avenue Jean Jaurès 77250 Moret-sur-Loing
Tel.: 33 (0) 1.60.70.80.20 – Fax: 33 (0) 1.60.70.80.21
chevalnoir@chateauxhotels.com
Gilles de CRICK
7 rooms: 61 € / 110 €
1 flat: 150 €
Breakfast: 10 €
Menu(s): 27 € / 60 € - **Carte:** 60 €
1/2 board: 69,5 € / 87 €

Open all year

equipments
telephone, internet, T.V.
Satellite, minibar

environment
architecture 18°, furniture 19°,
garden, terrace

leisure, relaxation
tennis 1 km, golf course 7 km,
horse-riding 6 km, hiking in
Fontainebleau forest

In the heart of the historic fortified town of Moret-sur-Loing, the cradle of Impressionnism, this former staging inn offers travellers a charming and romantic setting. Fine cuisine skilfully blending flavors and spices. The rooms are named after Sisley, Van Gogh, Monet etc.

Visa ● Diners ● MASTER CARD

Road map p. 619

A6 exit Fontainebleau, N6 dir. Sens

Orly/Charles-de-Gaulle:
60 km

Domaine de Bois Boudran 77370 Fontenailles
Tel.: 33 (0) 1.64.60.51.00 – Fax: 33 (0) 1.60.67.52.12

fontenailles@chateauxhotels.com
Soga MASASHI

48 rooms: 100 €
3 suites: 221 €
Breakfast: 9,5 €
Menu(s): 17 € / 40,50 € - **1/2 board:** 105 €

A unique site in the heart of Brie, less than an hour from Paris, 25 km from Fontainebleau and the mediaeval town of Provins, near Vaux-le-Vicomte château. Luxurious rooms, a naturally wooded 27-hole golf course, 240-acre park. Seasonal cuisine. Clubhouse bar, saunas, tennis courts, etc.

hotel annual closing
24/12 > 03/01
restaurant annual closing
24/12 > 03/01
equipments
lift, telephone, internet, T.V. Satellite, minibar, safe
environment
architecture 19e, park 100 ha, terrace 200 m², total calm
leisure, relaxation
horse-riding 2 km, sauna, fitness, jacuzzi, 27 hole golf course

Visa ● Diners ● JCB ● MASTER CARD

Road map p. 619

A5 exit Châtillon-la-Borde, D48 Provins Nangis

Orly/Charles-de-Gaulle: 60 km

| Île-de-France

Château de Berchères

Houdan I Berchères-sur-Vesgre
www.chateauxhotels.com/bercheres I reservation service: 33 (0) 1.40.07.00.20

18, rue du Château
28260 Berchères-sur-Vesgre
Tel.: 33 (0) 2.37.82.28.22 – Fax: 33 (0) 2.37.82.28.23

berthe res@chateauxhotels.com
Lina SCICARD – Yves BUCHIN
20 rooms: 99,09 € / 153 €
1 flat: 304,9 € / 335,39 €
Breakfast: 13,72 €

Open all year
equipments
lift, telephone, internet, T.V.
Satellite, baby-sitting

environment
architecture 18°, park 25 ha,
garden, terrace 200 m², total
calm

leisure, relaxation
golf course 6 km, horse-riding
6 km

*A haven of peace and serenity,
40 km from Paris by the A13
motorway, an 18th century
castle that speaks of history,
renovated this year around the
theme of fruit and vegetables.
60 acres of grounds, lake,
river, tranquillity, leisure activities - a place of rare enjoyment.*

Visa

Road map p. 619

A13 dir. Rouen, A12, N12 then Dir.
Dreux exit Center of Houdan, D933
dir. Anet

Île-de-France I

Orly: 68 km

47-49, rue des Bondons
77260 La Ferté-sous-Jouarre
Tel.: 33 (0) 1.60.22.00.98 – Fax: 33 (0) 1.60.22.97.01
bondons@chateauxhotels.com
Martine & Jean BUSCONI

9 rooms: 90 € / 100 €
3 flats: 100 € / 150 € - **2 suites:** 150 € / 200 €
Breakfast: 10 €
Menu(s): 39 € / 77 € - **Carte:** 51 €

XVIIIth century château in a 17.5 acre park. Rooms with bathroom, minibar, TV with Canal + and satellite channels, radio/alarm clock, hair dryer. Hearty breakfasts. 20 minutes from Eurodisneyland, 1 hour from Paris. Previously the property of G. Ornet, the author of the Maître de Forge.

Open all year
restaurant annual closing 02/01 > 06/02
equipments
telephone, internet, T.V. Satellite/Canal+, minibar, safe
environment
architecture 18e, park 7 ha, garden, terrace, total calm
leisure, relaxation
tennis 1 km, golf course 20 km, horse-riding 1 km, jacuzzi, bicycles

Visa ● Diners ● MASTER CARD

Road map p. 619

A4 exit 18 La Ferté-sous-Jouarre - N3 dir. Châlons

 Orly/Charles-de-Gaulle: 60 km

| Île-de-France

Manoir de Gressy
Roissy ı Gressy-en-France
www.chateauxhotels.com/gressy ı reservation service: 33 (0) 1.40.07.00.20

77410 Gressy-en-France
Tel.: 33 (0) 1.60.26.68.00 – Fax: 33 (0) 1.60.26.45.46
gressy@chateauxhotels.com
Véronique POITRAULT
85 rooms: 200 € / 260 €
5 suites: 260 €
Breakfast: 15 €
Menu(s): 33 € - **Carte:** 42 €

Open all year
equipments
lift, telephone, internet, T.V.
Satellite, baby-sitting
environment
architecture 17e, garden,
terrace 200 m^2
leisure, relaxation
heated pool, golf course 8 km,
horse-riding 10 km, sauna,
open-air lunch and ballroom
dancing at a guingette on the
banks of the Marne, mountain
bike, canoeing

*Located in the peaceful village
of Gressy, just 10 min from
Charles de Gaulle airport, Le
Manoir is a must for your week
ends, business meetings, or
as a stop-over for a restful
night. Discover the flavours of
the French cuisine at Le Cel-
lier du Manoir. Ideal for visiting
Paris and the region.*

Visa ● Diners ● JCB ● Master Card

Road map p. 619

A1-A3-A104, N2 dir. Soissons, exit ZI
de Mitry Compans, D212 exit Gressy

 Orly/Charles-de-Gaulle:
30 km

Moulin d'Orgeval
Saint-Germain-en-Laye | Orgeval
www.chateauxhotels.com/orgeval | reservation service: 33 (0) 1.40.07.00.20

73

Rue de l'Abbaye 78630 Orgeval
Tel.: 33 (0) 1.39.75.85.74 – Fax: 33 (0) 1.39.75.48.52
orgeval@chateauxhotels.com
Liliane DOUVIER
12 rooms: 114 € / 135 €
2 flats: 225 € / 250 €
Breakfast: 13 €
Menu(s): 36 € / 64 € - **Carte:** 53,5 € -
1/2 board: 115 € / 136 €

*28 km from Paris by the A13
highway, in a natural and luxu-
riant setting, a privileged world
amidst silence and birdsong.
Warm welcome, refined table,
individually decorated rooms,
tranquil and bright, all looking
onto a natural park. Rest, serenity, delicious cuisine.*

restaurant annual closing
20/12 > 06/01
restaurant weekly closing
sun(ev)
01/11 > 15/04
equipments
telephone, internet, T.V.,
minibar
environment
architecture, park 5 ha, terrace
110 m², total calm
leisure, relaxation
heated pool, tennis 5 km, golf
course 5 km, horse-riding
5 km, sauna

Visa ● Diners ● JCB ● MASTER
CARD

■ GOLF
D 153
D113
A14
✝
A 13
● **ORGEVAL**

Road map p. 619

A13 or A14 exit Poissy/Orgeval then
N13

Orly/Charles-de-Gaulle:
45 km

| Île-de-France

Château de Villiers-le-Mahieu

Thoiry **I** Villiers-le-Mahieu

www.chateauxhotels.com/villiersmahieu | reservation service: 33 (0) 1.40.07.00.20

78770 Villiers-le-Mahieu

Tel.: 33 (0) 1.34.87.44.25 – Fax: 33 (0) 1.34.87.44.40

villiersmahieu@chateauxhotels.com

Frédéric PESY

80 rooms: 121 € / 200 €

Breakfast: 14 €

Meals only for seminairs, banquets and groups.

hotel annual closing
22/12 > 03/01

equipments
lift, telephone, internet, T.V.
Satellite, minibar, safe

environment
architecture 13^e, park 20 ha,
garden, terrace 900 m^2, view,
total calm

leisure, relaxation
heated pool, golf course 8 km,
horse-riding 10 km

40 km from Paris, surrounded by a moat, this 13 th century medieval castle is situated in a 28-acre wooded park. Unique, spacious bedrooms provide all modern comforts. Charm and calm combined with quality service are the main attractions of this refined spot. Heated pool, tennis. Golf nearby.

Visa ● Diners ● MASTER CARD

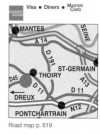

Road map p. 619

A13 then A12, N12, exit Pontchartrain/Thoiry/Villiers

Orly/Charles-de-Gaulle: 50/70 km

38, av. de la République
78640 Neauphle-le-Château
Tel.: 33 (0) 1.34.89.11.78 – Fax: 33 (0) 1.34.89.57.33
verbois @chateauxhotels.com
Eva & Kenneth BOONE
18 rooms: 90 € / 115 €
2 suites: 151 €
Breakfast: 11 €
Menu(s): 30 € - **Carte:** 45 € - **1/2 board:** 86 € / 99 €

29 km guest of Paris by high-
way. This 19 century estate,
overlooking the valley in a
charming village, invites you to
discover its Individually deco-
rated rooms and its privileged
welcome. Gastronomy in har-
mony with the seasons.

hotel annual closing
12/08 > 23/08 • 21/12 > 27/12
restaurant annual closing
12/08 > 23/08
equipments
telephone, internet, T.V.
Satellite, minibar, baby-sitting
environment
architecture 19ᵉ, furniture 18ᵉ,
park 3 ha, garden, terrace
140 m², view, vegetable
garden
leisure, relaxation
golf course 2 km

Visa ● Diners ● JCB ● MASTER CARD

NEAUPHLE-LE-CHÂTEAU
ROUEN PARIS
A 13
BOIS-D'ARCY
PONTCHARTRAIN
A 12
A 86
N 12
CD 912
ÉLANCOURT
VERSAILLES
N 10
TRAPPES

Road map p. 619

A13 then A12 then N12 exit Neauphle
dir. Dreux

Orly: 30 km

Relais de Courlande
Versailles ı Les Loges-en-Josas
www.chateauxhotels.com/courlande ı reservation service: 33 (0) 1.40.07.00.20

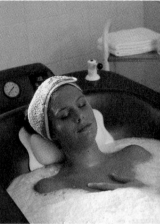

23, rue de la Division Leclerc
78350 Les Loges-en-Josas
Tel.: 33 (0) 1.30.83.84.00 – Fax: 33 (0) 1.39.56.06.72
courlande@chateauxhotels.com
Alain GRANCHAMP

51 rooms: 75 € / 138 €
2 suites: 182 €
Breakfast: 10 €
Menu(s): 27,5 € / 58 € - **Carte:** 48,8 €
1/2 board: 79,5 € / 95,5 €

Open all year
equipments
lift, telephone, internet, T.V.
Satellite
environment
architecture contemporaine,
park 2 ha, garden, terrace
100 m², total calm
leisure, relaxation
tennis 0.1 km, golf course
5 km, horse-riding 2 km,
beauty salon, balneo, sauna,
solarium

4 kilometers from the Château of Versailles, a manor farm-house built in the time of Louis XIV which has been converted into a convivial restaurant, offering the best of traditional fare. Among the amenities of the modern quiet and comfortable hotel is a balneotherapy and beauty treatment complex.

Visa ● Diners ● JCB ● MASTER CARD

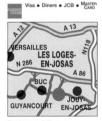

Road map p. 619

N118 then A86 exit Versailles / Jouy
en Josas

 Orly: 20 km

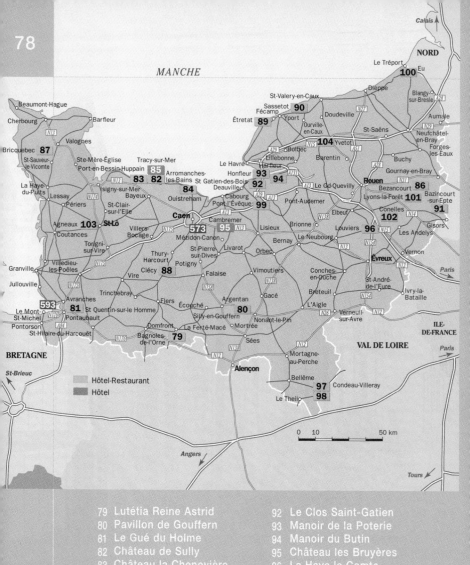

Boulevard Paul Chalvet
61140 Bagnoles-de-l'Orne
Tel.: 33 (0) 2.33.37.94.77 – Fax: 33 (0) 2.33.30.09.87
reineastrid@chateauxhotels.com
Olivier GOSSIN – Denise LEDUC
30 rooms: 55 € / 109 €
Breakfast: 9 €
Menu(s): 22 € / 57 € - **Carte:** 36 € -
1/2 board: 68 € / 83 €

A 1900's hotel in its calm flower garden, in a residential district, and situated near the center of the resort. Comfortable, individually decorated rooms, pastel couloured restaurant to savour a refined cuisine. A charming stopover.

hotel annual closing
15/10 > 25/03
restaurant annual closing
10/10 > 10/04
equipments
lift, telephone, T.V.
environment
architecture 1930, garden, terrace, view
leisure, relaxation
golf course 3 km, horse-riding 2 km, beauty salon, thermal baths, heated pool and tennis at 50 m

Visa ● Diners ● MASTER CARD

Road map p. 619

N12, From Caen, D562 dir. Flers, D18 dir. Bagnoles de l'Orne

Caen-Carpiquet: 85 km

Pavillon de Gouffern

Argentan **I** Silly-en-Gouffern

www.chateauxhotels.com/gouffern I reservation service: 33 (0) 1.40.07.00.20

61310 Silly-en-Gouffern

Tel.: 33 (0) 2.33.36.64.26 – Fax: 33 (0) 2.33.36.53.81

gouffern@chateauxhotels.com
M. TERNYNCK-THOMAS

19 rooms: 42 € / 76,5 €
1 suite: 106 €
Breakfast: 8 €
Menu(s): 14,5 € / 32 € - **Carte:** 38 €
1/2 board: 49,55 €

Open all year
hotel weekly closing
sun(ev)
15/11 > 15/04
restaurant weekly closing
mon(lun), sun(ev)
15/11 > 15/04
equipments
telephone, internet, T.V.
Canal+, baby-sitting
environment
architecture 18°, furniture
contemporain, park 80 ha,
garden, view, total calm
leisure, relaxation
golf course 7 km, horse-riding
5 km

In the charming and rich Normandie, a typical 18th and 19th century hunting lodge, set in its 200-acre wooden park. Comfort, tranquillity and the pleasure of the great french traditionnal cuisine...

Visa ● Diners ● MASTER CARD

SILLY-EN-GOUFFERN

LE BOURG-SAINT-LÉONARD

N 26

LE PIN AU HARAS

N 26

ORNE

ALMENÈCHES

Road map p. 619

A11 exit La Ferté Bernard - N26 dir.
Argentan-L'Aigle

 Caen: 50 km

14, rue des Estuaires
50220 St-Quentin-sur-le-Homme
Tel.: 33 (0) 2.33.60.63.76 – Fax: 33 (0) 2.33.60.06.77
holme@chateauxhotels.com
Annie & Michel LEROUX
10 rooms: 64,03 € / 83,85 €
Breakfast: 9,15 €
Menu(s): 24,40 € / 53,36 € - **Carte:** 56,42 € -
1/2 board: 77 € / 99,10 €

Between Normandie and Bretagne, near the bay of the splendid Mont Saint-Michel, the hotel enjoys the peaceful setting of a small village. Guestrooms are stylishly decorated, all overlooking the garden. Gastronomic specialities inspired by the sea.

hotel annual closing
02/01 > 25/01
restaurant annual closing
02/01 > 24/01
equipments
telephone, internet, T.V., safe
environment
garden, terrace, total calm
leisure, relaxation
golf course 30 km, horse-riding 2 km

Visa ● Diners ● MASTER CARD

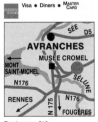

Road map p. 619

A13 exit Caen - N175 dir. Mont-St-Michel

Rennes: 80 km

ı Normandie

Château de Sully

Bayeux
www.chateauxhotels.com/sully | reservation service: 33 (0) 1.40.07.00.20

Route de Port-en-Bessin 14400 Bayeux
Tel.: 33 (0) 2.31.22.29.48 – Fax: 33 (0) 2.31.22.64.77
sully@chateauxhotels.com
Inka & Antoine BRAULT
22 rooms: 90 € / 131 €
Breakfast: 11 €
Menu(s): 28 € / 60 € - **Carte:** 36 €
1/2 board: 87,5 € / 108 €

hotel annual closing
25/11 > 10/03
restaurant annual closing
25/11 > 10/03
equipments
telephone, T.V. Satellite
environment
architecture 18e, park 3 ha,
garden
leisure, relaxation
heated pool/covered, golf
course 5 km, horse-riding 5 km

This 18th century château is situated between Bayeux and the Normandy landing beaches. Ancient charm and modern comfort in the renovated rooms (château and annex), overlooking the old large park. Gourmet restaurant with sea food, terroir and market products.

Visa ● Diners ● MasterCard

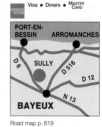

Road map p. 619

A13 exit Caen - N13 dir. Bayeux then
Port-en-Bessin

 Caen-Carpiquet: 25 km

Château La Chenevière
Bayeux I Port-en-Bessin
www.chateauxhotels.com/cheneviere I reservation service: 33 (0) 1.40.07.00.20

83

Escures-Commes 14520 Port-en-Bessin
Tel.: 33 (0) 2.31.51.25.25 – Fax: 33 (0) 2.31.51.25.20
cheneviere@chateauxhotels.com
Claude ESPRABENS

13 rooms: 150 € / 240 €
3 suites: 280 € / 350 €
Breakfast: 15 €
Menu(s): 40 € / 65 € - **Carte:** 31 € -
1/2 board: 131,5 € / 176,5 €

This Norman château, surrounded by forested grounds, is a refuge of peace and verdure. The elegant and spacious rooms are decorated with floral motifs while the radiant cuisine of Claude Esprabens plays with the seasons and foods from the sea.

hotel annual closing
03/01 > 12/02
restaurant annual closing
03/01 > 12/02
restaurant weekly closing
mon(lun), tue(lun)
12/02 > 03/01
mon(lun), tue(lun)
12/02 > 03/01
equipments
lift, telephone, internet, T.V.
Satellite, minibar, baby-sitting
environment
architecture 18e, furniture
contemporain, park 3 ha,
garden, terrace 145 m², view,
vegetable garden, total calm
leisure, relaxation
tennis 1 km, golf course 1 km,
horse-riding 1 km

Visa ● Diners ● JCB ● MASTER CARD

PORT-EN-BESSIN
ARROMANCHES
D 514
LONGUES-S-MER
D 6
N 13
D 516
ST-LÔ
BAYEUX
CAEN
N175 - A13

Road map p. 619

A13 dir. Cherbourg, N13 dir. Cherbourg Bayeux

Carpiquet: 25 km

Ferme de la Rançonnière

Bayeux I Crépon

www.chateauxhotels.com/ranconniere | reservation service: 33 (0) 1.40.07.00.20

Route d'Arromanches Crépon 14480 Crépon
Tel.: 33 (0) 2.31.22.21.73 – Fax: 33 (0) 2.31.22.98.39
ranconniere@chateauxhotels.com
Familles SILEHGEM & VEREECKE

35 rooms: 44 € / 104 €
7 suites: 120 € / 135 €
Breakfast: 10 €
Menu(s): 15 € / 35 € - **Carte:** 30 €
1/2 board: 52 € / 82 €

Open all year
equipments
lift, telephone, internet, T.V.
Satellite, baby-sitting
environment
architecture 13ᵉ, garden
leisure, relaxation
tennis 3 km, golf course
20 km, horse-riding 4 km,
thalassotherapy, 5 km from
D-day beaches

*Near Bayeux, Arromanches
and Caen, Crepon, a beautiful
village steeped in history...At
its heart, this magnificent 13th
and 15th century manor is
decorated in Normandie style.
Breakfast delicious as are the
succulent regional dishes. For
4 km from D-day Beach.*

Road map p. 619

A13 peripheral north exit 7 Creully-
Arromanches

 Caen-Carpiquet: 22 km

24, chemin de l'Eglise 14117 Tracy-sur-Mer
Tel.: 33 (0) 2.31.22.35.37 – Fax: 33 (0) 2.31.22.93.38
victoria@chateauxhotels.com
Robert SELMI
13 rooms: 57 € / 96 €
Breakfast: 7 €

A 19th century manor house, entirely renovated, with elegant rooms overlooking the park and the flower garden. Near the historic places of the landing beaches and a few minutes from Bayeux, a tourist town worldwide known for its 11th century cathedral, its tapestries and museums.

hotel annual closing
01/10 > 31/03
equipments
telephone, T.V.
environment
architecture 19e, furniture 19e, garden, terrace, total calm
leisure, relaxation
heated pool/covered, tennis 2 km, golf course 12 km, horse-riding 0.2 km

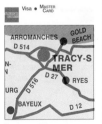

Road map p. 619

N13 exit Bayeux. D516 dir. Arromanches

✈ Caen: 30 km

Château du Landel

Gournay en Bray I Bezancourt
www.chateauxhotels.com/landel I reservation service: 33 (0) 1.40.07.00.20

76220 Bezancourt
Tel.: 33 (0) 2.35.90.16.01 – Fax: 33 (0) 2.35.90.62.47
landel@chateauxhotels.com
Yves & Annick CARDON
17 rooms: 77 € / 153 €
Breakfast: 9 €
Menu(s): 25 € / 40 € - **Carte:** 33 €
1/2 board: 76 € / 114 €

hotel annual closing
15/11 > 15/03
restaurant annual closing
15/11 > 15/03
equipments
telephone, internet
environment
architecture 17e, park 3 ha,
garden, total calm
leisure, relaxation
heated pool, golf course
25 km, horse-riding 7 km

Set amidst greenery, this fine 17th century house, once a staging post on the road to Saint-Jacques de Compostelle, offers all the appeal of life in a château. Warm welcome, tasteful decor, comfortable rooms and fine food promise a marvelous stay in a region with a rich heritage.

Visa ● MASTER CARD

Road map p. 619

A15-N14 dir. Dieppe/Gisors/Neuf-Marche/Bezancourt

Boss/Roissy CDG 40 km/ 90 km

4, cours du Château Intérieur des Remparts
50260 Bricquebec
Tel.: 33 (0) 2.33.52.24.49 – Fax: 33 (0) 2.33.52.62.71
vieuxchateau@chateauxhotels.com
Hubert HARDY
16 rooms: 53 € / 106 €
Breakfast: 7,62 €
Menu(s): 14,5 € / 30,5 € - **Carte:** 28 € -
1/2 board: 52 € / 68 €

An authentic mediaeval castle standing proudly amid its ramparts is the setting for this establishment offering restaurant in the old knights hall and old world charm in comfortable guest rooms. Visite of the Queen Victoria 1857 and Field Marshall Montgomery 1957.

hotel annual closing
01/01 > 01/02
restaurant annual closing
01/01 > 01/02
equipments
telephone, internet, T.V.
Canal+
environment
architecture 12º, terrace 50 m^2
leisure, relaxation
tennis 0.5 km, golf course
14 km, horse-riding 5 km

Visa ● MASTER CARD

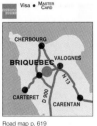

Road map p. 619

N13 exit Bricquebec, D900 dir. Bricquebec

 Maupertus-Cherbourg:
22 km

I Normandie

Moulin du Vey
Clécy
www.chateauxhotels.com/vey | reservation service: 33 (0) 1.40.07.00.20

Le Vey 14570 Clécy
Tel.: 33 (0) 2.31.69.71.08 – Fax: 33 (0) 2.31.69.14.14
vey@chateauxhotels.com
Denise LEDUC
12 rooms: 67 € / 94 €
Breakfast: 9 €
Menu(s): 22 € / 61 € - **Carte:** 53 €
1/2 board: 80 € / 90 €

hotel annual closing
30/11 > 28/12 ● 04/01 > 31/01
restaurant annual closing
30/11 > 28/12 ● 04/01 > 31/01
hotel weekly closing
sun(ev)
02/11 > 15/03
restaurant weekly closing
mon(lun), sun(ev)
02/11 > 15/03
equipments
telephone, T.V.
environment
architecture 19ª, garden,
terrace, view
leisure, relaxation
tennis 1 km, golf course 3 km,
horse-riding 7 km

35 km from Caen, in an enchanting setting in the heart of Norman Switzerland, an authentic mill on the banks of the Orne restored as a charming hotel. Individually decorated rooms. Many Norman specialities. On fine days, meals served on the terrace on the banks of the river.

Visa ● Diners ● MASTER CARD

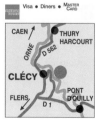

Road map p. 619

A13 exit 31: Flers-Alençon, then exit 11, D 562 dir. Flers-Laval then 133A dir. Le Vey

 Caen-Carpiquet: 35 km

Chemin de Saint-Clair 76790 Etretat

Tel.: 33 (0) 2.35.27.08.23 – Fax: 33 (0) 2.35.29.92.24
donjon@chateauxhotels.com
Omar ABODIB

17 rooms: 66 € / 166 €
4 suites: 176 € / 216 €
Breakfast: 12 €
Menu(s): 29 € / 54 € - **Carte:** 47 € -
1/2 board: 74 € / 160 €

Overlooking the Normandy village Etretat, this charming ivy-covered château set in a beautiful park provides a warm welcome. and a spectacular view of the surroundings. The spacious, comfortable rooms overlook the park, the sea or the cliffs. The expert cooking highlights delectable terroir products.

Open all year

equipments
telephone, internet, T.V.
Satellite/Canal+, minibar, safe,
baby-sitting

environment
architecture 19e, garden,
terrace, view, total calm

leisure, relaxation
heated pool, tennis 0.5 km,
golf course 1 km, horse-riding
3 km, sauna, hammam, jacuzzi

Visa ● Diners ● JCB ● MASTER CARD

Road map p. 619

A13 exit Pont de Tancarville dir Etretat
- A29 exit etretat

Le Havre: 20 km

Château de Sassetot

Fécamp I Sassetot-le-Mauconduit

www.chateauxhotels.com/sassetot | reservation service: 33 (0) 1.40.07.00.20

76540 Sassetot-le-Mauconduit

Tel.: 33 (0) 2.35.28.00.11 – Fax: 33 (0) 2.35.28.50.00

sassetot@chateauxhotels.com

Pierre-Frédérick GALLAND

26 rooms: 72 € / 145 €
3 suites: 183 € / 290 €
Breakfast: 10 €
Menu(s): 23 € / 54 € - **Carte:** 45,73 €
1/2 board: 70 € / 106,5 €

Open all year

equipments
telephone, internet, T.V.
Satellite, minibar

environment
architecture 18°, furniture
contemporain, park 11 ha,
garden, terrace 100 m², view,
total calm

leisure, relaxation
tennis 0.3 km, golf course
27 km, horse-riding 0.8 km

Former summer residence of the Austrian Empress Sissi, set within a wooded 25-acre park, discover the privileged lifestyle of this18th century chateau on the Côte d'Albâtre. Gastronomic restaurant. Nearby: the ivory and spice route not far from the cliffs overhanging the Petites Dalles beach.

Visa ● Diners ● MASTER CARD

Road map p. 619

A13 exit 25 Bourg/Achard or D913
dir. Fécamp

Le Havre: 45 km

27140 Bazincourt-sur-Epte

Tel.: 33 (0) 2.32.55.11.61 – Fax: 33 (0) 2.32.55.95.65

rapee@chateauxhotels.com

Philippe BERGERON

11 rooms: 77 € / 92 €
1 flat: 92 € - **1 suite:** 123 €
Breakfast: 10 €
Menu(s): 27 € / 36 € - **1/2 board:** 68 € / 75 €

A château with the appearance of an English manor-house in a wooded estate... The welcome is exceptional, the cuisine a festival. Decor refined... Discover Gisors, the capital of the Knights Templar, Giverny and Claude Monet's house, the Lyons forest, etc. Nearby walking trails, riding centres.

hotel annual closing
20/01 > 01/03 ● 15/08 > 01/09
restaurant annual closing
20/01 > 01/03 ● 15/08 > 01/09
equipments
telephone, T.V., safe
environment
architecture 19º, park 3 ha, garden, terrace 300 m², view, total calm
leisure, relaxation
heated pool, tennis 5 km, golf course 12 km, horse-riding 0.1 km

Visa

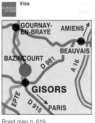

Road map p. 619

A16 exit Beauvais - A13 exit Vernon

Orly: 60 km

| Normandie

Le Clos Saint-Gatien
Honfleur | Saint-Gatien-des-Bois

www.chateauxhotels.com/saintgatien | reservation service: 33 (0) 1.40.07.00.20

4, rue des Brioleurs
14130 Saint-Gatien-des-Bois
Tel.: 33 (0) 2.31.65.16.08 – Fax: 33 (0) 2.31.65.10.27
saintgatien@chateauxhotels.com
M. & Mme.Michel RUFIN
58 rooms: 60 € / 144 €
Breakfast: 11 €
Menu(s): 16 € / 60 € - **Carte:** 23 €
1/2 board: 63 € / 105 €

Open all year
equipments
lift, telephone, internet, T.V.
Satellite/Canal+, minibar,
baby-sitting
environment
garden, terrace
leisure, relaxation
heated pool/covered, golf
course 2 km, horse-riding
0.5 km, sauna, jacuzzi

*Between Deauville, Trouville
and Honfleur, a comfortable
and individual atmosphere in
the setting of an old Norman
farm, semi-rustique, semi-
modern. Traditional and refined cuisine: foie gras in a
terrine, supreme of turbot, fillet
of beef with the marrow, Ivory
delight with coffee, etc.*

Visa ● Diners ● MASTER CARD

Road map p. 619

A13 exit Deauville and then Honfleur.
D579, D74 - A29 exit Airport St-Gatien

Deauville/St-Gatien: 2 km

Chemin Paul Ruel 14113 Cricqueboeuf
Tel.: 33 (0) 2.31.88.10.40 – Fax: 33 (0) 2.31.88.10.90
manoirpoterie@chateauxhotels.com
Ludovic CROSNIER
18 rooms: 104 € / 186 €
Breakfast: 11,5 €
Menu(s): 26 € / 34 € - **Carte:** 46 €

Between Honfleur and Trou-
ville, this Manor receives
guests with the warm hospital-
ity of the Normans with the flair
of a small chateau. Opulently
decorated rooms overlook the
sea or the countryside. Relax
in the bar or bask in front of the
fire in the lounge. Experience
the French lifestyle!

Open all year
equipments
lift, telephone, internet, T.V.
Satellite, minibar, safe,
baby-sitting
environment
park 2 ha, garden, terrace
70 m², view
leisure, relaxation
tennis 1.5 km, golf course
8 km, horse-riding 2 km,
balneo, jacuzzi, beach 300 m,
near casino

Visa ● Diners ● JCB ● Master Card

Road map p. 619
Paris - Honfleur A13 then D513

Deauville St-Gatien: 8 km

Manoir du Butin
Honfleur
www.chateauxhotels.com/butin | reservation service: 33 (0) 1.40.07.00.20

Phare du Butin 14600 Honfleur
Tel.: 33 (0) 2.31.81.63.00 – Fax: 33 (0) 2.31.89.59.23
butin@chateauxhotels.com
Véronique HEULOT
9 rooms: 120 € / 350 €
Breakfast: 10 €
Menu(s): 30 € / 46 € - **1/2 board:** 102 € / 217 €

hotel annual closing
12/11 > 06/12
restaurant annual closing
12/11 > 06/12
equipments
telephone, internet, T.V.,
minibar, baby-sitting
environment
architecture 18e, garden,
terrace, view, total calm
leisure, relaxation
tennis 2 km, golf course
15 km, horse-riding 8 km

15km from Deauville in a 2-acre park, this superb manor from the 18th century offers you both tranquillity and warm intimacy surrounded by a beautiful park overlooking the sea. Comfortable rooms. The restaurant proposes you a high class and delicious cuisine from Normandy in a refined setting.

Visa ● JCB ● MasterCard

Road map p. 619

from Paris: A14, A13, A29 exit 3.
Cross Honfleur then D513 by coast

Saint-Gatien: 8 km

www.chateauxhotels.com/bruyeres | reservation service: 33 (0) 1.40.07.00.20

Route du Cadran 14340 Cambremer
Tel.: 33 (0) 2.31.32.22.45 – Fax: 33 (0) 2.31.32.22.58
bruyeres@chateauxhotels.com
José MOTTI

13 rooms: 72 € / 168 €
Breakfast: 11 €

A 19th-century château in the heart of the Auge region, a land of stud farms and cider. Warm and peaceful atmosphere, perfectly equipped and luxuriously decorated personalised guestrooms. Gastronomic cuisine. Numerous leisure activities.

hotel annual closing
01/01 > 29/03

equipments
telephone, T.V. Satellite, minibar

environment
architecture 19e, park 10 ha, garden, terrace 60 m², total calm

leisure, relaxation
heated pool, tennis 1.5 km, golf course 20 km, horse-riding 10 km, horse-riding stables in Lisieux (12 km)

Visa ● Diners ● MASTER CARD

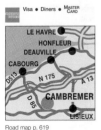

LE HAVRE
HONFLEUR
DEAUVILLE
CABOURG
D513
N 175
A 13
CAMBREMER
D 85
LISIEUX

Road map p. 619

A13 exit 29A "La Haie Tondue" dir- falaise

Deauville: 26 km

La Haye le Comte
Louviers
www.chateauxhotels.com/lahayecomte | reservation service: 33 (0) 1.40.07.00.20

4, route de La Haye-le-Comte 27400 Louviers
Tel.: 33 (0) 2.32.40.00.40 – Fax: 33 (0) 2.32.25.03.85
lahayecomte@chateauxhotels.com
Marie-Laure & Jean-Jacques MAGUET
16 rooms: 60 € / 85 €
Breakfast: 8,50 €
Menu(s): 16 € / 39 € - **Carte:** 22 €

hotel annual closing
28/12 > 15/01
restaurant annual closing
28/12 > 15/01
restaurant weekly closing
mon(lun), sun(ev)
01/11 > 31/03
equipments
telephone, internet, T.V.
Satellite/Canal+
environment
architecture 16e, park 5 ha,
terrace, view, total calm
leisure, relaxation
golf course 9 km, horse-riding
12 km, tennis, game of bowls

62 miles from Paris, on the road to Deauville, this charming 16th century manor house stands in a 12-acre park, crowned by 400 hundred-year old bow trees. In the restaurant, savour Normandy delights. Also: tennis, forest walks. Nearby: Giverny and Claude Monet's home.

Visa • MASTER CARD

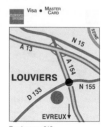

Road map p. 619
A13 exit Louviers

Rouen, Boos: 25 km

Nogent-le-Rotrou I Condeau

www.chateauxhotels.com/chateauvilleray I reservation service: 33 (0) 1.40.07.00.20

Villeray 61110 Condeau
Tel.: 33 (0) 2.33.73.30.22 – Fax: 33 (0) 2.33.73.38.28
chateauvilleray @ chateauxhotels.com
Muriel EELSEN

4 rooms: 100 € / 199 €
2 flats: 199 € / 275 € - **3 suites:** 190,56 € / 289,65 €
Breakfast: 13 €
Carte: 50 € - **1/2 board:** 165 € / 264 €

Perched on a hill overlooking the Huisne Valley, this elegant 18th and 19th century château combines the sophistication and simplicity of the rooms with the aristocratic distinction of the lounges. All around are 44 ha of walled estate grounds. An authentic and rural setting.

Open all year

equipments
telephone, internet, T.V., minibar, safe, baby-sitting

environment
architecture 18e, furniture 19e, park 44 ha, garden, terrace, view, total calm

leisure, relaxation
heated pool, golf course 18 km, horse-riding, canoeing

Visa ● Diners ● MASTER CARD

Road map p. 619

dir. Nogent-le-Rotrou D918 condé sur huisne

Orly: 120 km

| Normandie

Moulin de Villeray
Nogent-le-Rotrou I Condeau
www.chateauxhotels.com/villeray | reservation service: 33 (0) 1.40.07.00.20

Villeray 61110 Condeau
Tel.: 33 (0) 2.33.73.30.22 – Fax: 33 (0) 2.33.73.38.28
villeray@chateauxhotels.com
Christian EELSEN
19 rooms: 90 € / 206 €
3 flats: 145 € / 206 €
Breakfast: 12 €
Menu(s): 23 € / 60 € - **Carte:** 54 €
1/2 board: 87 € / 168 €

Open all year
equipments
telephone, internet, T.V.,
minibar, safe, baby-sitting
environment
architecture 18e, furniture 19e,
park 5 ha, garden, terrace,
view, total calm
leisure, relaxation
heated pool, golf course
18 km, horse-riding

At 75 min from Paris in the leafy Perche, this former mill offers you calm and well-being. For a meal on the terrace on the banks of the Huisne or in the old mill-house, the menu offers you specialities with all flavours. Fishing, canoeing, mountain-bikes, carriages, golf tariffs on request.

Visa ● Diners ● MasterCard

Road map p. 619

A11 - from Paris, exit Chartres N23 -
from Mans, exit La Ferté Bernard

Orly: 120 km

Pont-L'Evêque

Quetteville 14130 Pont-l'Evêque
Tel.: 33 (0) 2.31.65.62.40 – Fax: 33 (0) 2.31.64.24.52
hauquerie@chateauxhotels.com
13 rooms: 100 € / 160 €
4 suites: 140 € / 200 €
Breakfast: 10 €
Menu(s): 25 € / 52 € - **Carte:** 53 € -
1/2 board: 35 €

A short distance from Deauville and the pretty port of Honfleur, is a beautiful stud farm, as where it should be, the horse is king. The ambience is friendly, the service well trained. The comfortable rooms and the gastronomie cuisine compete to give a particularly pleasant stay.

hotel annual closing
01/01 > 28/02
restaurant annual closing
01/01 > 28/02
equipments
lift, telephone, T.V. Canal+, minibar, safe
environment
architecture 10e, park 25 ha, garden, terrace, total calm
leisure, relaxation
golf course 10 km, horse-riding 10 km

Visa • Master Card

Road map p. 619

A13 exit 28 Beuzeville, N175 dir. Pont l'Evêque

Domaine de Joinville

Rouen I Eu

www.chateauxhotels.com/joinville | reservation service: 33 (0) 1.40.07.00.20

Route du Tréport 76260 Eu
Tel.: 33 (0) 2.35.50.52.52 – Fax: 33 (0) 2.35.50.27.37
joinville@chateauxhotels.com
Ludovic ELOY
20 rooms: 76 € / 135 €
3 flats: 152 € / 200 € - **3 suites:** 160 €
Breakfast: 12 €
Menu(s): 25 € / 42 €

Open all year
restaurant annual closing
01/01 > 31/01
equipments
telephone, T.V., minibar
environment
architecture 19e, park 10 ha,
garden, terrace 90 m², view
leisure, relaxation
covered pool, golf course
30 km, horse-riding 3 km,
balneo with a charge, sauna,
jacuzzi

Listed historic monument. A luxury gastronomic stop-over, rooms furnished in different styles, a park surrounded by a wood. Christmas and New Year programmes. Fitness centre. Sauna, jacuzzi. Mountain-bikes for rent. To be discovered: the Bay of the Somme, the Marquenterre park.

Visa • MasterCard

Road map p. 619

A28 exit Blangy/Bresle - D49 Le
Tréport-Eu

Rouen: 90 km

27, place Benserade BP 4
27480 Lyons-La-Forêt
Tel.: 33 (0) 2.32.49.62.02 – Fax: 33 (0) 2.32.49.80.09
licorne@chateauxhotels.com
Famille BRUN
13 rooms: 65 € / 92 €
6 flats: 97 € / 130 €
Breakfast: 10 €
Menu(s): 30 € - **1/2 board:** 68 € / 82 €

In this pretty village in the middle of Europe's greatest beech forest, the setting has not changed in 200 years. La Licorne has been here since 1610. The fabled animal protects the mystery of this opulent, comfortable, cosy residence. Near Rouen, Giverny, Château-Gaillard, the Norman abbeys.

Visa ● Diners ● JCB ● Master Card

Road map p. 619

A13 exit Gaillon-les-Andelys, D316 dir. Les Andelys

hotel annual closing
16/12 > 21/01
restaurant annual closing
01/01 > 31/03●01/11 > 31/03
hotel weekly closing
mon, sun
01/11 > 31/03
restaurant weekly closing
mon, tue(lun)
01/04 > 31/10
equipments
telephone, T.V., safe
environment
architecture 17e, garden, terrace 100 m²
leisure, relaxation
tennis 1 km, golf course 30 km, horse-riding 6 km, mountain bikes for hire

Orly/Charles-de-Gaulle: 110 km

Moulin de Connelles

Rouen I Connelles

www.chateauxhotels.com/connelles | reservation service: 33 (0) 1.40.07.00.20

40, route d'Amfreville-sous- les-Monts
27430 Connelles
Tel.: 33 (0) 2.32.59.53.33 – Fax: 33 (0) 2.32.59.21.83
connelles @chateauxhotels.com
Hubert PETITEAU

7 rooms: 99, € / 145, €
4 suites: 138 € / 191 €
Breakfast: 12 €
Menu(s): 30 € / 50 € - **Carte:** 39,40 €
1/2 board: 89,5 € / 112,5 €

hotel annual closing
02/01 > 01/02
restaurant annual closing
02/01 > 01/02
hotel weekly closing
mon, sun(ev)
30/09 > 30/04
restaurant weekly closing
mon(lun),tue(lun), wen(lun),
thi(lun)
01/05 > 30/09
mon, tue(lun), sun(ev)
30/09 > 30/04

equipments
telephone, internet, T.V.
Satellite/Canal+, minibar, safe

environment
architecture 19ᵉ, park 3 ha,
garden, terrace 50 m², view,
total calm

leisure, relaxation
heated pool/covered, golf
course 5 km, horse-riding
10 km, sauna, jacuzzi, boat
trips, mountain bike

*One hour from Paris and
Deauville, this charming 19th
century manor house is set in
a 75 acres venerable park,
edged by two branches of the
Seine. Luxuriously decorated
suites and guest rooms, offering one of Normandy's most
refined restaurants. Rowing
boats can be rented for romantic outings.*

Road map p. 619

A14/A13 exit Louviers dir. Pont de
l'Arche N15, then St Pierre du V. then
Connelles

Rouen: 20 km

www.chateauxhotels.com/agneaux | reservation service: 33 (0) 1.40.07.00.20

Avenue Ste Marie 50180 Agneaux
Tel.: 33 (0) 2.33.57.65.88 – Fax: 33 (0) 2.33.56.59.21
agneaux@chateauxhotels.com
René & Jeanette GROULT
10 rooms: 75 € / 127 €
1 suite: 173 €
Breakfast: 10,06 €
Menu(s): 23 € / 56 € - **Carte:** 23 €

This historic, 13th century château sparkles like a jewel at the centre of a lush, green park with deer . Quiet serenity surrounds this outstanding site, only 30 km (19 miles) from the D Day beach and 70 km (43 miles) from Mont St-Michel. Gourmet regional delights served in the restaurant.

Open all year
equipments
telephone, T.V. Canal+, minibar

environment
architecture 13°, park, garden, terrace, view, total calm

leisure, relaxation
horse-riding 4 km

Visa ● MASTER CARD

Road map p. 619

A13 - N13 exit Bayeux dir. St-Lô-Coutances

Caen-Carpiquet: 60 km

Auberge du Val au Cesne

Yvetot

www.chateauxhotels.com/valcesne | reservation service: 33 (0) 1.40.07.00.20

Le Val au Cesne 76190 Yvetot
Tel.: 33 (0) 2.35.56.63.06 – Fax: 33 (0) 2.35.56.92.78
valcesne@chateauxhotels.com
Jérôme CAREL
5 rooms: 76 € / 76 €
Breakfast: 8 €
Menu(s): 25 € / 43 € - **Carte:** 53 €
1/2 board: 71 €

hotel annual closing
07/01 > 28/01 • 19/08 > 02/09
restaurant annual closing
07/01 > 29/01 • 19/08 > 03/09
equipments
telephone, internet, T.V.
environment
architecture 17°, garden, view
leisure, relaxation
tennis 5 km, golf course
20 km, horse-riding 2 km

A typical Norman inn nestling in a valley, surrounded by a wood. In the restaurant, traditional dishes made with regional products. Rooms isolated by a pleasure garden. In Yvetot, a round church lit by 1,000 sp. metres of stained-glass windows.

Visa ● MASTER CARD

Road map p. 619

A29 exit east of Yvetot or A13 exit "Pont de Brotonne", N15 and D5

 Rouen: 35 km

Bretagne

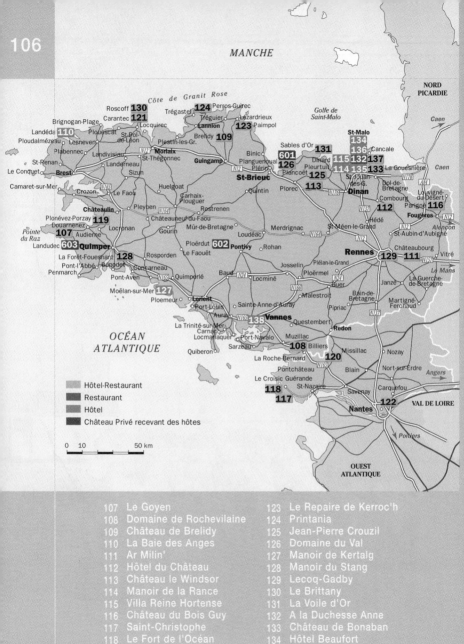

Audierne port pl. Jean Simon 29770 Audierne
Tel.: 33 (0) 2.98.70.08.88 – Fax: 33 (0) 2.98.70.18.77
goyen@chateauxhotels.com
Adolphe & Yvonne BOSSER
21 rooms: 48,78 € / 137,2 €
2 flats: 114,34 € / 138,73 € - **1 suite:** 137,2 € /
182,94 €
Breakfast: 9,15 €
Menu(s): 14,94 € / 65,55 € - **Carte:** 54,88 € -
1/2 board: 76,99 € / 121,2 €

Nestled in the center of the picturesque fishing port of Audierne, this fine house with its blue shutters looks out towards the sea. The tastefully decorated rooms, friendly service and the refreshing tang of the seafood cuisine, are guaranteed to win you over to this Breton region.

hotel annual closing
05/01 > 10/01 ● 02/11 > 26/12
restaurant annual closing
05/01 > 24/03 ● 02/11 > 26/12
restaurant weekly closing
mon
16/09 > 02/11
mon
01/04 > 15/06

equipments
lift, telephone, internet, T.V.,
minibar, safe, baby-sitting
environment
terrace 40 m², view
leisure, relaxation
tennis 2 km, golf course
30 km, horse-riding 15 km

Visa ● MASTER CARD

Road map p. 619

from Paris: A81 exit Rennes - from
Rennes: N24 dir. Lorient, N165 dir.
Quimper

Pluguffan-Quimper: 20 km

Bretagne

Pointe de Pen-Lan 56190 Billiers
Tel.: 33 (0) 2.97.41.61.61 – Fax: 33 (0) 2.97.41.44.85
rochevilaine@chateauxhotels.com
Bertrand JAQUET
34 rooms: 100 € / 260 €
3 suites: 282 € / 420 €
Breakfast: 14 €
Menu(s): 46 € / 89 € - **Carte:** 55 €
1/2 board: 93 € / 175 €

Open all year
equipments
lift, telephone, internet, T.V. Canal+, minibar, safe
environment
architecture 15/16ᵉ, garden, terrace, view, total calm
leisure, relaxation
heated pool/covered, tennis 0.3 km, golf course 30 km, horse-riding 1 km, beauty salon, balneo, sauna, hammam, fitness, jacuzzi

Bordered by the sea and set in beautiful gardens, this group of ancient buildings from Brittany's golden age is an ideal resting place with pool, fitness center, balneotherapy, riding and tennis. Chef Patrice Caillault's cuisine enjoys a fine reputation.

Visa ● Diners ● JCB ● Master Card

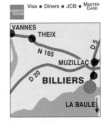

Road map p. 619

N165 exit Billiers/Muzillac and dir. Pen-Lan

Nantes: 80 km

22140 Brélidy

Tel.: 33 (0) 2.96.95.69.38 – Fax: 33 (0) 2.96.95.18.03

brelidy@chateauxhotels.com

Eliane & Pierre YONCOURT

9 rooms: 71,5 € / 130 €

1 suite: 178,5 € / 202 €

Breakfast: 9,15 €

Menu(s): 24,5 € / 31 € - **1/2 board:** 71,75 € / 101 €

Built on a remarkable feudal outcrop, a stately 16th century house with cosy rooms and tasteful decor, overlooking two rivers. Stroll through the 86-acre grounds where you may see deer, herons and dragonflies - an ideal base from which to explore Brittany, especially the Pink Granite coast and Isle of Bréhat.

hotel annual closing
02/11 > 31/03

restaurant annual closing
02/11 > 31/03

equipments
telephone, T.V.

environment
architecture 16e, furniture 16e, park, garden, terrace 120 m^2, view, total calm

leisure, relaxation
tennis 3 km, golf course 7 km, horse-riding 7 km, jacuzzi, river and lake fishing

Visa ● MASTER CARD

Road map p. 619

A11 then N12, exit Lannion-Tréguier, then D712 dir. Tréguier

Lannion: 30 km

La Baie des Anges

Brest ı Landeda

www.chateauxhotels.com/anges ı reservation service: 33 (0) 1.40.07.00.20

**350, route des Anges Port de l'Aber Wrac'h
29870 Landeda**
Tel.: 33 (0) 2.98.04.90.04 – Fax: 33 (0) 2.98.04.92.27
anges@chateauxhotels.com
Jacques BRIANT
18 rooms: 68 € / 122 €
2 suites: 138 € / 154 €
Breakfast: 10,5 €

hotel annual closing
03/01 > 15/02
equipments
internet, T.V. Canal+, safe
environment
architecture 10ᵉ, terrace, view,
total calm
leisure, relaxation
golf course 20 km, horse-riding
2 km, sauna, jacuzzi

On the Aber Wrac'h, one of the most exceptional corners of Brittany, this nicely renovated 19th century house faces its sun-yellow façade toward the sea. The large rooms are comfortable and the breakfasts are true gourmand poetry. A good address for discovering this fascinating region.

Visa ● MASTER CARD

Road map p. 619

Brest, D13 dir. "Port de l'Abert Wrac'h"

 Brest-Guipavas: 20 km

30, rue de Paris 35220 Châteaubourg
Tel.: 33 (0) 2.99.00.30.91 – Fax: 33 (0) 2.99.00.37.56
armilin@chateauxhotels.com
Marie-Line DOMELIER
31 rooms: 72 € / 102 €
1 suite: 140 € / 155 €
Breakfast: 10 €
Menu(s): 20 € / 35 € - **Carte:** 35 € -
1/2 board: 86 € / 100 €

Gateway from Brittany, this former mill, remodelled as a hôtel-restaurant provides 11 traditionnal rooms in the main building and 21 contemporary style rooms in a residence in the middle of 12 acres of wooded parkland. At the restaurant, over the river, you will find a regional cuisine, gourmande and refined.

hotel annual closing
23/12 > 07/01

restaurant annual closing
23/12 > 07/01

restaurant weekly closing
sun(ev)
01/11 > 28/02

equipments
lift, telephone, internet, T.V.
Satellite/Canal+, safe

environment
architecture 19e, furniture contemporain, park 5 ha, garden, terrace, view, vegetable garden

leisure, relaxation
golf course 15 km, horse-riding 10 km

Visa ● Diners ● MASTER CARD

Road map p. 619

N157 exit Châteaubourg

Rennes/Saint-Jacques:
25 km

Hôtel du Château
Combourg
www.chateauxhotels.com/hotelduchateau | reservation service: 33 (0) 1.40.07.00.20

1, place Chateaubriand 35270 Combourg
Tel.: 33 (0) 2.99.73.00.38 – Fax: 33 (0) 2.99.73.25.79
hotelduchateau@chateauxhotels.com
Christian & Marie-Thérèse PELE
35 rooms: 46 € / 122 €
Breakfast: 8,5 €
Menu(s): 16 € / 45 € - **Carte:** 27 €
1/2 board: 46 € / 119 €

hotel annual closing
13/04 > 19/04 • 15/12 > 15/01
restaurant annual closing
13/04 > 19/04 • 15/12 > 15/01
hotel weekly closing
sun(ev)
19/08 > 15/12
restaurant weekly closing
mon(lun)
14/07 > 18/08
mon(lun), sun(ev)
19/08 > 15/12
equipments
telephone, internet, T.V.
Satellite/Canal+, minibar
environment
architecture 18e, garden,
terrace 50 m², view
leisure, relaxation
tennis 1 km, golf course 10 km

In Combourg, the Hotel du Chateau allows you to dreamily gaze upon the romantic vistas beloved by Chateaubriand. Enjoy the tranquil surroundings from rooms overlooking the lake, the chateau or the garden. In the restaurant, courses inspired by Christian Pele delicately mix flavours of the sea and the country.

Visa • Diners • MASTER CARD

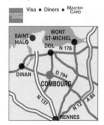

Road map p. 619

From Rennes, dir. Saint-Malo, exit Combourg

 Dinard-Pleurtuit: 40 km

Le Bois Billy
22130 Plorec-sur-Arguenon / Plancoët
Tel.: 33 (0) 2.96.83.04.83 − Fax: 33 (0) 2.96.83.05.36
lewindsor@chateauxhotels.com
Jean & Annie BOUVIER

21 rooms: 69 € / 145 €
2 suites: 190 € / 244 €
Breakfast: 12 €
Menu(s): 21,34 € / 60,98 € - **1/2 board:** 70 € / 107 €

20 km from the beaches of the Emerald Coast and beside the forest. A romantic château in a 11-acre park. Warm welcome. Cuisine with all the flavours of the sea and the kitchen garden. Dream-like rooms. Near Cap Fréhel, Mont St-Michel, Cancale, Saint-Malo, Dinard, Dinan. Golf, riding sailing.

hotel annual closing
14/01 > 12/02
restaurant annual closing
14/01 > 12/02
equipments
telephone, internet, T.V., safe, baby-sitting
environment
architecture 18e, furniture d'époque, park 11 ha, garden, terrace 95 m², view, vegetable garden, total calm
leisure, relaxation
tennis 3 km, golf course 15 km, horse-riding 6 km, swimming pool

Visa ● MASTER CARD

Road map p. 619

N12 St-Brieuc exit Jugon les Lacs

Manoir de la Rance
Dinard I Pleurtuit

www.chateauxhotels.com/rance | reservation service: 33 (0) 1.40.07.00.20

Le Château de Jouvente 35730 Pleurtuit
Tel.: 33 (0) 2.99.88.53.76 – Fax: 33 (0) 2.99.88.63.03

rance@chateauxhotels.com
Yvonne JASSELIN

7 rooms: 62 € / 138 €
2 suites: 137 € / 198 €
Breakfast: 9,15 €

hotel annual closing
15/11 > 15/03

equipments
telephone, T.V.

environment
architecture 19ᵉ, garden,
terrace, view, total calm

leisure, relaxation
tennis 3 km, golf course 7 km,
horse-riding 4 km,
thalassotherapy

XIXth century manor with refined decor. Large rooms facing the enchanting sea view. Large flowery terraces facing the sea, quiteness and rest in a large park on the banks of the Rance. Lovely horseback rides ont the banks of the river as far as Dinard and its beaches.

Road map p. 619

D114 dir. La Richardais/Le Minihic-
Sur-Rance

 Pleurtuit: 4 km

19, rue de la Malouine 35800 Dinard
Tel.: 33 (0) 2.99.46.54.31 – Fax: 33 (0) 2.99.88.15.88
reinehortense@chateauxhotels.com
Florence & Marc BENOIST
7 rooms: 150 € / 196 €
1 suite: 275 € / 335 €
Breakfast: 12 €

An original Belle Epoque villa, Reine Hortense ontained his name from its royal connections. The treasured objects once belonging to Hortense de Beauharnais give a personal quality to the surroundings. The Reine Hortense guest rooms, opening out over the sea, allow no respite to the eyes.

hotel annual closing
15/11 > 25/03
equipments
telephone, T.V.
environment
architecture 19ᵉ, garden, terrace, view
leisure, relaxation
golf course 3 km, horse-riding 1 km, thalassotherapy

Visa ● MasterCard

Road map p. 619

A11 exit Rennes, N157 exit Dinard

Dinard: 3 km

Château du Bois Guy

Fougères I Parigné
www.chateauxhotels.com/boisguy | reservation service: 33 (0) 1.40.07.00.20

Le Bois Guy 35133 Parigné
Tel.: 33 (0) 2.99.97.25.76 – Fax: 33 (0) 2.99.97.27.27
boisguy@chateauxhotels.com
Gérard FEVRIER
12 rooms: 53 € / 114 €
Breakfast: 9 €
Menu(s): 20 € / 58 € - **Carte:** 46 €
1/2 board: 61 € / 84 €

hotel annual closing
01/01 > 14/04●16/10 > 14/04
restaurant annual closing
01/01 > 14/04●16/10 > 14/04
hotel weekly closing
mon(lun), sun(lun)
15/04 > 15/10
restaurant weekly closing
mon, sat(lun), sun(ev)
15/04 > 15/10
equipments
telephone, internet, T.V.
Satellite
environment
architecture 17°, park 3 ha,
terrace 25 m^2, total calm
leisure, relaxation
tennis 10 km, golf course
30 km, horse-riding 5 km

*This Renaissance-style resi-
dence, only 30 min from Mont
St-Michel, offers calm in a rich,
historical setting. Tasteful
decoration surrounds you,
even in the cosiness of the
full-comfort rooms. The seasonal cooking is deliciously
inventive. A magic spot for all
those devoted to peace and
well-being.*

Visa ● Master Card

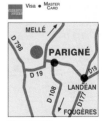

Road map p. 619

A84 exit 29, In Fougères dir. Flers
D177, D108 on your left dir. Parigné

Rennes: 60 km

www.chateauxhotels.com/saintchristophe | reservation service: 33 (0) 1.40.07.00.20

Place Notre-Dame 44500 La Baule
Tel.: 33 (0) 2.40.62.40.00 – Fax: 33 (0) 2.40.62.40.40
saintchristophe@chateauxhotels.com
Calixte JOÜON
27 rooms: 48 € / 124 €
5 flats: 61 € / 159 €
Breakfast: 8 €
Menu(s): 23 € / 30 € - **1/2 board:** 61 € / 92,50 €

100 m from the sea, in a residential district. 3 turn-of-the-century villas around a floral terrace, carefully-tended garden, antique furniture. Nearby: 2 water treatment centres, 8 km of fine sand which has earned this bay the title of Europe's most beautiful beach. Restaurant open all year round.

Open all year
equipments
telephone, internet, T.V., baby-sitting
environment
garden, terrace 300 m^2
leisure, relaxation
tennis 2 km, golf course 6 km, horse-riding 1.5 km, thalassotherapy

Visa • Diners • JCB • MASTER CARD

Road map p. 619

A11 Nantes, N165,N171 St-Nazaire exit Center of La Baule by D192

Nantes: 80 km

| Bretagne

Le Fort de l'Océan
Le Croisic
www.chateauxhotels.com/ocean | reservation service: 33 (0) 1.40.07.00.20

La pointe du Croisic 44490 Le Croisic
Tel.: 33 (0) 2.40.15.77.77 – Fax: 33 (0) 2.40.15.77.80
ocean@chateauxhotels.com
Valérie CRIAUD
7 rooms: 137,21 € / 198,19 €
2 suites: 243,92 €
Breakfast: 12,96 €
Menu(s): 40,4 € / 64,03 €

restaurant annual closing
12/11 > 20/12 • 06/01 > 10/02
restaurant weekly closing
mon(lun), tue(lun), wen(lun)
15/06 > 15/09
mon, tue
10/02 > 14/06 • 16/09 > 12/11
equipments
telephone, internet, T.V.
Satellite, minibar
environment
architecture 18e, garden,
terrace, view
leisure, relaxation
heated pool, tennis 10 km, golf
course 0.2 km, horse-riding
10 km

*At Le Croisic looms a Vauban
fortress in Breton granite while
in the garden are hydrangea,
lavender and umbrella pines.
The residence, towering upon
the rocks and soothed by the
rhythm of the tides, looks out
upon the sea. An breton eden.*

Road map p. 619

A11 then dir. Guérande/Le Croisic

 Nantes: 90 km

Manoir de Moëllien
Locronan I Plonévez-Porzay
www.chateauxhotels.com/moellien I reservation service: 33 (0) 1.40.07.00.20

119

29550 Plonévez-Porzay
Tel.: 33 (0) 2.98.92.50.40 – Fax: 33 (0) 2.98.92.55.21
moellien@chateauxhotels.com
M. & Mme. Bruno GARET
18 rooms: 62 € / 114 €
Breakfast: 8 €
Menu(s): 20 € / 34 € - **Carte:** 34 € -
1/2 board: 60 € / 88 €

In the tourist heart of southern Finistère, a historic XVIIth-century manor, entirely restored, with refined cuisine adapted to the seasons, and the tranquillity of rooms in an annex. A heaven of peace and greenery to find oneself again. Nearby: Locronan 2 km, fine sandy beaches, Quimper 20 km.

Visa ● Diners ● M̲A̲S̲T̲E̲R̲
C̲A̲R̲D̲

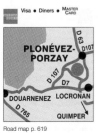

Road map p. 619

N165 exit north of Quimper, D107 dir. Douarnenez

hotel annual closing
03/11 > 22/03
restaurant annual closing
03/11 > 22/03
restaurant weekly closing
tue(lun), wen(lun), thi(lun)
23/03 > 15/06
tue(lun), wen, thi(lun)
20/09 > 03/11

equipments
telephone, internet, T.V.
Satellite, minibar

environment
architecture 17e, park 3 ha, garden, view, total calm

leisure, relaxation
tennis 2.5 km, horse-riding 3 km

Quimper - Pluguffan: 18 km

La Bretesche

Missillac

www.chateauxhotels.com/bretesche | reservation service: 33 (0) 1.40.07.00.20

Domaine de La Bretesche 44780 Missillac
Tel.: 33 (0) 2.51.76.86.96 – Fax: 33 (0) 2.40.66.99.47
bretesche@chateauxhotels.com
Christophe DELAHAYE
24 rooms: 120 € / 220 €
7 suites: 230 € / 285 €
Breakfast: 14 €
Menu(s): 35 € / 70 € - **Carte:** 55 € -
1/2 board: 110 € / 160 €

hotel annual closing
18/01 > 09/03

restaurant annual closing
18/01 > 09/03●04/11 > 14/11

restaurant weekly closing
sun(ev), mon
09/03 > 15/04●15/10 > 18/01
mon, tue(lun)
16/04 > 14/07●20/08 > 15/10

equipments
lift, telephone, internet, T.V.
Satellite/Canal+, minibar,
baby-sitting, valet parking

environment
architecture 19e, furniture 18e,
park 200 ha, garden, terrace
2500 m², view, total calm

leisure, relaxation
heated pool, horse-riding 4 km,
golf for beginners

In the heart of the Brière Regional Park, beside a magnificent golf course, a vast 500-acre domain where tradition meets innovation. Half-timbered beams and antique wood panelling, delicious fine cuisine, sumptuous rooms, completed by an original bar in the converted stables. A place of prestige.

Visa ● Diners ● JCB ● MASTER CARD

Road map p. 619

A11 then N165 exit Missillac-La Bretesche

Nantes Atlantique: 55 km

20, rue du Kelenn 29660 Carantec
Tel.: 33 (0) 2.98.67.00.47 – Fax: 33 (0) 2.98.67.08.25
carantec@chateauxhotels.com
Patrick JEFFROY
12 rooms: 110 € / 134,50 €
Breakfast: 11 €
Menu(s): 26 € / 60 € - **Carte:** 75 €
1/2 board: 183 € / 208 €

This hotel in Carantec, on a headland overlooking the bay of Morlaix. is an attractive Breton house where 12 rooms with a view on the sea, (5 with balconies) await you. Food tasting of the sea, nearby seaside trails bordered with mimosas, a fine sandy beach combine to make this a charming spot in a captivating region.

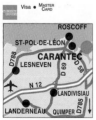

Road map p. 619
dir. morlaix, N12 exit Roscoff

hotel annual closing
07/01 > 21/01 ● 08/12 > 15/12
restaurant annual closing
07/01 > 21/01 ● 08/12 > 15/12
restaurant weekly closing
mon(lun), tue(lun)
16/06 > 22/09
equipments
lift, telephone, internet, T.V.
Satellite
environment
architecture 19°, furniture
contemporain, garden, terrace
100 m², view
leisure, relaxation
tennis 1.5 km, golf course
1 km, horse-riding 15 km,
beauty salon, thalassotherapy

Brest-Guipavas: 55 km

Le Domaine d'Orvault

Nantes I Orvault Nantes

www.chateauxhotels.com/domaineorvault | reservation service: 33 (0) 1.40.07.00.20

Chemin des Marais du Cens - Porte de Rennes
44700 Orvault Nantes
Tel.: 33 (0) 2.40.76.84.02 – Fax: 33 (0) 2.40.76.04.21
domaineorvault@chateauxhotels.com
Sylvain LEJEUNE
28 rooms: 78 € / 98 €
1 suite: 122 €
Breakfast: 10 €
Menu(s): 22 € / 44 € - **Carte:** 38 €
1/2 board: 99 € / 146 €

Open all year
restaurant weekly closing
sat(lun)
31/03 > 31/10
sat(lun), sun(ev)
31/10 > 31/03

equipments
lift, telephone, internet, T.V.
Satellite/Canal+, minibar

environment
park 1 ha, terrace 80 m², total
calm

leisure, relaxation
covered pool, golf course
2 km, sauna, fitness, jacuzzi,
paint-ball, mountain bikes

A few minutes away from Nantes, in the middle of a wooded park, this charming residence offers you a wealth of opportunities to unwind and enjoy. Peaceful surroundings, rooms with their own individual style, and creative cookery from the talented Thierry Bouhier: all the ingredients for your dream holiday.

Visa ● MASTER CARD

Road map p. 619

Ring road North Nantes exit Rennes
N° 37 dir. Grand Val. 1st road on the
right, after 2nd roundabout

Nantes Atlantique: 8 km

29, quai Morand 22500 Paimpol
Tel.: 33 (0) 2.96.20.50.13 – Fax: 33 (0) 2.96.22.07.46
kerroch@chateauxhotels.com
Jean-Claude BROC
11 rooms: 44,21 € / 114,34 €
1 flat: 99,09 € / 114,34 € - **1 suite:** 113,57 € / 166,17 €
Breakfast: 10,52 €
Menu(s): 21,34 € / 59,46 € - **Carte:** 35,06 €
1/2 board: 59,30 € / 94,37 €

A bourgeois XVIIIth century pirate's residence between Roscoff and Saint-Malo. Sound-proofed guestrooms with Directoire-style decor overlooking the bay of Paimpol. Fine dining in the restaurant or regional specialities and seafood available in the bistro between a fireplace and granite walls.

Visa • MASTER CARD

restaurant annual closing
01/12 > 25/12 ● 15/01 > 05/02
restaurant weekly closing
tue, wen(lun)
14/07 > 31/08
mon(lun), tue, wen(lun)
01/09 > 13/07
equipments
lift, telephone, internet, T.V.
Satellite/Canal+, minibar, safe
environment
architecture 18°, terrace, view
leisure, relaxation
tennis 1 km, golf course
20 km, horse-riding 5 km,
sea-fishing

ILE DE BRÉHAT
D 786
PAIMPOL
D 6
ST-QUAY-PORTRIEUX
LANVOLLON
BREST
D 7
N 12
GUINGAMP

Road map p. 619

West motorway exit Rennes, N12 dir.
St-Brieuc then Paimpol

Saint-Brieuc: 40 km

Printania

Perros-Guirec

www.chateauxhotels.com/printania | reservation service: 33 (0) 1.40.07.00.20

12, rue des Bons-Enfants 22700 Perros-Guirec
Tel.: 33 (0) 2.96.49.01.10 – Fax: 33 (0) 2.96.91.16.36
printania@chateauxhotels.com
Marie-Françoise LE CALVEZ
33 rooms: 82 € / 125 €
Breakfast: 11,5 €
Menu(s): 26 € - **Carte:** 20 €
1/2 board: 83 € / 100 €

hotel annual closing
01/01 > 14/01 ● 01/10 > 01/03
restaurant annual closing
01/01 > 14/01 ● 01/10 > 01/03
equipments
lift, internet, T.V.
Satellite/Canal+, safe
environment
architecture 19e, park, garden,
terrace, view, total calm
leisure, relaxation
heated pool/covered, golf
course 6 km, horse-riding
6 km, thalassotherapy

*A romantic villa built in the
1930's, perched on the rocky,
rose-colored granite coast, offering all the best in elegance,
comfort and quality. From the
restaurant and the rooms facing the sea, there is a breathtaking view out over the
ocean.*

Visa ● Diners ● Master Card

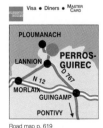

Road map p. 619

A81 exit Rennes, N12 exit Guingamp-
Lannion

Lannion: 6 km

20, Les Quais 22130 Plancoët
Tel.: 33 (0) 2.96.84.10.24 – Fax: 33 (0) 2.96.84.01.93
ecrin@chateauxhotels.com
Jean-Pierre CROUZIL
3 rooms: 75 € / 120 €
4 suites: 120 € / 160 €
Breakfast: 14 €
Menu(s): 55 € / 92 € - **1/2 board:** 85 € / 130 €

In a village on a coast resembling lacework, the gentle comfort of sound-proofed rooms. An exquisite cuisine of fresh produce: lobster, fish from the bay, traditionally raised fowl, 450 wines on the list. Nearby: Cap Fréhel, Mont St-Michel. Walks in the forest, mountain-bikes available, sea trips.

hotel annual closing
06/01 > 05/02
restaurant annual closing
06/01 > 05/02
equipments
telephone, T.V., minibar, baby-sitting
environment
architecture contemporaine
leisure, relaxation
sauna, solarium

Visa • MASTER CARD

Road map p. 619
N12 dir. Dinan

Dinard-Pleurtuit: 15 km

Château du Val

Planguenoual

www.chateauxhotels.com/val | reservation service: 33 (0) 1.40.07.00.20

22400 Planguenoual
Tel.: 33 (0) 2.96.32.75.40 – Fax: 33 (0) 2.96.32.71.50
val@chateauxhotels.com
Jean-Luc LE PAGE & Muriel HERVE
21 rooms: 86 € / 138 €
2 flats: 183 € / 244 € - **3 suites:** 198 €
Breakfast: 9 €
Menu(s): 30 € / 57 € - **Carte:** 54 €

Open all year
equipments
telephone, internet, T.V.
Canal+, safe
environment
architecture 15e, park 11 ha,
garden, total calm
leisure, relaxation
heated pool/covered from april
to september, balnéo, sauna,
jacuzzi, tennis covered,
squashes, golf course 5 km,
horse-riding 1 km, beach 1 km

15th and 19th century chateau, 800 metres from the sea,
in a historically listed park.
Rooms in the chateau and
17th-18th century farm-
houses. Indoor sports complex: tennis courts, two
squash courts, heated swimming pool, jetstream, spa,
sauna, body building. Ideal for
visiting Brittany.

Visa ● MASTER CARD

Road map p. 619

N12 exit D81 - St-René, D786 dir.
Le-Val-André

 St-Brieuc: 25 km

Route de Riec-sur-Belon
29350 Moëllan-sur-Mer
Tel.: 33 (0) 2.98.39.77.77 – Fax: 33 (0) 2.98.39.72.07
kertalg@chateauxhotels.com
Brann MANROT LE GOARNIC

8 rooms: 80 € / 160 €
1 flat: 195 €
Breakfast: 10 €

A haven of stone and moss, a legendary space between sky and sea: romantic charm, refined decor in the rooms, 218-acre park. Pont-Aven, city of the painters, is only 9 km away, the fine sandy beaches, 4 km. On the spot, walks in the forest, river fishing.

hotel annual closing
15/11 > 10/04

equipments
telephone, T.V., safe

environment
architecture 18°, park 85 ha, garden, terrace 150 m², view, total calm

leisure, relaxation
tennis 3 km, golf course 18 km, horse-riding 1 km

Visa ● MASTER CARD

Road map p. 619

N165 exit Quimperlé-centre - D116 then D24 dir. Moëlan

✈ Lorient: 19 km

Manoir du Stang

Quimper | La Forêt-Fouesnant

www.chateauxhotels.com/stang | reservation service: 33 (0) 1.40.07.00.20

29940 La Forêt-Fouesnant
Tel.: 33 (0) 2.98.56.97.37 – Fax: 33 (0) 2.98.56.97.37
stang@chateauxhotels.com
Guy HUBERT
24 rooms: 76 € / 150 €
Breakfast: 8 €
Menu(s): 29 €

hotel annual closing
31/10 > 31/03
restaurant annual closing
01/01 > 01/07 • 31/08 > 01/07
equipments
lift, telephone
environment
architecture 15ᵉ, furniture 18ᵉ,
park 40 ha, garden, terrace
150 m², view, total calm
leisure, relaxation
golf course 0.5 km,
horse-riding 2 km,
thalassotherapy, balneo

Beautiful Cornouaille manor house, in vast French-style gardens with lake, woods and 100-acre estate. Antique furniture, original panelling. Close to sea, harbor, fishing, boat trips to nearby islands (Glénans Islands). Nearby: golf, beaches, sailing school, swimming-pool, riding.

Road map p. 619

N165 exit Fouesnant then D44 then
D783 dir. Quimper

Quimper: 18 km

156, rue d'Antrain 35700 Rennes
Tel.: 33 (0) 2.99.38.05.55 – Fax: 33 (0) 2.99.38.53.40
lecoqgadby@chateauxhotels.com
Véronique BREGEON
9 rooms: 107 € / 148 €
1 suite: 244 € / 274 €
Breakfast: 18 €
Menu(s): 28,97 € / 54,88 € - **Carte:** 39,64 €
1/2 board: 148 € / 230 €

Located in a residential neigh-bourhood of Rennes, this im-posing bourgeois home has been an institution for nearly a century. The bedrooms are decorated with period furni-ture and oriental rugs. The inventive cooking is a savy mix of fish, seafood and regional produce from Brittany

Open all year
equipments
lift, telephone, internet, T.V.
Satellite, minibar, safe,
baby-sitting
environment
architecture 18e, furniture 18e,
garden, terrace 100 m²
leisure, relaxation
balneo, sauna, hammam,
tennis 2 km, golf course
10 km, horse-riding, beauty
salon

Visa ● Diners ● JCB ● MASTER CARD

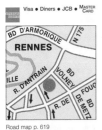

Road map p. 619

Exit Rennes North, dir. Beauregard

Rennes/Saint-Jacques:
15 km

Le Brittany
Roscoff
www.chateauxhotels.com/brittany | reservation service: 33 (0) 1.40.07.00.20

Boulevard Sainte Barbe 29681 Roscoff
Tel.: 33 (0) 2.98.69.70.78 – Fax: 33 (0) 2.98.61.13.29
brittany@chateauxhotels.com
Patricia CHAPALAIN
23 rooms: 90 € / 136 €
1 flat: 151 € / 200 € - **1 suite:** 151 € / 200 €
Breakfast: 11,5 €
Menu(s): 22,87 € / 49 € - **Carte:** 46 €
1/2 board: 90 € / 113 €

hotel annual closing
01/01 > 21/03●22/10 > 31/12
restaurant annual closing
01/01 > 21/03●22/10 > 31/12
equipments
lift, telephone, internet, T.V.
Satellite, safe, baby-sitting
environment
architecture 17°, terrace
60 m², view
leisure, relaxation
heated pool/covered, tennis
1 km, golf course 15 km,
horse-riding 5 km, beauty
salon, thalassotherapy, balneo,
sauna, hammam, jacuzzi,
painting lessons

On the old port of Roscoff, this Breton seaside manor house offers the highest standard of comfort. Heated and covered swimming pool. Gastronomic and recognized restaurant Le Yachtman. Nearby, sea water treatment centres, ferry services to Ireland and Great Britain. Numerous excursions possibilities.

Visa ● JCB ● MASTER CARD

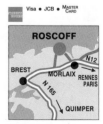

Road map p. 619
Speed road N12 exit Morlaix

Brest-Guipavas: 45 km

Sable d'or les Pins ∣ Frehel

www.chateauxhotels.com/voileor ∣ reservation service: 33 (0) 1.40.07.00.20

Allée des Acacias 22240 Frehel

Tel.: 33 (0) 2.96.41.42.49 – Fax: 33 (0) 2.96.41.55.45
voileor@chateauxhotels.com
Michel HELLIO

21 rooms: 80 € / 125 €
4 flats: 99 € / 228 € - **2 suites:** 142 € / 203 €
Breakfast: 11,5 €
Menu(s): 29 € / 68,6 € - **Carte:** 30,49 €
1/2 board: 88 € / 111 €

Michel Hellio is a creative chef who blends the savours of seafood and country produce with skill and elegance. A house of quality, opposite the most beautiful bay in Brittany, where the designer rooms are decorated in a subdued contemporary style. Near Cap Frehel.

hotel annual closing
01/01 > 11/03
restaurant annual closing
01/01 > 11/03
restaurant weekly closing
mon, tue(lun)
28/02 > 30/09
equipments
telephone, internet, T.V.
Satellite, safe, baby-sitting
environment
furniture contemporain,
garden, terrace, view
leisure, relaxation
tennis 1 km, golf course 2 km,
horse-riding 2 km, solarium,
golf

Road map p. 619

Road Rennes/St Brieuc, dir.
Lamballe/Erquy

Dinard: 35 km

A la Duchesse Anne

Saint-Malo Intra-Muros

www.chateauxhotels.com/duchesseanne | reservation service: 33 (0) 1.40.07.00.20

5, Place Guy La Chambre
35400 Saint-Malo Intra-Muros
Tel.: 33 (0) 2.99.40.85.33 – Fax: 33 (0) 2.99.40.00.28
duchesseanne@chateauxhotels.com
Serge & Maryvonne THIROUARD
Carte: 48 €

restaurant annual closing
01/12 > 01/02
restaurant weekly closing
mon(lun), wen
01/05 > 01/10
mon(lun), wen, sun(ev)
01/10 > 01/05
environment
terrace

Married to Charles VII, then to Louis XII, the Duchesse Anne fiercely defended her duchy which was joined to France in 1532. The restaurant is set in the pirates' city, under the ramparts: seafood products, grilled lobster, fine and seasonal fish, flat oysters, homemade foie gras...

Road map p. 619

N12 exit Saint-Malo

Dinard: 14 km

35350 La Gouesnière
Tel.: 33 (0) 2.99.58.24.50 – Fax: 33 (0) 2.99.58.28.41
bonaban@chateauxhotels.com
Vlasta SILER
30 rooms: 58 € / 153 €
2 suites: 206 € / 275 €
Breakfast: 10 €
Menu(s): 23 € / 49 € - **Carte:** 25 € -
1/2 board: 87 € / 182 €

This 17th century château, located on site that once overlooked the Brittany Steppes, blends the sumptuous past with the modernistic present. Spacious, comfortable and personalised rooms, a vast park and a gourmet restaurant are a tribute to tradition, wih an unexpected dash of creativity.

Open all year

equipments
lift, telephone, internet, T.V. Satellite, safe, baby-sitting

environment
architecture 17e, park 27 ha, garden, terrace 25 m², view, total calm

leisure, relaxation
golf course 12 km, horse-riding 1 km, thalassotherapy, thermal baths, jacuzzi

Visa ● MASTER CARD

Road map p. 619
D4 dir. La Gouesnière

Dinard: 15 km

Hôtel Beaufort

Saint-Malo **ı** Saint Malo
www.chateauxhotels.com/hotelbeaufort **ı** reservation service: 33 (0) 1.40.07.00.20

25, chaussée du sillon 35400 Saint Malo
Tel.: 33 (0) 2.99.40.99.99 – Fax: 33 (0) 2.99.40.99.62
hotelbeaufort@chateauxhotels.com
Mark & Sylvie PETERSON
22 rooms: 70 € / 170 €
Breakfast: 9,23 €

Open all year
equipments
lift, telephone, internet, T.V.
environment
architecture 19ᵉ, furniture
contemporain, view
leisure, relaxation
golf course 20 km, horse-riding
5 km, thalassotherapy

In exceptional surroundings, close to the Ramparts and overlooking the wide bay of Saint-Malo, the Hotel Beaufort, totally renovated in 2001, retains the charm of a private residence, where sophisticated decor is combined with friendly service suited to the individual's needs.

Road map p. 619

A11 Paris-Rennes, N137 Rennes/St-Malo, dir. Railway station-le Sillon

 Saint-Malo/Dinard/Pleurtuit:
15 km

Bretagne ı

La Malouinière des Longchamps

Saint-Malo I Saint-Jouan-des-Guerets

www.chateauxhotels.com/longchamps | reservation service: 33 (0) 1.40.07.00.20

35430 Saint-Jouan-des-Guerets
Tel.: 33 (0) 2.99.82.74.00 – Fax: 33 (0) 2.99.82.74.14
longchamps@chateauxhotels.com
Blandine GOGER
9 rooms: 64 € / 138 €
5 flats: 318 € / 820 €
Breakfast: 9 €

At the gates of the pirate city, in a flower garden, a warm welcome in a family atmosphere. Heated swimming pool, tennis, mini-golf, table-tennis, billiards. Near to the old city of Saint-Malo, Dinard, Dinan, Cap Fréhel, Cancale, Mont Saint-Michel, Jersey and Guernsey.

hotel annual closing
15/11 > 01/04
equipments
telephone, T.V. Satellite
environment
architecture 18e, garden, terrace 300 m², total calm
leisure, relaxation
heated pool, billiards, mini-golf, golf course 15 km, horse-riding 10 km, thalassotherapy, thermal baths, Mont-St-Michel

Visa ● MASTER CARD

Road map p. 619
N137 exit St-Jouan

Dinard: 12 km

La Villefromoy

Saint-Malo

www.chateauxhotels.com/villefromoy | reservation service: 33 (0) 1.40.07.00.20

7, boulevard Hébert 35400 Saint-Malo
Tel.: 33 (0) 2.99.40.92.20 – Fax: 33 (0) 2.99.56.79.49
villefromoy@chateauxhotels.com
Georges LE TOUMELIN
19 rooms: 76,22 € / 121,96 €
2 suites: 137,2 € / 213,43 €
Breakfast: 9 €

hotel annual closing
18/11 > 19/12
equipments
lift, telephone, internet, T.V.
Canal+
environment
architecture 19°, garden
leisure, relaxation
tennis 3 km, golf course
15 km, horse-riding 3 km,
thalassotherapy, thermal baths

This lovely Second Empire beachside residence successfully marries past luxury with modern comfort. The innate hospitality of your hosts will make your stay unforgettable. Near the hotel, the sea-side promenade leads to the pirate city with its many restaurants, bars and entertainments.

Visa ● Diners ● MASTER CARD

Road map p. 619

RN 137 exit St-Malo dir. "Thermes Marins"

Dinard: 15 km

GARE DE LA GOUESNIERE
35350 Saint-Méloir-des-Ondes
Tel.: 33 (0) 2.99.89.10.46 – Fax: 33 (0) 2.99.89.12.62
tirelguerin@chateauxhotels.com
Mesdames TIREL & GUERIN
48 rooms: 57,93 € / 137,2 €
2 suites: 137,20 € / 182,90 €
Breakfast: 9,15 €
Menu(s): 20 € / 70 € - **Carte:** 42,7 €
1/2 board: 59,50 € / 89,20 €

Visitors first come here for the cuisine which harmoniously combines classical tradition and lightness. Near the seaside resorts. 10 km from Saint-Malo and Cancale, famous for its oysters parks. In the district, Mont Saint-Michel, departure point for the Channel Islands and Great Britain.

hotel annual closing
08/12 > 08/01
restaurant annual closing
08/12 > 08/01
restaurant weekly closing
sun(ev)
01/10 > 31/03
equipments
lift, telephone, internet, T.V. Satellite, minibar, safe, baby-sitting
environment
furniture contemporain, garden, terrace 100 m²
leisure, relaxation
heated pool/covered, golf course 20 km, horse-riding 1 km, sauna, fitness, jacuzzi

Visa ● Diners ● JCB ● Master Card

Road map p. 619
N137 exit Châteauneuf, D76 dir.Cancale.

Dinard: 15 km

Villa Kerrasy

Vannes

www.chateauxhotels.com/kerasy | reservation service: 33 (0) 1.40.07.00.20

20, avenue Favrel et Lincy 56000 Vannes
Tel.: 33 (0) 2.97.68.36.83 – Fax: 33 (0) 2.97.68.36.84
kerasy@chateauxhotels.com
Jean-Jacques VIOLO
11 rooms: 90 € / 141 €
1 suite: 245 € / 282 €
Breakfast: 10 €

hotel annual closing
07/01 > 20/01 ● 11/11 > 01/12

equipments
telephone, internet, T.V.
Satellite, minibar, safe,
baby-sitting

environment
architecture contemporaine,
garden, terrace 40 m²

leisure, relaxation
tennis 1 km, golf course
10 km, horse-riding 2 km

A stone's throw from medieval Vannes, this hotel of character recalls the olden days of the East India company. Each room is decorated and named after one of the 12 legendary ports: Mocha, Canton, Pondicherry. Japanese garden, generous food with hints of spice. A place to dream of faraway travels.

Visa ● MASTER CARD

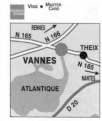

Road map p. 619

A11 then N166 exit Vannes Nantes - from Nantes: N165 exit Vannes Centre

 Lorient Lann Bihoué: 60 km

Bretagne |

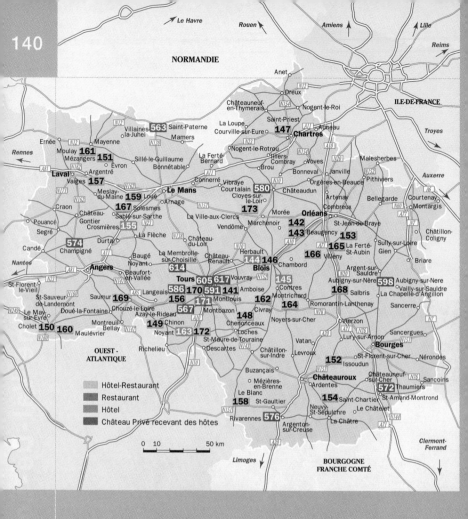

Centre Maine Val-de-Loire

Route de Chargé 37400 Amboise
Tel.: 33 (0) 2.47.57.23.67 – Fax: 33 (0) 2.47.57.32.50
pray@chateauxhotels.com
Ludovic LAURENTY – Adrien CARIOU
17 rooms: 89 € / 160 €
2 flats: 179 € / 230 €
Breakfast: 11 €
Menu(s): 29 € / 52 € - **Carte:** 50 €

The strength of this XIIIth century fortress' massive towers combines with the beauty of its Renaissance façade. An historical residence in a magic region, the Châteaux de la Loire. Traditionnal and new gastronomy, facing the 17th century tapestries and monumental fireplace in the dining room...

Visa ● Diners ● MASTER CARD

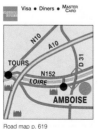

Road map p. 619

A10 exit Amboise. D31 dir. Amboise then D751 dir. Blois

hotel annual closing
02/01 > 10/02

restaurant annual closing
02/01 > 10/02

equipments
telephone, T.V., safe, baby-sitting

environment
architecture 13^e, furniture antique, park 5 ha, garden, terrace 30 m^2, view, vegetable garden

leisure, relaxation
heated pool, tennis 2 km, golf course 2 km, horse-riding 2 km, helicopter trips

Tours: 47 km

L'Abbaye
Beaugency
www.chateauxhotels.com/abbaye | reservation service: 33 (0) 1.40.07.00.20

2, quai de l'Abbaye 45190 Beaugency
Tel.: 33 (0) 2.38.44.67.35 – Fax: 33 (0) 2.38.44.87.92
abbaye@chateauxhotels.com
Armand AUPETIT – Nicolas MATHIEU
13 rooms: 68 € / 90 €
4 flats: 90 € / 106 €
Breakfast: 7,5 €
Menu(s): 30 €

Open all year
equipments
telephone, T.V., safe
environment
architecture 17e, terrace
150 m², view
leisure, relaxation
heated pool/covered, tennis
0.3 km, golf course 6 km,
horse-riding 10 km, 27 and
36-hole golf ranges

*17th abbey overlooking the
Loire ans its old bridge. Between Beauce and Sologne,
18 km from Chambord.
Rooms which were the former
monk's cells. Historical façade
and staircase. Traditional gastronomy : lobster in truffe
dressing, roasted veal kidneys
in Chinon wine.*

Visa ● Diners ● JCB ● MASTER CARD

Road map p. 619
A10 exit Meung-Baugency and N152

Orly/Charles-de-Gaulle:
150 km

12, rue des Eaux-Bleues 45190 Beaugency
Tel.: 33 (0) 2.38.44.68.15 – Fax: 33 (0) 2.38.44.10.01
tonnellerie@chateauxhotels.com
Marie-Christine POUEY
16 rooms: 70 € / 170 €
4 suites: 110 € / 200 €
Breakfast: 12 €
Menu(s): 25 € / 45 € - **Carte:** 55 € -
1/2 board: 100 € / 195 €

An hour and a half from Paris in the region of the great Loire châteaux, a former wine-merchant's house. The elegance of the decoration tunes perfectly with the food which adds modern notes to traditional specialities. Loire Valley wines. Near Bordes international golf course.

hotel annual closing
26/12 > 28/02
restaurant annual closing
26/12 > 28/02
restaurant weekly closing
tue(lun), wen(lun), thi(lun), fri(lun), sat(lun)
equipments
lift, telephone, internet, T.V. Satellite, baby-sitting
environment
architecture 19e, furniture 19e, garden, terrace
leisure, relaxation
heated pool, golf course 9 km, horse-riding 7 km

Visa ● MASTER CARD

Road map p. 619

A10 exit Mer or Beaugency them RN 152 to Tavers Centre

Orly: 130 km

Château de Moulins

Blois | **Herbault**

www.chateauxhotels.com/moulins | reservation service: 33 (0) 1.40.07.00.20

Landes-le-Gaulois 41190 Herbault
Tel.: 33 (0) 2.54.20.17.93 – Fax: 33 (0) 2.54.20.17.99
moulins@chateauxhotels.com
Gilbert ENFOUX
19 rooms: 107 € / 153 €
6 flats: 182 €
Breakfast: 8 €

Open all year

equipments
telephone, internet, T.V.,
minibar, safe

environment
architecture 17e, park 90 ha,
garden, terrace 200 m², view,
total calm

leisure, relaxation
tennis 2 km, golf course 9 km,
horse-riding 8 km

In the valley of the chateaux, between Blois and Vendôme, a wooded estate of 225 acres with private hunting and fishing. An enchanting setting whose origins date back to the 13 th century withs its vast lounge with fireplace, its box-cellings and golden atmosphere, its comfortable rooms.

Visa • JCB • MASTER CARD

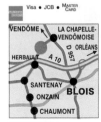

Road map p. 619

A10 exit Blois, dir. Vendôme

Le Breuil: 2 km

Route de Fougères 41700 Cheverny

Tel.: 33 (0) 2.54.44.20.20 – Fax: 33 (0) 2.54.44.30.40

breuil@chateauxhotels.com

M. & Mme. Jean-Louis TETENOIRE

16 rooms: 83 € / 140 €
2 suites: 199 € / 245 €
Breakfast: 11 €

Between Loire and Sologne, in a 75-acre wooded park, XVIIIth-century château: gleaming old furniture, rooms painted in pastel colours, the pomp of the great drawing-room. Near all the famous Châteaux de la Loire: Blois, Chambord, Chaumont, Amboise, Chenonceau, Cheverny.

hotel annual closing
15/11 > 15/03

hotel weekly closing
mon, sun (out of season)

equipments
telephone, T.V., minibar

environment
architecture 18e, park 30 ha, garden, total calm

leisure, relaxation
tennis 4 km, golf course 3.5 km, horse-riding 1 km

Visa ● MASTER CARD

Road map p. 619

A10 exit Blois - D52 dir. Cheverny

Orly/Charles-de-Gaulle: 190 km

Le Médicis

Blois

www.chateauxhotels.com/medicis | reservation service: 33 (0) 1.40.07.00.20

Route d'Angers 2, allée François 1ᵉʳ
41000 Blois
Tel.: 33 (0) 2.54.43.94.04 – Fax: 33 (0) 2.54.42.04.05
medicis@chateauxhotels.com
Christian GARANGER
12 rooms: 83 € / 112 €
1 suite: 112 €
Breakfast: 11 €
Menu(s): 20 € / 61 € - **Carte:** 30 €
1/2 board: 80 € / 92 €

hotel annual closing
02/01 > 02/02
restaurant annual closing
02/01 > 02/02
hotel weekly closing
sun
15/10 > 15/04
restaurant weekly closing
sun(ev)
15/10 > 15/04
equipments
telephone, T.V. Canal+,
minibar
environment
architecture 19ᵉ
leisure, relaxation
tennis 3 km, golf course
12 km, horse-riding 3 km

Le Medicis situated in the François 1st resting place, with it's highly reputed food and the comfort of its twelve bedrooms, each with a personal touch to enhance your stay, air conditionned, sound proofed, bathroom, mini-bar, television channel and one suite with jaccuzi.

Visa ● Diners ● MASTER CARD

Road map p. 619

A10 exit Blois, dir. Town center, station and Angers

Centre Maine Val-de-Loire

Tours: 60 km

Manoir des Prés du Roy   147
Chartres I Saint-Prest
www.chateauxhotels.com/presroy | reservation service: 33 (0) 1.40.07.00.20

Allée des Prés du Roy 28300 Saint-Prest
Tel.: 33 (0) 2.37.22.27.27 – Fax: 33 (0) 2.37.22.24.92
presroy@chateauxhotels.com
Joëlle GOND
18 rooms: 56 € / 115 €
Breakfast: 8,30 €
Menu(s): 22,11 € / 35,06 € - **Carte:** 22 €

45 minutes from Paris and 5 minutes from Chartres, on the Eure river, is this pretty 16th century manor. Set in 30 acre park, the manor offers rooms with absolute comfort and charm. The chief will delight you with recipes in tune with seasons. Relax in the park, play tennis or billiards.

Open all year
equipments
lift, T.V., minibar
environment
architecture 16e, park 12 ha, terrace
leisure, relaxation
golf course 10 km

Visa ● MasterCard

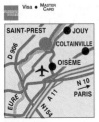

Road map p. 619
A11 exit 2 Chartres - A10 dir. Rouen

Aérodrôme de Champhol:
6 km

Le Bon Laboureur

Chenonceaux
www.chateauxhotels.com/laboureur | reservation service: 33 (0) 1.40.07.00.20

6, rue du Docteur Bretonneau
37150 Chenonceaux
Tel.: 33 (0) 2.47.23.90.02 – Fax: 33 (0) 2.47.23.82.01
laboureur@chateauxhotels.com
M. JEUDI
24 rooms: 65 € / 120 €
3 suites: 145 € / 180 €
Breakfast: 8,5 €
Menu(s): 30 € / 65 € - **Carte:** 45 €
1/2 board: 70 € / 105 €

hotel annual closing
12/11 > 20/12 ● 06/01 > 07/02
restaurant annual closing
12/11 > 20/12 ● 06/01 > 07/02
hotel weekly closing
wen, thi
15/10 > 01/04
restaurant weekly closing
tue(lun), thi(lun), sat(lun)
20/03 > 15/10
tue(lun), wen(ev), thi
15/10 > 01/04

equipments
telephone, T.V. Satellite, safe,
baby-sitting

environment
architecture 18ᵉ, park 3 ha,
garden, terrace 200 m²,
vegetable garden

leisure, relaxation
heated pool, tennis 0.4 km,
golf course 25 km, horse-riding
5 km

The pastel colours of the Loire Valley pervade this XVIIIth century Post house. Scattered among four charming houses, the rooms or apartments are bright and comfortable. In fine weather, the excellent cuisine is served on the patio that opens onto the flower garden. A pleasant stopping place.

Visa ● MASTER CARD

Road map p. 619

A10 exit Amboise, D40 dir. village-centre

 Tours: 30 km

Château de Danzay

D749 37420 Chinon
Tel.: 33 (0) 2.47.58.46.86 – Fax: 33 (0) 2.47.58.84.35
danzay@chateauxhotels.com
Jacques SARFATI
5 rooms: 160 € / 260 €
2 suites: 260 € / 280 €
Breakfast: 14 €
Menu(s): 50 € - **1/2 board:** 144 € / 194 €

Château built in 1461 by the squire of Louis XI. Enchanting peaceful setting. Park, terrace, luxury rooms. Candlelight dinners, delightful cuisine, Loire wines. Near Azay-le-Rideau, Chenonceau and other châteaux.

hotel annual closing
20/10 > 01/04
restaurant annual closing
30/09 > 01/05
equipments
T.V.
environment
architecture 15e, park 3 ha, garden, terrace, view, total calm
leisure, relaxation
heated pool, tennis 2 km, golf course 12 km, horse-riding 2 km

Visa • MASTER CARD

BOURGUEIL LANGEAIS
D 10 D 35 TOURS
D 749 N 152 LOIRE
SAUMUR RIGNY-USSÉ
CHINON D 751
POITIERS

Road map p. 619
A10 exit 24 dir. Chinon

Tours: 50 km

Centre Maine Val-de-Loire

Château de la Tremblaye
Cholet
www.chateauxhotels.com/tremblaye | reservation service: 33 (0) 1.40.07.00.20

Route des Sables 49300 Cholet
Tel.: 33 (0) 2.41.58.40.17 – Fax: 33 (0) 2.41.58.20.67
tremblaye@chateauxhotels.com
Allyson & Thierry GUIMARD
11 rooms: 84 € / 126 €
2 suites: 160 € / 209 €
Breakfast: 8,40 €
Menu(s): 19,82 € / 36,44 €

hotel annual closing
30/09 > 13/10
restaurant annual closing
30/09 > 13/10
restaurant weekly closing
mon(lun), sun(ev)
equipments
telephone, T.V.
environment
architecture 19º, park 4 ha,
garden, terrace, total calm
leisure, relaxation
heated pool, tennis 4 km, golf
course 4 km, horse-riding
2 km, bicycle hire at the hotel

Built in 1862 on the historic site of the Battle of Cholet, this magnificent château features tastefully decorated rooms from different eras (Empire, colonial). They overlook the pond and the vast tree-filled park. Enjoy the charm of the sitting rooms and revel in the refined, original cooking. Warm Welcome.

Visa ● Diners ● MASTER CARD

Road map p. 619

A11 exit Angers, N160 dir. Cholet

Relais du Gué de Selle
Evron-Mézangers
www.chateauxhotels.com/gueselles | reservation service: 33 (0) 1.40.07.00.20

151

Route de Mayenne 53600 Evron-Mézangers
Tel.: 33 (0) 2.43.91.20.00 – Fax: 33 (0) 2.43.91.20.10
gueselles@chateauxhotels.com
Didier PARIS & Didier PESCHARD
24 rooms: 47 € / 86 €
6 suites: 86 € / 108 €
Breakfast: 8 €
Menu(s): 18 € / 41 € - **Carte:** 42 €
1/2 board: 48 € / 80 €

An old restored farm, between a lake and forest, in a 200-acre park. Large dining-room with fireplaces and beams, lounges and terraces with view. To be tasted: lobster turnover with foie gras, fillet of pike/perch, the best wines of the Loire. Sailing, swimming, golfing, sauna, solarium...

Visa ● Master Card

Road map p. 619

A81 exit 2 Vaiges - D7 dir. Evron-Mayenne

hotel annual closing
22/12 > 10/01 ● 07/02 > 27/02
restaurant annual closing
22/12 > 10/01 ● 07/02 > 27/02
hotel weekly closing
mon(ev), fri(ev), sun(ev)
01/10 > 30/05
restaurant weekly closing
mon(lun)
01/07 > 30/09
mon, fri(ev), sun(ev)
01/10 > 30/05
equipments
telephone, internet, T.V.
Satellite/Canal+, minibar
environment
architecture 19ᵉ, park 80 ha,
garden, terrace 250 m², view
leisure, relaxation
heated pool, golf course
30 km, horse-riding 1 km,
sauna, solarium, fitness,
microlight flying (12 km)

Boulevard Stalingrad 36100 Issoudun
Tel.: 33 (0) 2.54.03.59.59 – Fax: 33 (0) 2.54.03.13.03
cognette@chateauxhotels.com
Alain NONNET

11 rooms: 60 € / 121 €
3 suites: 124 € / 229 €
Breakfast: 10 €
Menu(s): 21 € / 65 € - **Carte:** 54 €
1/2 board: 73 € / 104 €

Open all year
equipments
telephone, internet, T.V.
Satellite, minibar, safe
environment
architecture, garden, terrace
15 m², total calm
leisure, relaxation
golf course 10 km, horse-riding
1 km

An inn since 1789, frequently visited by Balzac, where he wrote La Rabouilleuse. Master Chef of France, Mr. Nonnet, and his family offer superb gourmet cuisine and exceptional comfort, in individually furnished rooms, and an extremely warm welcome. Extensive menu with Berry specialities.

Visa ● Diners ● MASTER CARD

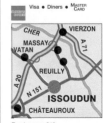

Road map p. 619

A20 or N151 dir. Issoudun. City centre.

Aérogare de Fay: 8 km

Route de Marcilly 45240 La Ferté Saint-Aubin
Tel.: 33 (0) 2.38.64.84.00 – Fax: 33 (0) 2.38.64.84.20
leschenes@chateauxhotels.com
Jean ELIA
23 rooms: 81 € / 110 €
1 flat: 144 €
Breakfast: 11 €
Menu(s): 40 € / 50 € - **Carte:** 45 €

In the heart of the Sologne, at the edge of the forest, this charming and traditional old house is a peaceful haven set in 30 acres of woodland. Large, comfortable rooms. Sophisticated cuisine using fresh produce complimented by fine Loire valley wines. For all nature-lovers.

hotel annual closing
01/02 > 15/02 ● 22/12 > 04/01
restaurant annual closing
01/02 > 15/02 ● 22/11 > 04/01
equipments
telephone, internet, T.V., safe, baby-sitting, valet parking
environment
park 72 ha, garden, terrace, view, vegetable garden, total calm
leisure, relaxation
tennis 4 km, golf course 5 km, horse-riding 4 km, balneo, swimming pool 2km

Visa

Road map p. 619

A71 exit La Ferté-St-Aubin, N20 - North D921

Orly: 100 km

Château de la Vallée Bleue

La Chatre I Saint-Chartier

www.chateauxhotels.com/valleebleue I reservation service: 33 (0) 1.40.07.00.20

Route de Verneuil 36400 Saint-Chartier
Tel.: 33 (0) 2.54.31.01.91 – Fax: 33 (0) 2.54.31.04.48
valleebleue@chateauxhotels.com
Gérard GASQUET

13 rooms: 65 € / 120 €
2 suites: 130 € / 165 €
Breakfast: 10 €
Menu(s): 35 € - **1/2 board:** 70 € / 110 €

hotel annual closing
04/11 > 15/03
restaurant annual closing
04/11 > 15/03
equipments
telephone, internet, T.V., minibar, safe
environment
architecture 19e, furniture 19e, park 4 ha, garden, terrace, view, vegetable garden, total calm
leisure, relaxation
tennis 7 km, golf course 18 km, horse-riding 15 km

In a 10-acre park, romantic halting-place in George Sand's doctor castle. Gastronomic restaurant with regional specialities. Exhaustive wine list, aperitifs and after dinner drinks. Swimming-pool for adults and flounder-basin for children. Terrace in summer, dinner by the fireside in winter.

Visa ● MasterCard

Road map p. 619

A20 exit 12 dir. Montluçon (La Châtre), D943, D69-A71 exit 8, D951 dir. La Châtre, D69

Châteauroux: 30 km

La Flèche ⏐ Crosmières

www.chateauxhotels.com/potardiere ⏐ reservation service: 33 (0) 1.40.07.00.20

Route de Bazouges 72200 Crosmières
Tel.: 33 (0) 2.43.45.83.47 – Fax: 33 (0) 2.43.45.81.06
potardiere@chateauxhotels.com
Marie-Yvonne & François BENOIST
12 rooms: 60 € / 100 €
1 flat: 110 € - **4 suites:** 100 € / 150 €
Breakfast: 8 €

A manor house in Angevin style dating from the 17th and 19th centuries. The national stud takes up residence from March to July in the meadows and vast stables. A superb place for nature-lovers who can enjoy cosy rooms and renovated suites, as well as numerous leisure activities in the grounds.

Visa ● MASTER CARD

Road map p. 619

A11 exit La Flèche/Sablé or Durtal

Open all year

equipments
telephone, internet, T.V. Satellite, minibar, baby-sitting

environment
architecture 18ᵉ, park 12 ha, garden, terrace 150 m², view, total calm

leisure, relaxation
heated pool (form may to sept.), golf course 18 km, paintball, clay-pigeon shooting

Marce/Angers: 20 km

Château de Rochecotte

Langeais

www.chateauxhotels.com/rochecotte | reservation service: 33 (0) 1.40.07.00.20

St-Patrice 37130 Langeais
Tel.: 33 (0) 2.47.96.16.16 – Fax: 33 (0) 2.47.96.90.59
rochecotte@chateauxhotels.com
Gérard PASQUIER
32 rooms: 122 € / 192 €
3 flats: 256 €
Breakfast: 14,5 €
Menu(s): 37 € / 58 € - **Carte:** 77 €
1/2 board: 107,50 € / 141 €

hotel annual closing
28/01 > 24/02
restaurant annual closing
28/01 > 24/02
restaurant weekly closing
mon, thi(lun)
01/04 > 30/10
mon
01/11 > 30/03
equipments
lift, telephone, internet, T.V.
Satellite, safe
environment
architecture 18º, furniture 18º,
park 12 ha, garden, terrace
300 m², view, total calm
leisure, relaxation
heated pool, tennis 10 km, golf
course 30 km, horse-riding
10 km, solarium, jacuzzi, table
tennis

*This castle overlooking the
Loire, once the Prince of Tall-
eyrand's property, appeals
both to the eye and the imagination - classical architecture,
Italian terrace, the French gardens, elegant salons, suites
and guest rooms. The excellent food is a tribute to the
grandeur of a distinguished
past.*

Visa ● MASTER CARD

Road map p. 619

A10 exit nº 20 Ste-Radegonde,
N152 dir. Saumur then D35 dir. Bourgueil

 Tours: 30 km

Rue du Fief aux Moines 53480 Vaiges
Tel.: 33 (0) 2.43.90.50.07 – Fax: 33 (0) 2.43.90.57.40
commerce@chateauxhotels.com
Samuel OGER

28 rooms: 52 € / 83 €
Breakfast: 7 €
Menu(s): 17,5 € / 45 € - **Carte:** 40 € -
1/2 board: 49 € / 55 €

Between the prehistoric site of Saulges, the Gallo-Roman ruins of Jublain and the medieval village of Sainte-Suzanne, five generations of the same family have retained charm and authenticity in this residence. Good meals, a large room, a fireplace, an air-conditioned veranda overlooking the garden.

hotel annual closing
04/01 > 28/01
restaurant annual closing
04/01 > 28/01
hotel weekly closing
fri (ev), sun (ev)
30/09 > 30/04
restaurant weekly closing
fri(ev), sun(ev)
30/09 > 30/04
equipments
lift, telephone, internet, T.V.
Canal+, minibar
environment
garden, terrace 30 m²
leisure, relaxation
tennis 0.5 km, golf course
20 km, sauna

Visa ● Diners ● MASTER CARD

Road map p. 619

A81 exit n° 2 inside the village or N157
dir. Paris-Brest

✈ Rennes: 90 km

Domaine de l'Etape

Le Blanc

www.chateauxhotels.com/etape | reservation service: 33 (0) 1.40.07.00.20

Route de Belâbre 36300 Le Blanc
Tel.: 33 (0) 2.54.37.18.02 – Fax: 33 (0) 2.54.37.75.59
etape@chateauxhotels.com
Nicole SEILLER
35 rooms: 36,59 € / 88,42 €
Breakfast: 7,93 €
Menu(s): 19,82 € / 53,36 € - **Carte:** 39 €

Open all year

equipments
telephone, T.V.

environment
architecture 19e, park 210 ha,
garden, terrace, view, total
calm

leisure, relaxation
tennis 5 km, golf course 5 km,
horse-riding 5 km, beauty
salon, solarium

Delightful 19th-century residence in a vast 500 acres park and 45 acres lake for fishing and boating. Horse riding year-round. Airfield nearby, with flying club, parachuting and glidding. You are in the Brenne nature reserve, in the Berry, the country of a thousand lakes with many bird sanctuaries.

Visa ● Diners ● MASTER CARD

Road map p. 619

D10 dir. Belâbre

Poitiers: 60 km

11-13, rue de la Libération 72540 Loué
Tel.: 33 (0) 2.43.88.40.03 – Fax: 33 (0) 2.43.88.62.08
ricordeau@chateauxhotels.com
Jean-Yves HERMAN
8 rooms: 88,42 € / 103,67 €
5 suites: 114,35 € / 129,58 €
Breakfast: 9,91 €
Menu(s): 19,82 € / 68 € - **Carte:** 30,49 €
1/2 board: 68,60 € / 75,47 €

An 18th century stagecoach relay. Rooms overlooking the terrace. delicious specialities. Landscaped garden, river with boats. A stop-over not to be missed between Normandy, Touraine and Brittany, two hours from Paris. Near the Solesme Abbey and the Malicorne faience factory.

hotel annual closing
28/01 > 01/03
restaurant annual closing
28/01 > 01/03
hotel weekly closing
sun(ev),mon
restaurant weekly closing
sun(ev),mon
equipments
lift, telephone, internet, T.V.
Satellite/Canal+
environment
architecture 19^e, park 3 ha,
garden, terrace, vegetable
garden, total calm
leisure, relaxation
heated pool, tennis 3 km, golf
course 25 km, horse-riding
8 km

Visa ● Diners ● MASTER CARD

Road map p. 619

A11 or A81 exit Sablé or D157 dir.
Laval

Rennes: 100 km

Château Colbert

Maulévrier

www.chateauxhotels.com/colbert | reservation service: 33 (0) 1.40.07.00.20

Place du Château 49360 Maulévrier
Tel.: 33 (0) 2.41.55.51.33 – Fax: 33 (0) 2.41.55.09.02
colbert@chateauxhotels.com
Dominique POPIHN-CIROT
23 rooms: 45,73 € / 91,47 €
Breakfast: 7 €
Menu(s): 26,68 € / 38,87 € - **Carte:** 34,3 €

hotel annual closing
29/01 > 01/03
restaurant annual closing
29/01 > 01/03
equipments
lift, telephone, internet, T.V.,
minibar, baby-sitting
environment
architecture 18°, park 4 ha,
garden, terrace 400 m², total
calm
leisure, relaxation
tennis 1 km, golf course
12 km, horse-riding 6 km

Located between the châteaux of the Loire and the Atlantic beaches, this beautiful 19th century residence is a haven of peace and warmth. All fully-equipped rooms offer the height of modern comfort, while the cooking is a gourmet's delight. Also a marvellous place for nature lovers.

Visa ● Diners ● MASTER CARD

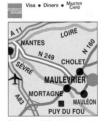

Road map p. 619

A10 exit Angers, dir. Cholet/Poitiers /
A87 exit Chollet South (beginning
2002)

Nantes: 70 km

Domaine du Bas Mont 53100 MOULAY
Tel.: 33 (0) 2.43.00.48.42 – Fax: 33 (0) 2.43.08.10.58
marjolaine@chateauxhotels.com
Jean-Marie CHAPIN
17 rooms: 49 € / 66 €
Breakfast: 7,5 €
Menu(s): 15 € / 49 € - **1/2 board:** 50 € / 65 €

5 km from Mayenne, near a lovely river, this house of character stands on 5 acres of parkland. Here, friendly service, nature and relaxation are the keystone to your stay. The bright airy rooms and shaded terrace look out onto the centenary chestnut trees

Visa ● MASTER CARD

Road map p. 619

from Laval: N162 dir. Mayenne - from Mayenne: N162 dir. Laval

hotel annual closing
01/01 > 06/01 ● 11/02 > 24/02
restaurant annual closing
01/01 > 06/01 ● 11/02 > 24/02
equipments
telephone, internet, T.V. Satellite, minibar
environment
architecture contemporaine, furniture contemporain, park 2 ha, garden, terrace, view, total calm
leisure, relaxation
french billiards, tennis 5 km, golf course 20 km, horse-riding 10 km

Château de la Menaudière

Montrichard
www.chateauxhotels.com/menaudiere | reservation service: 33 (0) 1.40.07.00.20

B.P. 15 41401 Montrichard
Tel.: 33 (0) 2.54.71.23.45 – Fax: 33 (0) 2.54.71.34.58
menaudiere@chateauxhotels.com
Geneviève SEGUI
26 rooms: 61 € / 137 €
1 flat: 244 €
Breakfast: 14,5 €
Menu(s): 22 € / 50,50 € - **Carte:** 45,73 €
1/2 board: 91,50 € / 122 €

hotel annual closing
18/11 > 28/02
restaurant annual closing
18/11 > 28/02
hotel weekly closing
sun(ev), mon
01/10 > 30/11
sun(ev), mon
01/03 > 30/04
restaurant weekly closing
sun(ev), mon
01/10 > 30/11
sun(ev), mon
01/03 > 30/04
equipments
telephone, internet, T.V.
Satellite, minibar, safe
environment
architecture 16e, park 15 ha,
garden, terrace, total calm
leisure, relaxation
heated pool, golf course
20 km, horse-riding 10 km,
golf - different levels and
options, tennis

In a large park very close to Chenonceau, in the heart of the Touraine, this castle whose foundations go back to 1443, offers you elegant and individually decorated rooms, two restaurants, lounge, bar. The warm and refined welcome, the delicacy of the cuisine makes this a privileged place.

Visa ● Diners ● JCB ● MASTER CARD

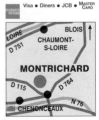

Road map p. 619

A10 exit Blois, D115 dir. Montrichard

Tours: 40 km

Château de Brou
Sainte-Marne-de-Touraine I Noyant-de-Touraine
www.chateauxhotels.com/brou | reservation service: 33 (0) 1.40.07.00.20

163

37800 Noyant-de-Touraine
Tel.: 33 (0) 2.47.65.80.80 – Fax: 33 (0) 2.47.65.82.92
brou@chateauxhotels.com
Bernadette & Christian GIRAULT
10 rooms: 90 € / 150 €
2 suites: 180 € / 260 €
Breakfast: 12 €

A authentic Xvth century chateau set in 250 acre park overlooking the Coutineau valley. Original decorations. The Richelieu, Joan of Arc, Henry IV and Balzac rooms are eminently comfortable and welcoming. A haven of peace in the heart of the Loire region.

hotel annual closing
02/01 > 28/03
hotel weekly closing
sun(ev)
11/11 > 02/01
equipments
telephone, internet, T.V.
Satellite, minibar, baby-sitting
environment
architecture 15ᵉ, park 100 ha,
garden, terrace, view,
vegetable garden, total calm
leisure, relaxation
tennis 3 km, golf course
25 km, horse-riding 4 km,
jacuzzi, music at the Château
weekend packages

Visa ● Diners ● MASTER CARD

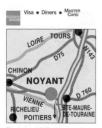

Road map p. 619

A10 exit 25 Ste-Maure, D760 dir.
Chinon-Richelieu

St Symphorien-Tours: 40 km

Le Clos du Cher

Saint-Aignan **I** Noyers-sur-Cher
www.chateauxhotels.com/closcher | reservation service: 33 (0) 1.40.07.00.20

Route de Saint-Aignan 41140 Noyers-sur-Cher
Tel.: 33 (0) 2.54.75.00.03 – Fax: 33 (0) 2.54.75.03.79
closcher@chateauxhotels.com
Michèle GALLOPIN
10 rooms: 59,46 € / 88,42 €
Breakfast: 9,15 €
Menu(s): 15,24 € / 53,36 € - **Carte:** 47 €
1/2 board: 60,22 € / 108,24 €

Open all year
equipments
telephone, internet, T.V.
Satellite, minibar, baby-sitting
environment
architecture 19e, garden,
terrace 30 m², total calm
leisure, relaxation
heated pool, tennis 1 km, golf
course 30 km, horse-riding
0.5 km, beauty salon

Deep in château country, between Touraine, Sologne and Berry, a luxurious and cosy hotel offering modern comforts. The restaurant will introduce you to the delights of French cuisine in the tradition of the region. On the banks of the Cher, let yourself be charmed by the romance of the forests.

Visa ● Diners ● MASTER CARD

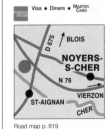

Road map p. 619

A10 exit Blois dir. Châteauroux - N76
between Tours et Vierzon

Orly/Charles-de-Gaulle:
250 km

Centre Maine Val-de-Loire I

Les Muids N20 45240 La Ferté-Saint-Aubin
Tel.: 33 (0) 2.38.64.65.14 – Fax: 33 (0) 2.38.76.50.08
muids@chateauxhotels.com
Rachel JENEVIN
21 rooms: 65 € / 145 €
1 suite: 175 €
Breakfast: 11 €
Menu(s): 20 € / 42 € - **Carte:** 21 €

Built in the XVIIIth century by an Irish officer in love with the Sologne, this beautifully modernised residence has maintained its original charm. Enjoy the comfortable bedrooms and suite, or the wood-panelled salons and dining rooms. Traditional cooking and selected vintage wines will seduce you.

restaurant annual closing
27/01 > 27/02
equipments
telephone, T.V. Satellite
environment
architecture 18°, park 33 ha, terrace
leisure, relaxation
golf course 2 km, horse-riding 7 km, thalassotherapy, balneo, sauna, hammam, fitness

Visa ● Diners ● MASTER CARD

Road map p. 619

A10 La Source - N20, 4km to the south of Ferté-Saint-Aubin

Orly: 130 km

Les Bouillants 41220 Villeny
Tel.: 33 (0) 2.54.98.23.94 – Fax: 33 (0) 2.54.98.23.99
chenesrouges@chateauxhotels.com
Nicole LAMBERT de LOULAY
9 rooms: 100 € / 122 €
1 suite: 138 €
Breakfast: 12 €
Menu(s): 27 € / 57 € - **1/2 board:** 92 € / 107 €

hotel annual closing
01/01 > 22/03
restaurant annual closing
01/01 > 22/03
hotel weekly closing
mon(lun), sun(lun)
01/09 > 31/05
mon, sun
01/09 > 31/05
restaurant weekly closing
closed at lunchtime
equipments
telephone, internet, T.V., safe
environment
park 2 ha, garden, terrace,
view, total calm
leisure, relaxation
heated pool, tennis 7 km, golf
course 15 km, horse-riding
7 km

An hour and a half from Paris, deep in the heart of the Sologne, a stately residence on the shore of its own private lake. Comfortable rooms, forest walks and fine food, with the emphasis on local game, are among the attractions of this relaxing spot. Fishing in the lake and shooting nearby.

Visa • MASTER CARD

Road map p. 619

A10 exit Orléans La Source, dir. D15 and D18

Tours: 95 km

16, place Dom Gueranger 72300 Solesmes
Tel.: 33 (0) 2.43.95.45.10 – Fax: 33 (0) 2.43.95.22.26
solesmes@chateauxhotels.com
Bertrand JAQUET
32 rooms: 72 € / 112 €
Breakfast: 10 €
Menu(s): 23 € / 54 € - **1/2 board:** 62 € / 78 €

The sound of plain chant at the Abbey of Solesmes diffuses a feeling of peace throughout this old house where rest and good food have always had their place. Didier Serre, a talented chef, gives free rein to his inspiration whilst never betraying tradition. Excellent wine list, cosy guestrooms.

Visa ● Diners ● MASTER CARD

Open all year
restaurant weekly closing
sun(ev)
01/11 > 31/03
equipments
lift, telephone, T.V.
Satellite/Canal+, minibar, safe
environment
architecture 19ᵉ, garden
leisure, relaxation
tennis 3 km, golf course 3 km, horse-riding 4 km, sauna, solarium, fitness, jacuzzi

SORTIE 2 — ALENÇON
N 157 — A 81
VAIGES — LE MANS
SORTIE 1
SOLESMES
SABLÉ D306 — SORTIE 10
ANGERS NANTES — LA FLÈCHE

Road map p. 619

A11 exit Sablé, N157-D4 dir. Solesmes. A81 exit Vaiges

Le Mans: 45 km

Domaine de Valaudran

Salbris

www.chateauxhotels.com/valaudran | reservation service: 33 (0) 1.40.07.00.20

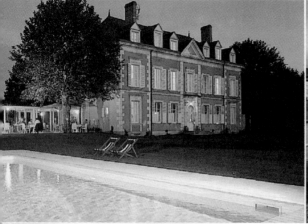

Avenue de Romorantin 41300 Salbris
Tel.: 33 (0) 2.54.97.20.00 – Fax: 33 (0) 2.54.97.12.22
valaudran@chateauxhotels.com
Famille DEBOIS-FROGE
27 rooms: 68,6 € / 99,09 €
4 flats: 150,92 €
Breakfast: 10,67 €
Menu(s): 18,29 € / 36,59 €

Open all year
hotel weekly closing
sun(lun)
15/09 > 15/04
restaurant weekly closing
mon(lun), sat(lun), sun
15/09 > 15/04
equipments
telephone, T.V., minibar,
baby-sitting
environment
architecture 19e, park 2 ha,
garden, terrace 45 m², view,
vegetable garden, total calm
leisure, relaxation
heated pool, tennis 2 km, golf
course 20 km, horse-riding
3 km

Luxury, calm and exquisite delight are the words to describe this XIXth century residence at the heart of Sologne. A haven of tranquility in a 5-acre park with heated pool. Breakfast is served on the sunlight terrace. Let the chef spoil you with his creative cooking based on local fresh products.

Visa • Diners • MASTER CARD

Road map p. 619

A71 exit Salbris (300 m from toll),
D724 dir. Salbris-centre

Orly: 120 km

32, quai Mayaud 49400 Saumur
Tel.: 33 (0) 2.41.67.30.30 – Fax: 33 (0) 2.41.67.51.00
anneanjou@chateauxhotels.com
Jean-René CAMUS
41 rooms: 51 € / 127 €
1 suite: 155 €
Breakfast: 9 €
Menu(s): 29 € / 55 € - **Carte:** 45 €
1/2 board: 123 € / 199 €

A private 18th century mansion transformed into a sumptuous hotel, with a historically graded façade and wrought-iron staircase beneath a trompe-l'oeil ceiling. Guestrooms overlooking the Loire or a 14th century chateau. On the 1st floor, 5 rooms have retained their original decor (Louis XVI, Empire)

Open all year
restaurant weekly closing
sun
01/01 > 31/12
equipments
lift, telephone, internet, T.V.
Satellite, minibar
environment
architecture 18e, furniture 18e,
garden, view
leisure, relaxation
tennis 1 km, golf course 5 km,
horse-riding 5 km

Visa ● Diners ● JCB ● MASTER CARD

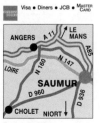

Road map p. 619

A11 dir. Nantes, A85 At Saumur, Left
bank, dir.Fontevraud or Chinon

Angers-Marcé: 30 km

67, rue de Beaulieu 37300 Joué les Tours
Tel.: 33 (0) 2.47.53.20.26 – Fax: 33 (0) 2.47.53.84.20

beaulieu@chateauxhotels.com
Jean-Pierre & Loraine LOZAY
19 rooms: 89,94 € / 129,60 €
Breakfast: 11,43 €
Menu(s): 35,85 € / 68,60 €
1/2 board: 83,85 € / 102,90 €

Open all year
equipments
telephone, T.V. Satellite, minibar

environment
architecture 18ᵉ, park 3 ha, garden, terrace, view

leisure, relaxation
golf course 3 km, horse-riding 8 km

This exquisite XVIIIth century gentleman's residence, with French garden and flower-filled park is situated in the heart of the Loire Valley. A superbly restful stay accompanied by unforgettable gourmet delights. Jean-Pierre Lozay, Master Chef of France will serve you his expert creations.

Visa ● MASTER CARD

Road map p. 619

A10 exit n° 24. N585 exit Savonnières/Villandry then twice on your left

Tours 02: 8 km

Route du Ripault 37250 Veigné
Tel.: 33 (0) 2.47.26.01.12 – Fax: 33 (0) 2.47.34.04.71
fleuri@chateauxhotels.com
Martine & Alain CHAPLIN
Menu(s): 19,80 € / 48 € - **Carte:** 34,30 €

Lost in a green ocean on the banks of the Indre and in the midst of the Loire Valley châteaux, this XVIth century mill belonged to Rohan-Guéméné, Dukes of Montbazon. Prestigious wine list: old vintages from the Loire Valley going back to 1890. Farmhouse chesseboard. Modern and classical cuisine. 9 rooms and 1 suite for all nature lovers.

Visa ● JCB ● MASTER CARD

Road map p. 619

A10 exit 24 then rocade direction N10

hotel annual closing
01/02 > 08/03●17/12 > 25/12

restaurant annual closing
01/02 > 08/03●17/12 > 25/12

hotel weekly closing
mon
01/04 > 11/11
sun (ev), mon
12/11 > 30/03

restaurant weekly closing
mon, thi(lun)
01/04 > 11/11
mon, thi(lun), sun(ev)
12/11 > 30/03

environment
architecture 16ᵉ, furniture contemporain, garden, terrace 80 m², total calm

leisure, relaxation
tennis 3 km, golf course 15 km, horse-riding 3 km

Les Hauts de Sainte-Maure

Sainte-Maure-de-Touraine
www.chateauxhotels.com/saintemaure | reservation service: 33 (0) 1.40.07.00.20

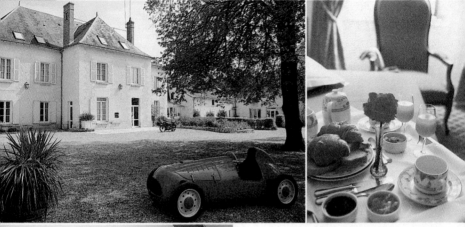

2/4, avenue Charles-de-Gaulle
37800 Sainte-Maure-de-Touraine
Tel.: 33 (0) 2.47.65.50.65 – Fax: 33 (0) 2.47.65.60.24
saintemaure@chateauxhotels.com
Jérôme & Frédéric MOUREY
29 rooms: 74,7 € / 175,32 €
Breakfast: 9,91 €
Menu(s): 22,11 € / 54,88 € - **Carte:** 42,69 €
1/2 board: 83,85 € / 106,71 €

hotel annual closing
01/01 > 01/02
restaurant annual closing
01/01 > 02/02
hotel weekly closing
sun
01/10 > 01/05
restaurant weekly closing
mon(lun)
01/05 > 01/10
mon(lun), sun
01/10 > 01/05

equipments
lift, telephone, internet, T.V.
Satellite/Canal+, minibar
environment
architecture 16ᵉ, furniture 18ᵉ,
garden, terrace 120 m²,
vegetable garden
leisure, relaxation
heated pool, tennis 1 km, golf
course 30 km, horse-riding
5 km

An old 16th century staging inn, the Hostellerie is a cluster of historical buildings, set in flower-filled gardens amidst centenary trees. Heated swimming pool, small family collection of vintage cars. At La Poste restaurant, the Mourey brothers take great delight in running the proceedings.

Visa ● Diners ● JCB ● MASTER CARD

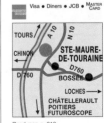

Road map p. 619

A10 exit 25 Sainte-Maure, N10 dir. Tours

 Tours: 30 km

41160 La-Ville-aux-Clercs
Tel.: 33 (0) 2.54.80.62.83 – Fax: 33 (0) 2.54.80.66.03
foret@chateauxhotels.com
M. AUTEBON - M. & Mme. REDON
16 rooms: 50,31 € / 62,5 €
2 suites: 83,85 € / 111,29 €
Breakfast: 8 €
Menu(s): 26 € / 45,75 € - **Carte:** 45 €
1/2 board: 75 €

Not far from Paris (42 minutes by TGV train), a haven of peace in the heart of the Vendôme forest, the Manoir was once a hunting lodge. Surrounded by 5 acres of parkland, this stately residence beautifully combines the warmth of its welcome with the elegance of the decor.

Open all year
hotel weekly closing
mon(lun), sun(lun)
01/10 > 31/03
restaurant weekly closing
mon, sun(ev)
01/10 > 31/03
equipments
telephone, internet, T.V.
Canal+
environment
architecture 19ᵉ, park 2 ha,
garden, terrace 60 m², view,
total calm
leisure, relaxation
tennis 1 km, golf course
15 km, horse-riding 15 km

Visa ● MASTER CARD

Road map p. 619

A11 exit Thivars - N10 direction Tours

Tours: 70 km

How to book ?

→ At the Châteaux & Hôtels reservation centre:
- Tél : 00 33 (0) 1 40 07 00 20
- Fax : 00 33 (0) 1 40 07 00 30

→ By Internet:
- www.chateauxhotels.com
- resa@chateauxhotels.com

→ Directly with the establishement required

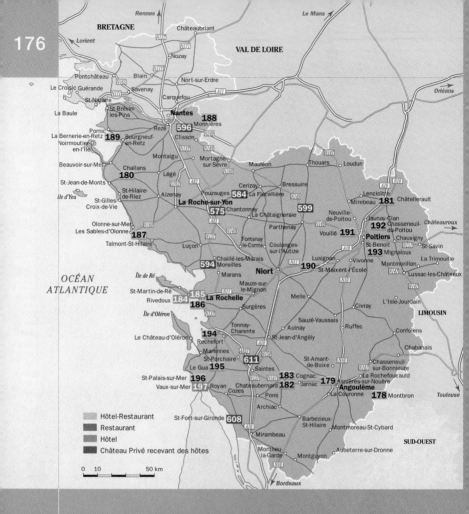

pour bien manger, bien dormir,
mais aussi bien acheter,

CHAMPÉRARD
2002

9500 adresses
pour manger vrai tous les jours

Restaurants et Hôtels de week-end

boulangers, pâtissiers, bouchers, charcutiers, Vins de l'année

PLON

le Guide Champérard
vous est indispensable.

Château Sainte-Catherine

Angoulême I Montbron

www.chateauxhotels.com/saintecatherine | reservation service: 33 (0) 1.40.07.00.20

Route de Marthon 16220 Montbron
Tel.: 33 (0) 5.45.23.60.03 – Fax: 33 (0) 5.45.70.72.00
saintecatherine@chateauxhotels.com
Florence CROCQUET
10 rooms: 54 € / 84 €
2 flats: 91 € / 122 € - **2 suites:** 91,47 € / 121,96 €
Breakfast: 7,62 €
Menu(s): 22 € / 25 € - **Carte:** 29 €
1/2 board: 54 € / 69 €

Open all year

equipments
telephone, internet, T.V.,
baby-sitting

environment
architecture 17ᵉ,
garden, terrace 300 m²,
view, total calm

leisure, relaxation
golf course 5 km, horse-riding
4 km

XVIIth century château where Josephine de Beauharnais stayed. Cosy, modern comforts with vast park in the heart of the lush Charente region. Refined cuisine and a host of leisure activities, for a superb stay. Cycling tours, canoes/ kayaks, walks, Querroy grottoes, Cognac caves, Roman art...

Visa ● Diners ● MASTER CARD

Road map p. 619

D16 between Marthon and Montbron

Champniers-Angoulême:
20 km

Lieu-Dit 16290 Asnieres-sur-Nouère
Tel.: 33 (0) 5.45.90.83.00 – Fax: 33 (0) 5.45.96.91.14
mainebrun@chateauxhotels.com
Sophie MENAGER
16 rooms: 74 € / 116 €
2 suites: 160 €
Breakfast: 10 €
Menu(s): 18 € / 34 € - **Carte:** 38 €
1/2 board: 73 € / 105 €

A haven of peace in a restored mill, in the Cognac vineyards...Private loggia in all the luxurious rooms, overlooking the river and the garden. Gastronomic relay and famous wine cellar.

hotel annual closing
01/01 > 31/01 ● 01/11 > 31/01
restaurant annual closing
01/01 > 31/01 ● 01/11 > 31/01
hotel weekly closing
mon
01/02 > 14/04
restaurant weekly closing
mon(lun)
15/04 > 29/09
mon, tue(lun), sun(ev)
01/02 > 14/04

equipments
telephone, internet, T.V.
Satellite/Canal+, minibar
environment
architecture 18º, furniture 18º,
park 18 ha, garden, terrace
60 m², total calm
leisure, relaxation
tennis 8 km, golf course
12 km, horse-riding 8 km

Visa ● Diners ● JCB ● MASTER CARD

Road map p. 619

A10 exit Saintes or Poitiers. N141/
Cognac

Bordeaux: 120 km

Château de la Vérie

Challans
www.chateauxhotels.com/verie | reservation service: 33 (0) 1.40.07.00.20

Rte de St-Gilles Croix de Vie 85300 Challans
Tel.: 33 (0) 2.51.35.33.44 – Fax: 33 (0) 2.51.35.14.84

verie@chateauxhotels.com
Jean-François MARTIN
23 rooms: 53,40 € / 155,50 €
Breakfast: 9,15 €
Menu(s): 19,10 € / 48,80 €
1/2 board: 55,70 € / 106,75 €

Open all year
equipments
telephone, internet, T.V.
Satellite/Canal+, minibar, safe

environment
architecture 16e, park 17 ha,
garden, terrace 300 m², view,
vegetable garden, total calm

leisure, relaxation
golf course 15 km, canoeing,
sandsailing on 30-km long
beach

*Welcome to France's second
most sunny area! Close to the
coast, this 16th century classified château set in 42 acre
park invites you to discover a
haven of natural beauty and a
gourmet stopover: Jean-
François Delanné, Maître Cui-
sinier de France. Special re-
duced rates at 5 nearby golf
courses.*

Visa ● Diners ● MASTER CARD

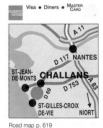

Road map p. 619
A83 exit Montaigu

Nantes: 60 km

74, boulevard Blossac 86100 Châtellerault
Tel.: 33 (0) 5.49.93.33.00 – Fax: 33 (0) 5.49.93.25.19
hotelmoderne@chateauxhotels.com
M. & Mme. Christian PROUST
21 rooms: 61 € / 130 €
2 flats: 123 € / 140 €
Breakfast: 8,1 €
Menu(s): 10,50 € / 38 € - **Carte:** 57,17 €

10 minutes from the Futuro-scope Park, 50 km from the first of the Loire châteaux, near the vast atlantic beaches. A famous stopover for C. Proust's imaginative and inventive cuisine. Grill for the more simple meals. Near to the Saint Cyr and Roche-Posay golf courses.

restaurant annual closing
15/11 > 05/12

equipments
lift, telephone, internet, T.V.
Satellite/Canal+

environment
architecture 19e, garden, view

leisure, relaxation
heated pool/covered, tennis
2 km, golf course 15 km,
horse-riding 3 km

Visa ● Diners ● MASTER CARD

Road map p. 619

A10 exit Châtellerault

Poitiers: 35 km

Château de l'Yeuse

Cognac I Châteaubernard

www.chateauxhotels.com/yeuse | reservation service: 33 (0) 1.40.07.00.20

65, rue de Bellevue quartier de l'Echassier
16100 Châteaubernard

Tel.: 33 (0) 5.45.36.82.60 – Fax: 33 (0) 5.45.35.06.32

yeuse@chateauxhotels.com
Céline DESMAZIERES

21 rooms: 84 € / 138 €
1 flat: 365 € / 440 € - **3 suites:** 168 € / 228 €
Breakfast: 12 €
Menu(s): 23 € / 52 € - **Carte:** 53 €
1/2 board: 125 € / 225 €

hotel annual closing
01/01 > 21/01

restaurant annual closing
01/01 > 21/01

restaurant weekly closing
sat(lun)
01/05 > 30/09
sat(lun), sun(ev)
01/10 > 30/04

equipments
lift, telephone, internet, T.V.,
minibar, safe

environment
architecture 19ᵉ, garden,
terrace, view, total calm

leisure, relaxation
tennis 3 km, golf course 4 km,
horse-riding 10 km, hammam,
jacuzzi

This XIXth century building en-circled by 2 ha of grounds overlook Charente valley. It is the mandatory rendezvous for the gourmets of the Charente who come to revel with exquis-ite dishes and rare wines. The terrace is pleasant, the rooms charming and the welcome elegant.

Visa ● Diners ● JCB ● MASTER CARD

Road map p. 619

Châteaubernard D15, dir. St-Brice
then Quartier de l'Echassier

Angoulême: 50 km

Cognac

www.chateauxhotels.com/pigeonsblancs | reservation service: 33 (0) 1.40.07.00.20

110, rue Jules Brisson 16100 Cognac
Tel.: 33 (0) 5.45.82.16.36 – Fax: 33 (0) 5.45.82.29.29
pigeonsblancs@chateauxhotels.com
Famille TACHET
6 rooms: 60 € / 95 €
Breakfast: 9 €
Menu(s): 20 € / 53 € - **1/2 board:** 76 € / 95 €

The hosts help you to discover and like their beautiful region. A refined welcome, comfort, talented cuisine retain the typical local touch. On fine days, meals on the terrace, calm of the gardens so close to the old city, the port and the ageing casks of the famous Cognac.

hotel annual closing
01/01 > 15/01

hotel weekly closing
sun(lun)
15/01 > 31/12

restaurant weekly closing
mon(lun), sun(ev)
15/01 > 31/12

equipments
telephone, T.V. Canal+, baby-sitting

environment
architecture 17ᵉ, furniture 19ᵉ, garden, terrace 25 m², view, vegetable garden

leisure, relaxation
tennis 1 km, golf course 3 km, horse-riding 1 km, river cruises on the Charente

Visa ● Diners ● MASTER CARD

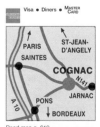

Road map p. 619

A10 exit Pons/St-Jean d'Y. Quartier Saint-Jacques

Angoulême: 45 km

Auberge de la Marée

La Rochelle I Rivedoux-Plage
www.chateauxhotels.com/maree | reservation service: 33 (0) 1.40.07.00.20

Sur le port - Ile de Ré 17940 Rivedoux-Plage
Tel.: 33 (0) 5.46.09.80.02 – Fax: 33 (0) 5.46.09.88.25
maree@chateauxhotels.com
Daniel BERNARD
30 rooms: 58 € / 155 €
Breakfast: 10 €

hotel annual closing
01/01 > 23/03•11/11 > 12/04

equipments
telephone, internet, T.V.

environment
garden, terrace 100 m²

leisure, relaxation
heated pool, tennis 0.8 km, golf course 25 km, horse-riding 3 km, jacuzzi, thalassotherapy 3 km, balneotherapy 3 km

An inn located on the small harbor of this island. Patio, gardens, pool, waterfall, solarium, rose garden... All together create the atmosphere of a vast private residence. A dream island, bordered by white sand dunes, villages in the pine woods facing the ocean, the kingdom of migrating birds.

Visa • MASTER CARD

Road map p. 619
A10 exit Pont de l'île de Ré

 La Rochelle/Île-de-Ré: 4 km

3, rue de la Monnaie 17000 La Rochelle
Tel.: 33 (0) 5.46.50.65.65 – Fax: 33 (0) 5.46.50.63.19
monnaie@chateauxhotels.com
Gisèle VERGNON – Geneviève BAUDON
31 rooms: 68,6 € / 102 €
4 suites: 144,83 € / 190 €
Breakfast: 9,5 €

In the heart of the historic city, at the entrance of the old port, the charm of a XVIIth-century residence with privileged comfort and tranquillity: refined guestrooms and suites, quiet sitting room for breakfast, interior courtyard, winter garden, lounge. Beach 100m away.

Open all year

equipments
lift, telephone, internet, T.V. Canal+, minibar, safe

environment
architecture 17°, garden, terrace 45 m², view, total calm

leisure, relaxation
tennis 1 km, golf course 7 km, horse-riding 8 km, day cruise on a catamaran

Visa ● Diners ● MASTER CARD

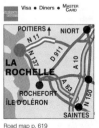

Road map p. 619
La Rochelle/île-de-Ré dir. town center

La Rochelle/Île-de-Ré: 8 km

Résidence de France
La Rochelle
www.chateauxhotels.com/residence | reservation service: 33 (0) 1.40.07.00.20

43, rue du minage 17000 La Rochelle
Tel.: 33 (0) 5.46.28.06.00 – Fax: 33 (0) 5.46.28.06.03
residence@chateauxhotels.com
Nicolas IGNATIEW
22 rooms: 64,03 € / 109,75 €
14 flats: 79,27 € / 183 € - **11 suites:** 91,5 € / 221,05 €
Breakfast: 7,62 €
Menu(s): 15 € / 20 € - **Carte:** 30 €

Open all year
equipments
lift, telephone, T.V., safe,
baby-sitting
environment
architecture 16e, garden,
terrace 30 m²
leisure, relaxation
tennis 2.5 km, golf course
10 km, horse-riding 10 km

In the heart of the old city of La Rochelle, a hearty welcome awaits you at this ensemble of two buildings linked by a gallery, a 16th century inn facing the famous arcades and a contemporary building overlooking the garden. The food combines French tradition with local specialities.

Visa ● Diners ● MASTER CARD

Road map p. 619
A10 exit 33 South of Niort, N11

 La Rochelle-Ile de Ré: 6 km

5, promenade Godet
85100 Les Sables-d'Olonne
Tel.: 33 (0) 2.51.95.37.71 – Fax: 33 (0) 2.51.95.37.30
atlantic@chateauxhotels.com
Jean-Etienne BLANCHARD
30 rooms: 70 € / 122 €
Breakfast: 9 €
Menu(s): 19 € / 41 € - **Carte:** 13 € -
1/2 board: 55 € / 93 €

Looking out to sea, located at the center of the bay of Sables d'Olonne, this contemporary hotel offers 30 luxurious air-conditioned rooms. Seaside atmosphere and relaxation, by the indoor pool or at the "Sloop" restaurant where you can sample the finest sea-food.

Open all year
restaurant weekly closing
fri, sun
01/10 > 28/03
equipments
lift, telephone, internet, T.V.
Satellite/Canal+, minibar, safe
environment
terrace 30 m², view
leisure, relaxation
heated pool/covered, tennis
1 km, golf course 11 km,
horse-riding 10 km, casino
1km

Visa ● Diners ● MASTER CARD

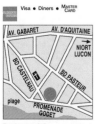

Road map p. 619

A11 Nantes-Paris then A83 exit Montaigu La Roche s/Yon, N160

Nantes-Atlantique: 95 km

Château de la Colaissière

Nantes ı Saint-Sauveur-de-Landemont

www.chateauxhotels.com/colaissiere ı reservation service: 33 (0) 1.40.07.00.20

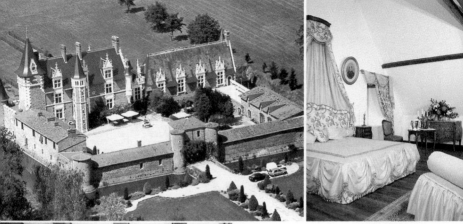

49270 Saint-Sauveur-de-Landemont
Tel.: 33 (0) 2.40.98.75.04 – Fax: 33 (0) 2.40.98.74.15

colaissiere@chateauxhotels.com
Olivier LEINEKUGEL LE COCQ

15 rooms: 100 € / 300 €
1 flat: 200 € / 230 €
Breakfast: 11 €
Menu(s): 25 € / 53 € - **1/2 board:** 145 € / 275 €

hotel annual closing
02/01 > 31/01

restaurant annual closing
02/01 > 31/01

restaurant weekly closing
mon

equipments
telephone, T.V. Canal+,
minibar, safe, baby-sitting

environment
architecture 15/16e, park
16 ha, garden, terrace 50 m²,
view, total calm

leisure, relaxation
heated pool, golf course 8 km,
horse-riding 8 km

Near Nantes, a true Renaissance jewel, former property of the Dukes of Anjou and Bretagne. Majestic interior, period furniture, antique tapestries, sumptuous guest rooms, gourmet restaurant. And last but not least, excellent Loire wines.

Visa ● JCB ● MASTER CARD

Road map p. 619

A11 exit Ancenis - D763 dir. Liré,
St-Laurent-des Autels

 Nantes-Atlantique: 35 km

Rue de la Noue fleurie
44760 La Bernerie-en-Retz
Tel.: 33 (0) 2.51.74.60.06 – Fax: 33 (0) 2.51.74.60.02
gressiere@chateauxhotels.com
Suzanne GRANDJEAN
15 rooms: 49 € / 110 €
Breakfast: 8 €
Menu(s): 21 € / 43 € - **1/2 board:** 49 € / 83 €

Built by the Marquis de Charettte in 1870, this chateau retains the values of the old-style hotels. On a hill overlooking the sea, peace, comfort and warm welcome. Rooms individually decorated. In a Marie-Antoinette decor, you will savour a traditional regional cuisine, accompanied by vintage wines.

Open all year

equipments
telephone, internet, T.V. Satellite

environment
architecture 11ᵉ, park 4.5 ha, garden, terrace, total calm

leisure, relaxation
golf course 6 km, horse-riding 6 km, thalassotherapy, sauna

Visa • **Master Card**

Road map p. 619

A11 and A83 exit Nantes - D751 dir. Pornic

Nantes: 30 km

Le Logis Saint-Martin

Niort I Saint-Maixent-l'Ecole

www.chateauxhotels.com/saintmartin | reservation service: 33 (0) 1.40.07.00.20

Chemin de Pissot 79400 Saint-Maixent-l'Ecole
Tel.: 33 (0) 5.49.05.58.68 – Fax: 33 (0) 5.49.76.19.93
saintmartin@chateauxhotels.com
Ingrid & Bertrand HEINTZ
10 rooms: 85 € / 115 €
1 suite: 125 €
Breakfast: 13 €
Menu(s): 29 € / 68 € - **Carte:** 55 €
1/2 board: 90 € / 125 €

hotel annual closing
01/01 > 01/02
restaurant annual closing
01/01 > 01/02
hotel weekly closing
mon
16/10 > 14/03
restaurant weekly closing
mon, tue(lun), sat(lun)
15/03 > 15/10
mon, tue(lun), sat(lun)
16/10 > 14/03
equipments
telephone, internet, T.V.
Satellite
environment
architecture 17e, furniture 17e,
park 3 ha, garden, terrace,
view, total calm
leisure, relaxation
tennis 1 km, golf course
20 km, horse-riding 1 km

In a wooded park on the banks of the Sèvre, a few minutes from Niort, Poitiers and La Rochelle, a 17th century residence entirely renovated. A relaxing stay where traditions and quality are combined. Regional products and great vintage wines have pride of place for the most appreciative gourmets.

Visa ● Diners ● JCB ● MASTER CARD

Road map p. 619

A10 exit n° 31 dir. St-Maixent L'Ecole
N11

Poitiers: 40 km

La Chapelle 86190 Vouillé

Tel.: 33 (0) 5.49.51.80.43 – Fax: 33 (0) 5.49.51.90.09

perigny@chateauxhotels.com

Didier BROQUERAULT

36 rooms: 65 € / 150 €

6 flats: 115 € / 150 € - **2 suites:** 125,01 € / 152,45 €

Breakfast: 11,5 €

Menu(s): 22 € / 48 € - **Carte:** 45,73 €

This XVIth century château near Poitiers is at the heart of a protected 113-acre park. 36 tastefully decorated bedrooms, 2 suites and 4 spacious villas will make your stay calm and peaceful. At the Périgny restaurant or on the flower terrace, you can enjoy fine seasonal cooking.

Open all year

equipments
lift, telephone, internet, T.V., safe, baby-sitting

environment
architecture 16ª, park 30 ha, garden, terrace, view, total calm

leisure, relaxation
heated pool, golf course 15 km, horse-riding 15 km, 3 tennis

Visa ● Diners ● JCB ● MASTER CARD

Road map p. 619

A10 exit n° 29 north of Poitiers - N149 dir. Nantes

Poitiers-Biard: 8 km

10, place du Champ de Foire
86360 Chasseneuil-du-Poitou
Tel.: 33 (0) 5.49.52.86.66 – Fax: 33 (0) 5.49.52.86.32
ribaudiere@chateauxhotels.com
William MIGEON

39 rooms: 70 € / 135 €
2 suites: 125 € / 145 €
Breakfast: 11,5 €
Menu(s): 21,5 € / 46 € - **Carte:** 20 €
1/2 board: 80 € / 99 €

Open all year

equipments
lift, telephone, internet, T.V.
Satellite, minibar

environment
architecture 19ᵉ, garden,
terrace 100 m²

leisure, relaxation
heated pool, tennis 0.8 km,
golf course 20 km, horse-riding
10 km

Near Poitiers, 3 min from the Futuroscope, a XIXth century residence whose original decor you will like very much. The tranquillity of its land-scaped park bordering the river invites you to have a memorable stay. Wide recep-tion hall, summer garden, con-ference room. Access by the A10 motorway.

Visa ● Diners ● JCB ● MASTER CARD

Road map p. 619

A10 exit Futuroscope - N10 dir. Chas-
seneuil centre

Poitiers-Biard: 10 km

635, route de Beauvoir 86550 Mignaloux
Tel.: 33 (0) 5.49.55.47.47 – Fax: 33 (0) 5.49.55.31.95
beauvoir@chateauxhotels.com
Jean-Philippe HUBAU
43 rooms: 65 € / 175 €
2 flats: 150 €
Breakfast: 9 €
Menu(s): 14,5 € / 36,5 € - **1/2 board:** 92 € / 179 €

*The Manoir de Beauvoir, near
the Futuroscope, provides the
astounding spectacle of
wooded nature, dotted with
bodies of water around the
structure form of an international 18-hole golf course. The
variety of services and the ef-
ficiency of the teams make
this an ideal spot to combine
rest and work.*

Open all year

equipments
lift, telephone, T.V. Canal+,
minibar, baby-sitting

environment
architecture 19ᵉ, park 90 ha,
garden, terrace 200 m², view,
total calm

leisure, relaxation
heated pool, tennis 2 km,
horse-riding 8 km, golf,
courses for for beginners,
games room

Visa ● Diners ● JCB ● MASTER CARD

Road map p. 619

A10 exit 29 Poitiers Nord - N147
dir.Limoges

Poitiers-Biard: 21 km

La Corderie Royale

Rochefort

www.chateauxhotels.com/corderieroyale | reservation service: 33 (0) 1.40.07.00.20

Rue Audebert BP 275 17300 Rochefort
Tel.: 33 (0) 5.46.99.35.35 – Fax: 33 (0) 5.46.99.78.72
corderieroyale@chateauxhotels.com
Jacques REY & Marie-José RENUCCI-EVEN

42 rooms: 58 € / 156 €
3 suites: 144 € / 237 €
Breakfast: 9,5 €
Menu(s): 25 € / 52 € - **Carte:** 45 €
1/2 board: 81 € / 108 €

hotel annual closing
02/02 > 06/03
restaurant annual closing
02/02 > 06/03
hotel weekly closing
mon, sun
01/11 > 30/03
restaurant weekly closing
mon, sun(ev)
01/11 > 30/03
equipments
lift, telephone, internet, T.V.
Satellite/Canal+, minibar
environment
architecture 17^e, furniture
contemporain, garden, terrace
250 m^2, view, total calm
leisure, relaxation
tennis 0.2 km, golf course
10 km, horse-riding 5 km,
thermal baths, sauna, fitness

Hôtel de la Corderie Royale is located in a beautiful country setting on the banks of the Charente river near the centre of Rochefort. The famous arsenal built by Colbert lies close to this relaxing hotel. Elegant features, fine cuisine. Not to be missed: the port and the Corderie royale...

Visa ● Diners ● JCB ● **MASTER CARD**

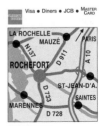

Road map p. 619
A10 exit n° 24

La Rochelle Laleu: 30 km

2, rue du Bassin « Châlons » 17600 Le Gua
Tel.: 33 (0) 5.46.22.82.72 – Fax: 33 (0) 5.46.22.91.07
chalons@chateauxhotels.com
Martine & Guy BOUQUET
14 rooms: 47 € / 86 €
Breakfast: 11 €
Menu(s): 19 € / 60 € - **Carte:** 34 € -
1/2 board: 83 € / 122 €

The Moulin de Châlons welcomes the visitor with its beautiful romantic surroundings of wooded parkland and winding river. You will find here a time-honoured tradition of fine food - gastronomy and relaxation in a convivial atmosphere within close reach of the major tourist attractions.

hotel annual closing
06/01 > 29/01
restaurant annual closing
06/01 > 29/01
hotel weekly closing
mon, sun(ev)
01/10 > 01/05
restaurant weekly closing
mon, sun(ev)
01/10 > 01/05
equipments
telephone, T.V., safe
environment
architecture 18e, garden,
terrace 100 m^2
leisure, relaxation
tennis 10 km, golf course
12 km, horse-riding 10 km

Road map p. 619

A10 exit Saintes dir. Ile oléron, Nancras, Le Gua

✈ Royan-Medis: 8 km

Primavera

Royan I Saint-Palais-sur-Mer

www.chateauxhotels.com/primavera I reservation service: 33 (0) 1.40.07.00.20

12, rue du Brick 17420 Saint-Palais-sur-Mer
Tel.: 33 (0) 5.46.23.20.35 – Fax: 33 (0) 5.46.23.28.78
primavera@chateauxhotels.com
M. & Mme. Jean-Jacques CORMAU
45 rooms: 60 € / 170 €
Breakfast: 10 €
Menu(s): 20 € / 45 € - **Carte:** 25 €

hotel annual closing
02/02 > 18/02●15/11 > 20/12
restaurant annual closing
02/02 > 18/02●15/11 > 20/12
restaurant weekly closing
mon(ev)
01/04 > 30/09
mon, tue(lun), wen(lun)
01/10 > 31/03
equipments
lift, telephone, internet, T.V.
environment
architecture 12°, park 2 ha,
garden, terrace, view
leisure, relaxation
heated pool/covered, golf
course 1 km, horse-riding
1 km, thalassotherapy, thermal
baths

*Lush 5-acre park for calm and
relaxation with heated indoor
pool. Golf course, riding centre and zoo are nearby. Sumptuous cuisine featuring shell-
fish and grilled fish. Casino
and discotheques nearby for
evening entertainment. Walks
along the seashore and excursions in the country.*

Visa ● Diners ● MASTER CARD

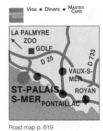

Road map p. 619

A10 exit 35 Saintes, dir. La Palmyre
and D25

Rochefort: 40 km

Parc des Fées Route de Saint-Palais
17640 Vaux-sur-Mer
Tel.: 33 (0) 5.46.39.00.75 – Fax: 33 (0) 5.46.38.29.99
rohan@chateauxhotels.com
Michèle & Jean-Maurice SEGUIN
43 rooms: 48 € / 118 €
Breakfast: 9,15 €

In this residence with the charm of an English cottage, set in extensive parkland by the sea, the Duchess of Rohan held a literary salon. Direct access to the fine sandy beach. Sunny terrace set among pine trees. Nearby:18-hole golf course, sailing, riding. Rooms with period furniture.

hotel annual closing
11/11 > 25/03

equipments
telephone, T.V. Satellite, safe, baby-sitting

environment
architecture 19ᵉ, garden, terrace

leisure, relaxation
heated pool, golf course 4 km, horse-riding 4 km

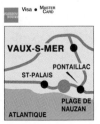

Visa ● MASTER CARD

Road map p. 619

A10 exit Saintes, D25 dir. St-Palais/mer

La Rochelle: 75 km

CHATEAU LAGREZETTE

VIN DE CAHORS

Tout un
Terroir
dans un château

•

Médaille d'or
Paris
salon de l'agriculture

•

Propriété
vendangée à la main
depuis 1503

•

Visite
des caves
souterraines

•

Dégustation
Vente - Expédition
Documentation
sur commande

•

ALAIN DOMINIQUE PERRIN
DOMAINE DE LAGREZETTE

46140 CAILLAC FRANCE TÉL. 05 65 20 07 42 FAX 05 65 20 06 95
site internet : www.chateau-lagrezette.tm.fr

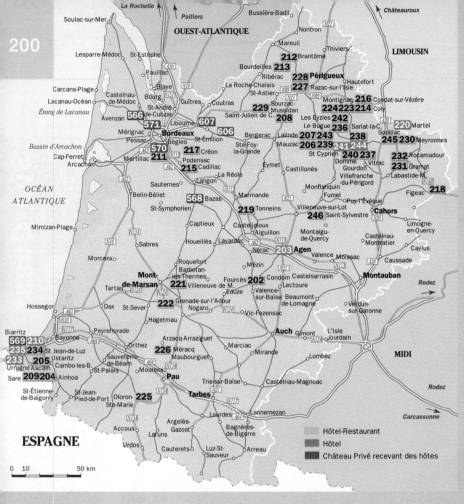

200

Hôtel-Restaurant
Hôtel
Château Privé recevant des hôtes

0   10   50 km

ESPAGNE

Sud-Ouest

CHÂTEAU PAPE CLÉMENT
Grand Cru Classé de Graves

CHÂTEAU FOMBRAUGE
Grand Cru de Saint-Emilion

CHÂTEAU LA TOUR CARNET
Grand Cru Classé en 1855 - Haut-Médoc

"Bernard Magrez est propriétaire de ces trois Châteaux, qui figurent parmi les plus anciens du Bordelais.
Les vignes du Château Pape Clément ont en effet été plantées en 1143,
celles du Château Fombrauge en 1459 et celles du Château La Tour Carnet en 1229
Il perpétue, pour l'élevage de ses vins, les traditions familiales et les exigences qualitatives
qui ont été transmises par ses prédécesseurs de génération en génération. "

www.pape-clement.com   www.fombrauge.com   www.latourcarnet.com

Château de Fourcès

Agen I Fourcès

www.chateauxhotels.com/fources | reservation service: 33 (0) 1.40.07.00.20

32250 Fourcès
Tel.: 33 (0) 5.62.29.49.53 – Fax: 33 (0) 5.62.29.50.59
fources@chateauxhotels.com
Comtesse Patrizia BARSAN

12 rooms: 100 € / 155 €
6 suites: 214 € / 224 €
Breakfast: 12 €
Menu(s): 16,63 € / 48,78 € - **Carte:** 33,54 €
1/2 board: 104 € / 144 €

hotel annual closing
01/01 > 24/03
restaurant annual closing
01/01 > 24/03
equipments
lift, telephone, internet, T.V.,
minibar, safe
environment
architecture 13°, garden,
terrace, view, total calm
leisure, relaxation
tennis 0.5 km, golf course
15 km, horse-riding 9 km,
horse-riding, bicycle
rides,car-racing

An intimate and sumptuous 13th century castle in the unique surroundings of the circular fortified town of Fourcès. Very comfortable and light guestrooms and suites, each separately decorated while respecting the prestigious architecture. Charming restaurant. Large sitting room. Leisure activities.

Visa ● Diners ● JCB ● MASTER CARD

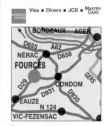

Road map p. 619

A62 exit Darmazan 6, D930 dir.
Nérac-Mézin

Agen/Toulouse/Bordeaux:
45 km

1 ter, place des Jacobins 47000 Agen
Tel.: 33 (0) 5.53.47.03.31 – Fax: 33 (0) 5.53.47.02.80
jacobins@chateauxhotels.com
Stéphane CAPMARTY-BUJAN – Gisèle BUJAN
15 rooms: 76,22 € / 122 €
Breakfast: 12 €

Hotel in a charming location, facting the 11th and 12th century Jacobian church, close to the Museum and Centre Culturel. Old furniture, confort, garden... Easy reach for lakes, walks and sports.

Open all year

equipments
telephone, internet, T.V.
Satellite/Canal+, minibar

environment
architecture 19ᵉ, garden, terrace, view, total calm

leisure, relaxation
golf course 5 km, horse-riding 10 km

Road map p. 619

A62 exit Agen

Agen: 3.5 km

Hôtel Ithurria

Ainhoa

www.chateauxhotels.com/ithurria | reservation service: 33 (0) 1.40.07.00.20

64250 Ainhoa
Tel.: 33 (0) 5.59.29.92.11 – Fax: 33 (0) 5.59.29.81.28
ithurria@chateauxhotels.com
Maurice ISABAL

26 rooms: 107 € / 122 €
2 flats: 129 € / 214 €
Breakfast: 9 €
Menu(s): 28 € / 43 € - **Carte:** 44 €
1/2 board: 84 € / 92 €

hotel annual closing
03/11 > 17/04
restaurant weekly closing
wen
15/09 > 03/11
wen
17/04 > 30/06
equipments
lift, telephone, T.V. Satellite,
safe
environment
architecture 17ᵉ, garden
leisure, relaxation
tennis 5 km, golf course 5 km,
horse-riding 6 km, sauna,
hiking, 5 signposted walking
trails

A 17th century Basque dwelling, a listed historical building. This building, previously an inn on the to St. Jacques de Compostella pilgrimage route, is also an excellent gastronomic stop-over, just 30 mn from the beaches. There are walking trails in the hills which will open up to you.

Visa • MASTER CARD

Road map p. 619

A63 exit n° 5 Bayonne south. D932,
dir. Espagne

 Biarritz: 28 km

Rue Principale 64480 Ustaritz
Tel.: 33 (0) 5.59.93.00.56 – Fax: 33 (0) 5.59.93.16.54
patoula@chateauxhotels.com
Pierre GUILHEM
9 rooms: 65 € / 90 €
Breakfast: 10 €
Menu(s): 20 € / 35 € - **1/2 board:** 62 € / 74 €

A lovely stop-over in a calm garden on the banks of the Nive river. Walks in the forest, golf courses, beaches, Spain, Basque mountains... The Patoula is also a restaurant that celebrates regional products. Breakfasts and regional meals under the flowering pergola at the water's edge.

hotel annual closing
20/10 > 27/10•05/01 > 05/02
restaurant annual closing
20/10 > 27/10•05/01 > 27/02
hotel weekly closing
mon
15/09 > 15/06
restaurant weekly closing
mon, fri(lun)
15/06 > 15/09
mon, fri(lun), sun(ev)
15/09 > 15/06
equipments
telephone, T.V.
environment
architecture 19e, garden,
terrace 75 m², view
leisure, relaxation
golf course 4 km, horse-riding
1 km, thalassotherapy, thermal
baths

Visa ● MASTER CARD

Road map p. 619

A63 exit south of Bayonne, D932 dir.
Cambo

Biarritz-Parme: 12 km

La Métairie

Bergerac I Lalinde

www.chateauxhotels.com/metairie I reservation service: 33 (0) 1.40.07.00.20

Mauzac 24150 Lalinde
Tel.: 33 (0) 5.53.22.50.47 – Fax: 33 (0) 5.53.22.52.93
metairie@chateauxhotels.com
Johner HEINZ
9 rooms: 95 € / 130 €
1 suite: 155 € / 190 €
Breakfast: 13 €
Menu(s): 29 € / 46 € - **Carte:** 46 €
1/2 board: 94 € / 107 €

hotel annual closing
01/11 > 23/03

restaurant annual closing
01/11 > 31/03

equipments
telephone, T.V. Satellite, minibar, baby-sitting

environment
architecture 19ᵉ, park 4 ha, garden, terrace 60 m², view, total calm

leisure, relaxation
tennis 3 km, golf course 15 km, horse-riding 1 km

The Métairie in Périgord offers a warm hospitality. For a real getaway to a relaxing country-side location, sample our sublime traditional cuisine with a unique contemporary touch. A host of Prehistorical tourist sites. 20 km from Bergerac and its airport. 7 km from the Lalinde Heliport.

Visa ● Diners ● MASTER CARD

Road map p. 619

A10 exit Libourne or A62 exit Marmande

Bergerac: 20 km

1, rue de la Tour 24150 Lalinde
Tel.: 33 (0) 5.53.61.01.82 – Fax: 33 (0) 5.53.24.74.60
lechateau@chateauxhotels.com
Guy GENSOU
7 rooms: 50,35 € / 153 €
Breakfast: 9,91 €
Menu(s): 21,35 € / 36,6 € - **1/2 board:** 56 € / 115 €

Perched above the "River of Good Hope", this attractive 13th-19th c. château offers all the ingredients for a memorable stay - rooms with a view of the Dordogne, classical country cooking where you can feast on foie gras in countless ways, and savour succulent roasts such as pigeon, quail, rack of lamb or ostrich.

Visa ● Diners ● MASTER CARD

LIMOGES
PÉRIGUEUX N89
LASCAUX
BORDEAUX D 710
LE BUGUE
BERGERAC
AGEN LALINDE

Road map p. 619

D29 between Bergerac and Sarlat

hotel annual closing
11/11 > 13/02 ● 19/09 > 25/09
restaurant annual closing
11/11 > 13/02 ● 19/09 > 25/09
hotel weekly closing
sun
11/11 > 31/03
restaurant weekly closing
mon, tue(lun)
31/03 > 30/06
mon, tue(lun), sun(ev)
11/11 > 31/03
equipments
telephone, T.V.
environment
architecture 13e, furniture contemporain, terrace 65 m^2, view
leisure, relaxation
tennis 2 km, golf course 10 km

Manoir du Grand Vignoble

Bergerac ı Saint-Julien-de-Crempse

www.chateauxhotels.com/grandvignoble ı reservation service: 33 (0) 1.40.07.00.20

Le Grand Vignoble
24140 Saint-Julien-de-Crempse
Tel.: 33 (0) 5.53.24.23.18 – Fax: 33 (0) 5.53.24.20.89
grandvignoble@chateauxhotels.com
Denis PETE

42 rooms: 58 € / 104 €
2 suites: 149 € / 240 €
Breakfast: 9 €
Menu(s): 23 € / 43 € - **Carte:** 34 €
1/2 board: 55 € / 83 €

hotel annual closing
15/11 > 30/03
restaurant annual closing
15/11 > 30/03
equipments
telephone, internet, T.V.
Satellite, minibar, baby-sitting
environment
architecture 17e, park 43 ha,
garden, terrace, total calm
leisure, relaxation
heated pool, golf course
20 km, horse-riding, sauna,
jacuzzi, mountain bikes for hire

*12 km from Bergerac, in the
heart of Périgord, a manor
built during the reign of Louis
XIV, set in 12 acres of meadows and woods. Open-air,
heated swimming-pool, tennis, sauna, gymnasium, pony-
club with 40 animals; Olympic
riding school. Traditional cuisine in the restaurant "Le Pour-
pre et Or".*

Visa ● MASTER CARD

Road map p. 619

A10 to Libourne then A89 to Muss-
idan then 1.dir. Villamblard second
direction St Julien de Crempse

 Bergerac: 16 km

64310 Sare
Tel.: 33 (0) 5.59.54.20.46 – Fax: 33 (0) 5.59.54.27.04
arraya@chateauxhotels.com
Jean-Baptiste FAGOAGA
20 rooms: 60,25 € / 90,75 €
1 flat: 115,1 € / 128,82 €
Breakfast: 8 €
Menu(s): 20,58 € / 29,73 € - **Carte:** 36,5 € -
1/2 board: 60,6 € / 75,95 €

In the village square, 12 km from the sea and golf courses, a beautiful XVIth century residence in the style of the region. Refined decor. A gastronomic stop-over. Boutique with home products and Basque linen. Rides on horseback, excursions to the border, climbs, prehistoric grottoes nearby.

hotel annual closing
01/01 > 28/03●05/11 > 28/03
restaurant annual closing
01/01 > 02/04●05/11 > 31/03
restaurant weekly closing
mon(lun), sun(ev)
07/04 > 30/06
mon(lun), sun(ev)
22/09 > 21/10
equipments
telephone, internet, T.V.
Satellite, safe
environment
architecture 16ᵉ, furniture 17ᵉ,
garden, terrace, view
leisure, relaxation
tennis 0.1 km, golf course
8 km, horse-riding 2 km,
thalassotherapy, thermal baths

Visa ● MASTER CARD

Road map p. 619

A63 exit North of St-Jean-de-Luz, D4 dir. Ascain

✈ Biarritz-Parme: 25 km

I Sud Ouest

Château du Clair de Lune

Biarritz
www.chateauxhotels.com/clairlune | reservation service: 33 (0) 1.40.07.00.20

48, avenue Alan-Seeger Route d'Arbonne
64200 Biarritz
Tel.: 33 (0) 5.59.41.53.20 – Fax: 33 (0) 5.59.41.53.29
clairlune@chateauxhotels.com
Danièle BEYRIERE
17 rooms: 70 € / 156 €
Breakfast: 10 €

Open all year

equipments
telephone, T.V. Satellite,
minibar, baby-sitting

environment
architecture 19ᵉ, furniture 19ᵉ,
park 8 ha, garden, terrace
80 m², view

leisure, relaxation
tennis 3 km, golf course 1 km,
horse-riding 2 km

Enter into the Château du Clair de Lune as into a dream and forget the world...Floral terrace, immense park, secret paths. Chose romantic manor rooms or those in the Hunting Lodge with a terrace. Numerous golf courses, water treatments.

Visa ● Diners ● MASTER CARD

Road map p. 619

A63 exit Biarritz dir. Arbonne

Biarritz-Parme: 3 km

Chemin de Smith Haut Lafitte
33650 Bordeaux-Martillac
Tel.: 33 (0) 5.57.83.83.83 – Fax: 33 (0) 5.57.83.83.84
caudalie@chateauxhotels.com
Bénédicte RODE – M. & Mme. CATHIARD
40 rooms: 175 € / 240 €
9 suites: 290 € / 425 €
Breakfast: 20 €
Menu(s): 30 € / 55 € - **Carte:** 30/70 €

In the midst of classed vintage Graves wines, the world's only wine-therapy complex opened in 1999. The hotel boasts beautifully decorated rooms and suites, fine gastronomic cuisine and an unusual fitness centre which uses substances derived from grape vines.

Open all year

equipments
lift, telephone, internet, T.V. Satellite, minibar, safe, baby-sitting, valet parking

environment
architecture, park 65 ha, garden, terrace 60 m^2, view, total calm

leisure, relaxation
heated pool, horse-riding 10 km, beauty salon, balneo, hammam, fitness, jacuzzi, tennis, golf, cycling, cookery classes, wine tasting, châteaux visits

Visa ● Diners ● MASTER CARD

Road map p. 619

A62 dir. Toulouse, exit 1 Martillac

Bordeaux-Mérignac: 16 km

Château de la Côte

Brantôme

www.chateauxhotels.com/cote | reservation service: 33 (0) 1.40.07.00.20

Biras-Bourdeilles 24310 Brantôme
Tel.: 33 (0) 5.53.03.70.11 – Fax: 33 (0) 5.53.03.42.84
cote @ chateauxhotels.com
Michel & Olivier GUILLAUME
13 rooms: 75 € / 140 €
3 suites: 110 € / 120 €
Breakfast: 10 €
Menu(s): 27 € / 56 € - **Carte:** 43 €
1/2 board: 78 € / 123 €

hotel annual closing
05/01 > 15/03●15/11 > 25/12
restaurant annual closing
05/01 > 15/03●15/11 > 25/12
restaurant weekly closing
mon(lun), tue(lun), wen(lun),
thi(lun), fri(lun), sat(lun)
equipments
telephone, internet, T.V.,
minibar, safe, baby-sitting
environment
architecture 15ᵉ, park 6 ha,
garden, terrace, view, total
calm
leisure, relaxation
tennis 3 km, golf course
13 km, horse-riding 2 km

Discover the charm of yester-years in one of the most beau-tiful chateaux-hotels in Perig-ord. A resting place refined by its gastronomy, by the beauty of its architecture and by the quality of its hospitality in the finest perigourdin tradition. In the region of grottoes and Ro-manesque churches.

Road map p. 619

D939 dir. Angoulême-Périgueux and
D106 E1 dir. Biras-Lisle

✈ Périgueux: 20 km

Le Bourg 24310 Bourdeilles
Tel.: 33 (0) 5.53.45.45.35 – Fax: 33 (0) 5.53.45.45.20
griffons@chateauxhotels.com
Lucile & Bernard LEBRUN
10 rooms: 76 € / 90 €
Breakfast: 7,8 €
Menu(s): 20,50 € / 35 € - **Carte:** 38 € -
1/2 board: 67,5 € / 74,5 €

In one of the loveliest baronies of Périgord, near castle and river, you will appreciate the convivial welcome at this elegant 16th century house. The patio garden and all the rooms, with wooden beams and fireplaces, overlook the Dronne. Delicious, healthy regional cuisine. A romantic place.

Visa ● MASTER CARD

hotel annual closing
20/10 > 20/04

restaurant weekly closing
mon(lun), fri(lun)
01/07 > 30/08
mon(lun), tue(lun), wen(lun),
thi(lun), fri(lun)
20/04 > 30/06

equipments
telephone, internet, T.V., safe

environment
architecture 16e, garden,
terrace 70 m², view, total calm

leisure, relaxation
tennis 0.2 km, golf course
25 km, horse-riding 4 km

Road map p. 619

from Paris, A20 exit Limoges, N21
dir. Thiviers, dir. Brantôme, dir. Riberac/
Bourdeille

Périgueux: 25 km

Manoir d'Hautegente

Brive-la-Gaillarde I Coly

www.chateauxhotels.com/hautegente I reservation service: 33 (0) 1.40.07.00.20

24120 Coly

Tel.: 33 (0) 5.53.51.68.03 – Fax: 33 (0) 5.53.50.38.52

hautegente@chateauxhotels.com

Edith & Patrick HAMELIN

13 rooms: 82 € / 191 €

2 suites: 137 € / 191 €

Breakfast: 12 €

Menu(s): 41 € / 58 € - **1/2 board:** 89 € / 145 €

hotel annual closing
02/11 > 01/04

restaurant annual closing
03/11 > 01/04

equipments
telephone, T.V. Satellite, minibar

environment
architecture 14ᵉ, park, garden, terrace, view, total calm

leisure, relaxation
heated pool, tennis 2 km, golf course 20 km, horse-riding 12 km

A charming and verdant XIVth century residence with comfortable, elegant rooms overlooking floral gardens and a trout steam. Dinings rooms and private salons with large fireplace. A terrace besides the brook for refined, varied dining. Personalized welcome, trail bike rental, canoeing, etc.

Visa ● Diners ● ᴹᴬˢᵀᴱᴿ ᶜᴬᴿᴰ

Road map p. 619

A20 exit 51 Brive. D62 dir. Sarlat/ Souillac

Périgueux-Brive: 50 km

Départementale 10 33410 Cadillac
Tel.: 33 (0) 5.56.76.92.00 – Fax: 33 (0) 5.56.62.11.59
tour@chateauxhotels.com
Monique CHAPUT

31 rooms: 60 € / 105 €
1 suite: 183 € / 275 €
Breakfast: 10 €
Menu(s): 15 € / 52 € - **Carte:** 26 € -
1/2 board: 61 € / 80 €

20 min from Bordeaux, in the heart of the vineyards, at the foot of the château of the Dukes of Epernon. A park bordered by the river. Comfort, tranquillity. Regional and original specialities. Billiards, sports and leisure activities. Historical and vineyard châteaux.

Open all year

restaurant annual closing
01/01 > 30/04 ● 01/11 > 30/12

restaurant weekly closing
fri(ev), sat, sun
01/02 > 30/04

equipments
lift, telephone, internet, T.V.
Satellite/Canal+, minibar

environment
architecture contemporaine, furniture contemporain, park 4 ha, garden, terrace 100 m², view, total calm

leisure, relaxation
tennis 0.05 km, golf course 15 km, horse-riding 10 km, sauna

Visa ● MASTER CARD

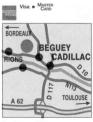

Road map p. 619

A62 exit 2 - N113 & D10 dir. Toulouse

Bordeaux-Mérignac: 40 km

Sud Ouest

Château de la Fleunie

Montignac | Condat-sur-Vézère
www.chateauxhotels.com/fleunie | reservation service: 33 (0) 1.40.07.00.20

24570 Condat-sur-Vézère
Tel.: 33 (0) 5.53.51.32.74 – Fax: 33 (0) 5.53.50.58.98
fleunie@chateauxhotels.com
Didier MORTIER
32 rooms: 55 € / 122 €
1 suite: 152,45 €
Breakfast: 10 €
Menu(s): 22 € / 43 € - **1/2 board:** 58 € / 93 €

hotel annual closing
01/01 > 01/03
equipments
T.V.
environment
architecture 12ᵉ, park 106 ha, garden, terrace, view, total calm
leisure, relaxation
golf course 25 km, horse-riding 8 km, sauna, gym

In the heart of black Périgord, 5 km from Lascaux, near Montignac, Sarlat, les Eyzies, 12th-15th century château in a 265-acre park. Quietness, comfort, away-from-it-all, spacious rooms. Refined and authentic cuisine, two tennis courts, walks, wildlife park, canoes-kayaks, riding.

Visa ● Diners ● MASTER CARD

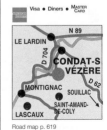

Road map p. 619

A20 exit Brive then N89 dir. Bordeaux then D764 dir. Montignac

Brive: 25 km

Route de Branne 33670 Créon

Tel.: 33 (0) 5.56.23.20.85 – Fax: 33 (0) 5.56.23.38.84
camiac@chateauxhotels.com
Jean-Marc PERRIN
10 rooms: 140 € / 450 €
Breakfast: 12 €
Menu(s): 27 € / 45 € - **Carte:** 16 €

23 km from Bordeaux, built in 1834 with a contemporary interior. A ideal stop-over and a wonderful starting point for visiting the region and its most famous wine Châteaux: Margaux, Mouton Rotschild, Ausone. Oenologie lessons, horse tricking, VTT and VIP service can be organised.

restaurant annual closing
02/11 > 23/03

equipments
lift, telephone, internet, T.V.
Satellite, baby-sitting

environment
architecture 19^e, park 8 ha,
garden, terrace, view, total
calm

leisure, relaxation
golf course 18 km,
horse-riding, bicycle track

Visa ● Diners ● MASTER CARD

Road map p. 619

Bordeaux East exit 24 dir. Bergerac
by D936

Bordeaux-Mérignac: 45 km

Château du Viguier du Roy

Figeac
www.chateauxhotels.com/viguierroy | reservation service: 33 (0) 1.40.07.00.20

Rue Droite (E. Zola) 46100 Figeac
Tel.: 33 (0) 5.65.50.05.05 – Fax: 33 (0) 5.65.50.06.06
viguierroy@chateauxhotels.com
Anne SECORDEL-MARTIN
16 rooms: 130 € / 200 €
2 flats: 275 € / 370 € - **3 suites:** 230 € / 275 €
Breakfast: 14 €
Menu(s): 23 € / 57 € - **Carte:** 39 €

hotel annual closing
01/01 > 06/04 ● 28/10 > 06/04
restaurant annual closing
17/11 > 23/11
restaurant weekly closing
mon(lun), sat(lun)
01/05 > 15/10
mon, sat(lun), sun(ev)
15/10 > 30/04
equipments
lift, telephone, internet, T.V.
Satellite, minibar, safe,
baby-sitting, valet parking
environment
architecture 12ᵉ, garden,
terrace, view, total calm
leisure, relaxation
heated pool, horse-riding 3 km,
jacuzzi

The prestige of a historic monument. Tranquillity of the interior gardens and cloister. Library, chapel, comfort, and refined decoration. Tea-room, bar, jacuzzi. In the heart of the mediaeval town, the famous Figeac. In the neighbourhood, many pleasant excursions possible.

Visa ● Diners ● MASTER CARD

Road map p. 619
A20 exit 54 - D2 dir. Figeac

Rodez-Marcillac: 55 km

36-38, cours de l'Yser 47400 Tonneins
Tel.: 33 (0) 5.53.84.34.34 – Fax: 33 (0) 5.53.84.31.31
garonne@chateauxhotels.com
6 rooms: 130 € / 161 €
Breakfast: 15 €
Menu(s): 26 € / 69 € - **Carte:** 53 €

In the heart of Gascony, above the quays of the old port, looking out over the fertile expanse of gardens and orchards that Stendhal liked to compare to Tuscany. In the guestrooms, the key words are light and space.

restaurant annual closing
01/01 > 15/01●26/10 > 10/11

equipments
lift, telephone, internet, T.V. Satellite, minibar, safe, baby-sitting, valet parking

environment
architecture contemporaine, furniture contemporain, view, total calm

leisure, relaxation
tennis 0.5 km, golf course 17 km, horse-riding 10 km, beauty salon, quad bike circuit

Visa ● Diners ● MASTER CARD

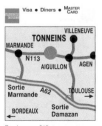

Road map p. 619

A62 exit 5 Marmande or 6 Damazan, N113 dir. Tonneins/Town-center

Agen: 36 km

Relais Sainte-Anne

Martel

www.chateauxhotels.com/sainteanne | reservation service: 33 (0) 1.40.07.00.20

rue du Pourtanel 46600 Martel
Tel.: 33 (0) 5.65.37.40.56 – Fax: 33 (0) 5.65.37.42.82
sainteanne@chateauxhotels.com
Pierre BETTLER
10 rooms: 42 € / 135 €
4 flats: 88 € / 135 € - **2 suites:** 160 € / 195 €
Breakfast: 11 €

hotel annual closing
15/11 > 25/03

equipments
telephone, internet, T.V.
Satellite, minibar, safe

environment
architecture 19^e, garden,
terrace 100 m^2, total calm

leisure, relaxation
heated pool, tennis 5 km, golf
course 18 km, horse-riding
5 km, jacuzzi

In the attractive medieval village of Martel, this hotel of character, sheltered by magnificent grounds, is an ideal place to stay to sense the charm of the region. Bright rooms, heated swimming-pool, breakfast served on the terrace - and the angels in the chapel watching over your rest.

Visa ● Diners ● JCB ● MASTER CARD

Road map p. 619

A20 exit 54 Gramat, N140 dir.
Gramat-Figeac

Brive: 30 km

Place de la Boiterie
40190 Villeneuve-de-Marsan

Tel.: 33 (0) 5.58.45.20.08 – Fax: 33 (0) 5.58.45.34.14

garrapit@chateauxhotels.com

Hervé GARRAPIT (fils) – Maïthé GARRAPIT

8 rooms: 69 € / 138 €
Breakfast: 14 €
Menu(s): 31 € / 58 € - **Carte:** 53 € -
1/2 board: 81 € / 115 €

The enjoyment of food and pleasures of comfort are joined together in this luminous and elegant coaching inn located in the Armagnac Landais. The stylish rooms are reply to the creativity of a chef in love with delicate savours that combine with generosity the subtleties of the tastes of a gourmand region.

Open all year

equipments
telephone, internet, T.V. Satellite/Canal+, minibar

environment
architecture 18e, furniture 16e, garden, total calm

leisure, relaxation
tennis 0.5 km, golf course 8 km, horse-riding 4 km, swimming pool, SPA, jacuzzi covered during winter

Road map p. 619

A62 exit Langon dir. Pau, then Villeneuve de Marsan

Pau Uzein: 65 km

Pain Adour et Fantaisie

Mont-de-Marsan I Grenade-sur-l'Adour

www.chateauxhotels.com/fantaisie | reservation service: 33 (0) 1.40.07.00.20

14-16, place des Tilleuls
40270 Grenade-sur-l'Adour
Tel.: 33 (0) 5.58.45.18.80 – Fax: 33 (0) 5.58.45.16.57

fantaisie@chateauxhotels.com
Philippe GARRET

9 rooms: 64,02 € / 121,95 €
1 suite
Breakfast: 11,43 €
Menu(s): 27,44 € / 82,32 € - **Carte:** 22,87 €
1/2 board: 96,04 € / 185,98 €

hotel annual closing
18/02 > 28/02
restaurant annual closing
18/02 > 28/02
equipments
telephone, T.V. Canal+,
minibar, safe, baby-sitting
environment
architecture 17e, terrace, view
leisure, relaxation
tennis 0.5 km, golf course
10 km, horse-riding 1 km,
jacuzzi

Beautiful 17th-18th century residence in the heart of the south-west. Creative cuisine based on superb regional produce. Regional wines and Bas Armagnacs. Meals served on the terrace on the river bank, in the lounge with glossy wood panelling. Bright, spacious rooms, charming and tranquil.

Visa ● Diners ● MASTER CARD

Road map p. 619

A62 exit Aiguillon - N124 between
Mont-de-Marsan and Aire sur Adour

Pau: 65 km

Place d'Armes 24290 Montignac

Tel.: 33 (0) 5.53.50.53.92 – Fax: 33 (0) 5.53.51.02.23

laroseraie@chateauxhotels.com

Vincent NOURRISSON

14 rooms: 72 € / 105 €
Breakfast: 10 €
Menu(s): 19 € / 30 € - **Carte:** 30 € -
1/2 board: 70 € / 90 €

In the heart of a mediaeval village, on the banks of the river, a lovely 19th century residence turned into a charming and gentle hotel, for a restful stay, gastronomic discoveries. 25 km from Sarlat and Les Eyzies. Visit to the grottoes, prehistoric sites, numerous châteaux.

Visa ● MASTER CARD

Road map p. 619

hotel annual closing
15/11 > 01/04

restaurant annual closing
15/11 > 01/04

restaurant weekly closing
mon(lun), tue(lun), wen(lun), thi(lun), fri(lun)
01/04 > 15/06

equipments
telephone, T.V., safe

environment
architecture 19^e, garden, terrace 100 m^2, view

leisure, relaxation
tennis 1 km, golf course 25 km, horse-riding 10 km, canoeing, kayak, mountain bike

Relais du Soleil d'Or

Montignac I Lascaux

www.chateauxhotels.com/soleilor | reservation service: 33 (0) 1.40.07.00.20

16, rue du 4 Septembre 24290 Lascaux
Tel.: 33 (0) 5.53.51.80.22 – Fax: 33 (0) 5.53.50.27.54

soleilor@chateauxhotels.com
Marcel BRENNER

28 rooms: 54,00 € / 84,00 €
2 flats: 143,3 € / 173,79 €
2 suites: 121,96 € / 152,45 €
Breakfast: 8,84 €
Menu(s): 18,29 € / 43,45 €
1/2 board: 61,50 € / 76,68 €

hotel annual closing
14/01 > 12/02

restaurant annual closing
14/01 > 12/02

restaurant weekly closing
mon(lun), sun(ev)
03/11 > 28/03

equipments
telephone, internet, T.V.
Satellite/Canal+, minibar

environment
architecture 18º, garden,
terrace 300 m², total calm

leisure, relaxation
tennis 0.5 km, golf course
30 km, horse-riding 7 km,
canoeing

*One mile from the Lascaux
caves, in a charming village of
Périgord Noir, on the Vézère
river, is situated this former
coaching inn where hospitality
is foremost. Discover art de
vivre in this setting where time
flows at the river's pace. Traditional cuisine highlighting
regional dishes.*

Visa ● Diners ● MASTER CARD

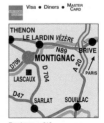

Road map p. 619

A20 exit Brive - N89 dir. Montignac-
Lascaux

 Brive: 30 km

Bd des Pyrénées 64400 Oloron-Sainte-Marie
Tel.: 33 (0) 5.59.39.70.70 – Fax: 33 (0) 5.59.39.24.47
alysson@chateauxhotels.com
Gaëlle DODARD
32 rooms: 60,98 € / 82,32 €
Breakfast: 7,62 €
Menu(s): 20,58 € / 38,11 €

Facing the Pyrenees, the starting point for numerous tours (sea and mountain), a friendly setting in typical architecture. Spacious, comfortable, sound-proofed rooms. Air-conditioned restaurant, with bay windows looking onto the garden and the swimming pool, where you can savour excellent meals.

Open all year
restaurant weekly closing
sat(lun)
01/05 > 30/09
fri(ev), sat
01/10 > 01/05
equipments
lift, telephone, internet, T.V. Canal+
environment
garden, terrace, view
leisure, relaxation
tennis 0.2 km, golf course 30 km, horse-riding 2 km, jacuzzi, 4x4 excursions for groups

Visa ● Diners ● MASTER CARD

Road map p. 619

A64 exit Salies or Pau dir. Saragosse/
Col du Somport

Pau: 32 km

Château de Méracq

Pau I Méracq

www.chateauxhotels.com/meracq | reservation service: 33 (0) 1.40.07.00.20

64410 Méracq

Tel.: 33 (0) 5.59.04.53.01 – Fax: 33 (0) 5.59.04.55.50

meracq@chateauxhotels.com

Jean-Pierre GUERIN-RECOUSSINE

6 rooms: 63 € / 87 €
2 suites: 126 € / 150 €
Breakfast: 9 €
Menu(s) : 28 € / 40 € - **1/2 board:** 70 € / 90 €

Open all year
reservation only
from 01/11 > 31/03

equipments
telephone, internet

environment
architecture 18°, park 3 ha,
garden, terrace 100 m², view,
vegetable garden, total calm

leisure, relaxation
tennis 1 km, golf course
25 km, horse-riding 10 km

Just 20 minutes from Pau, an hour from the sea and the mountains, on the road to Spain and the Guggenheim museum, this pretty late XVIIth century castle will open your eyes to the Bearn region. A must for all gourmets: full-flavoured regional dishes lovingly prepared by the chefs. Terroir cuisine.

Visa ● Diners ● JCB ● MASTER CARD

Road map p. 619

A64 exit Pau then N134 dir. Bordeaux

Pau Uzein: 12 km

Château de Lalande
Périgueux I Razac-sur-l'Isle
www.chateauxhotels.com/lalande | reservation service: 33 (0) 1.40.07.00.20

227

3 route de Saint-Astier 24430 Razac-sur-l'Isle
Tel.: 33 (0) 5.53.54.52.30 – Fax: 33 (0) 5.53.07.46.67
lalande@chateauxhotels.com
Michèle & Louis SICARD
15 rooms: 50 € / 80 €
2 flats: 82 € / 107 €
Breakfast: 7 €
Menu(s): 23 € / 49 € - **Carte:** 38 € -
1/2 board: 56 € / 68 €

Tranquillity and gastronomy in a vast park in the heart of Périgord: to discover Lascaux, Sarlat, Périgueux, the Bergerac and Bordeaux vineyards. With his frank and generous regional cuisine, Louis Sicard will make you appreciate the virtues of this magnificent province with its 1,000 châteaux.

hotel annual closing
01/01 > 15/03●05/11 > 31/12
restaurant annual closing
05/11 > 15/03●05/11 > 31/12
equipments
telephone, T.V. Satellite
environment
architecture 18^e, park 3 ha, garden, terrace 2000 m^2, total calm
leisure, relaxation
tennis 1 km, golf course 10 km, horse-riding 2 km

Visa ● MASTER CARD

Road map p. 619

N 2089 direction Bordeaux and D3

Périgueux-Bassillac: 20 km

Château des Reynats

Périgueux/Chancelade
www.chateauxhotels.com/reynats | reservation service: 33 (0) 1.40.07.00.20

15, avenue des Reynats
24650 Périgueux/Chancelade
Tel.: 33 (0) 5.53.03.53.59 – Fax: 33 (0) 5.53.03.44.84
reynats@chateauxhotels.com
Philippe ETCHEBEST – Jean-Michel DESPREZ

8 rooms: 106 € / 116 €
5 suites: 131 € / 171 €
Breakfast: 12,5 €
Menu(s): 27 € / 51 € - **Carte:** 53 €
1/2 board: 97,5 € / 102,5 €

hotel annual closing
02/01 > 05/02
restaurant annual closing
01/01 > 05/02
restaurant weekly closing
mon(lun), sat(lun), sun(lun)
01/05 > 31/10
mon, sat(lun), sun
01/11 > 30/04
equipments
lift, telephone, internet, T.V.,
minibar, safe
environment
architecture 19°, park 3 ha,
terrace 100 m²
leisure, relaxation
heated pool, golf course
0.2 km, horse-riding 1 km,
sightseeing, prehistoric sites

In the heart of Perigord, 10 minutes from the centre of Périgueux, a chateau that combines the charm and elegance of an authentic 19th century residence. Entirely renovated in 1991, it has retained a certain good life style. All the sites of Périgord are nearby: Lascaux, the Dordogne Valley...

Visa • Diners • JCB • MASTER CARD

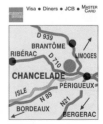

Road map p. 619
N89, D710 dir. D1

Périgueux-Boulazac: 10 km

www.chateauxhotels.com/chaufourg | reservation service: 33 (0) 1.40.07.00.20

« Le Chaufourg » 24400 Sourzac

Tel.: 33 (0) 5.53.81.01.56 – Fax: 33 (0) 5.53.82.94.87
chaufourg@chateauxhotels.com
Georges DAMBIER

5 rooms: 136 € / 229 €
4 suites: 274,50 € / 300 €
Breakfast: 14,50 €
Carte: 53 €

Between the park, meadows and gardens, overlooking the Isle river, a 17th century family residence, full of charm, elegance, comfort. Your host is happy to share his joy of living with you in Périgord... Trips on the river, walks in the woods, fishing, riding, golf and the high points of prehistory.

hotel annual closing
15/11 > 01/03

equipments
telephone, internet, T.V., safe

environment
architecture 17e, park 4 ha, garden, terrace, view

leisure, relaxation
tennis 1 km, golf course 30 km, horse-riding 10 km

Visa ● Diners ● MASTER CARD

Road map p. 619

Autoroute A89 exit n° 13

Bergerac: 30 km

La Terrasse

Rocamadour I Meyronne

www.chateauxhotels.com/laterrasse | reservation service: 33 (0) 1.40.07.00.20

46200 Meyronne

Tel.: 33 (0) 5.65.32.21.60 – Fax: 33 (0) 5.65.32.26.93

laterrasse@chateauxhotels.com

Gilles LIEBUS

11 rooms: 53 € / 121 €
1 flat: 282 € - **3 suites:** 121 € / 228 €
Breakfast: 9 €
Menu(s): 23 € / 45 € - **Carte:** 50 €
1/2 board: 56 € / 91 €

hotel annual closing
01/01 > 01/03

restaurant annual closing
15/11 > 01/03

equipments
telephone, internet, T.V.
Satellite, minibar, safe

environment
architecture 16e, garden,
terrace, view

leisure, relaxation
tennis 1 km, golf course
15 km, horse-riding 5 km

This entirely restored feudal chateau is reflected in the waters of the Dordogne river. Inside, the charm of the past mingles with the comfort of the present. Relax by the pool, in a shaded garden and enjoy a warm welcome in one of France's most beautiful regions. Panoramic restaurant.

Visa ● Diners ● MASTER CARD

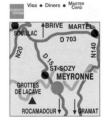

Road map p. 619

A20 exit Souillac, D703 dir Gramat

Brive: 35 km

8, place de la République 46500 Gramat
Tel.: 33 (0) 5.65.38.73.18 – Fax: 33 (0) 5.65.38.84.50
lionor@chateauxhotels.com
René MOMMEJAC
15 rooms: 51 € / 79 €
Breakfast: 9,45 €
Menu(s): 21 € / 47 € - **Carte:** 49 € -
1/2 board: 66,45 € / 85,45 €

Near Rocamadour, on the main square of the little town of Gramat, an ancient residence with a facade of local stone. High-class cuisine based on regional cooking, vintage wines from the Cahors region. Fine dining-room, large shaded terrace. Practical modern-style decoration in the bedrooms.

Visa ● Diners ● JCB ● MASTER CARD

Road map p. 619

A20 exit 54, N140 dir. Brive-Montpellier

hotel annual closing
15/12 > 15/01
restaurant annual closing
15/12 > 15/01
restaurant weekly closing
thi, fri
01/01 > 15/12
equipments
lift, telephone, internet, T.V. Satellite/Canal+, baby-sitting
environment
architecture 18^e, garden, terrace 90 m^2, vegetable garden
leisure, relaxation
tennis 0.6 km, golf course 20 km, horse-riding 1 km

Brive: 54 km

Les Vieilles Tours
Rocamadour
www.chateauxhotels.com/vieillestours | reservation service: 33 (0) 1.40.07.00.20

La Fage 46500 Rocamadour

Tel.: 33 (0) 5.65.33.68.01 – Fax: 33 (0) 5.65.33.68.59

vieillestours@chateauxhotels.com
M. & Mme. Virginie CAULOT – Roger ZOZZOLI

16 rooms: 52 € / 78 €
1 suite: 94 €
Breakfast: 8 €
Menu(s): 21 € / 55 € - **Carte:** 40 €
1/2 board: 61 € / 74 €

hotel annual closing
15/11 > 31/03
restaurant annual closing
15/11 > 31/03
equipments
telephone, internet, T.V.
Satellite, minibar
environment
architecture 17e, furniture 19e,
garden, terrace 80 m², view,
total calm
leisure, relaxation
tennis 3 km, golf course
30 km, horse-riding 3 km

A stone's throw from Rocamadour, a warm welcome awaits you at this 17th century country manor flanked by two towers including a splendid 13th century falconry. Spacious period-furnished rooms, a place to relax in style. Inventive regional-flavoured cuisine from a master of the art.

Visa ● Diners ● MASTER CARD

Road map p. 619

D673 dir. Payrac/Gourdon from Rocamadour

Brive: 58 km

64122 Saint-Jean de Luz
Tel.: 33 (0) 5.59.54.31.15 – Fax: 33 (0) 5.59.54.62.51
urtubie@chateauxhotels.com
Laurent de CORAL
10 rooms: 60 € / 130 €
Breakfast: 10 €

Owned by the same family since its construction in 1341, a fortified chateau enlarged and transformed in the 16th and 18th centuries. Louis XI stayed there in 1463, lands raised to a viscounty by Louis XIV in 1654. Vast rooms in the oldest part of the château. Period furniture. Good quality restaurant nearby.

Visa • MASTER CARD

Road map p. 619

A63 exit south of St-Jean-de-Luz. N10 dir. Urrugne

✈ Biarritz: 15 km

hotel annual closing
15/11 > 15/03

equipments
telephone, internet, T.V.
Satellite

environment
architecture 16ᵉ, furniture 18ᵉ, park 6 ha, garden

leisure, relaxation
golf course 3 km, horse-riding 10 km, beauty salon, thalassotherapy, sauna, hammam, fitness, jacuzzi, tennis in the park

| Sud Ouest

La Réserve

Saint-Jean-de-Luz

www.chateauxhotels.com/reserve | reservation service: 33 (0) 1.40.07.00.20

Rond-point Sainte-Barbe
64500 Saint-Jean-de-Luz
Tel.: 33 (0) 5.59.51.32.00 – Fax: 33 (0) 5.59.51.32.01

reserve@chateauxhotels.com
Henri BOUTIN

33 rooms: 70 € / 148 €
2 suites: 92 € / 270 €
Breakfast: 11 €
Menu(s): 26 € / 32 € - **Carte:** 40 €

Open all year
equipments
telephone, internet, T.V., safe,
baby-sitting

environment
park 3 ha, garden, terrace
300 m², view, total calm

leisure, relaxation
heated pool, golf course 3 km,
horse-riding 8 km, sauna

A unique spot on the Basque coast, facing the sea and mountains, a charming hotel on 7.5 acres of grounds, where you can enjoy a relaxing and invigorating stay. Traditional style rooms with balcony or loggia. Fine regional food on the panoramic terrace. Smugglers' path leading down to the beach.

Visa ● Diners ● MASTER CARD

Road map p. 619

A63 exit North of St-Jean de Luz or
N10 Bayonne/Biarritz

 Biarritz-Parme: 10 km

Lehen Tokia 235
Saint-Jean-de-Luz ı Ciboure
www.chateauxhotels.com/lehentokia | reservation service: 33 (0) 1.40.07.00.20

1, chemin Achotarreta 64500 Ciboure
Tel.: 33 (0) 5.59.47.18.16 – Fax: 33 (0) 5.59.47.38.04
lehentokia@chateauxhotels.com
M. PERSONNAZ
6 rooms: 77 € / 145 €
1 suite: 183 € / 214 €
Breakfast: 9,15 €

Above the Bay of Saint-Jean-de-Luz is the villa Lehen Tokia - "the first place" in Basque - built by Hiriart. Respect is inspired here from the beauty of the rooms and decoration of the era. Monumental stained-glass windows and unimpeded view over the Bay.

hotel annual closing
15/11 > 15/12 • 07/01 > 17/01

equipments
telephone, internet, T.V., minibar, safe

environment
architecture, garden, terrace, view, total calm

leisure, relaxation
tennis 2 km, golf course 1 km, thalassotherapy, sauna, golf

Visa ● Diners ● MASTER CARD

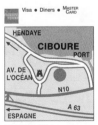

Road map p. 619

A63 exit south of St-Jean-de-Luz, N10

Biarritz: 12 km

Domaine de la Barde

Sarlat-la-Caneda I Le Bugue

www.chateauxhotels.com/barde | reservation service: 33 (0) 1.40.07.00.20

Route de Périgueux 24260 Le Bugue
Tel.: 33 (0) 5.53.07.16.54 – Fax: 33 (0) 5.53.54.76.19
barde@chateauxhotels.com
André DARNAUD
18 rooms: 72 € / 196 €
Breakfast: 11 €
Menu(s): 21,5 € / 53 € - **1/2 board:** 70 € / 132 €

hotel annual closing
01/01 > 11/04 • 15/10 > 11/04
restaurant annual closing
01/01 > 11/04
equipments
lift, telephone, T.V. Satellite, safe
environment
architecture 18ᵉ, park 4 ha, garden, terrace, view
leisure, relaxation
heated pool, golf course 17 km, horse-riding 10 km, sauna, fitness, tennis

Former repaire noble, Domaine de la Barde offers carefully restored 18th manor house, mill, 17th forge in 10 acres meadows, gardens, streams; in park, orangery (sauna, ping-pong, mini-fitness), near of heated swimming-pool, tennis. To be visited: the Périgord Noir, its châteaux and grottoes.

Visa • MASTER CARD

Road map p. 619
A20 exit Brive then N89 then D710

Périgueux: 35 km

Route de Montfort 24200 Vitrac-Sarlat
Tel.: 33 (0) 5.53.31.52.52 – Fax: 33 (0) 5.53.29.36.88
rochebois@chateauxhotels.com
Anne HILLEBRAND

34 rooms: 130 € / 375 €
4 flats: 345 € / 420 € - **2 suites:** 300 € / 375 €
Breakfast: 14 €
Menu(s): 29 € / 54 € - **Carte:** 54 € -
1/2 board: 117 € / 262 €

Rochebois is a noble and elegant residence, imbued with the seductive art of fine living. In the shaded gardens, trickling fountains and murmuring breezes in the mulberry trees gracefully mingles with wafts of honeysuckle and jasmine. Subtel Italian-inspired decoration. Golf, swimming pool.

hotel annual closing
15/11 > 25/03
restaurant annual closing
15/11 > 25/03
equipments
lift, telephone, internet, T.V.
Satellite, minibar, safe,
baby-sitting, valet parking
environment
architecture 19ᵉ, park 30 ha,
garden, terrace, view,
vegetable garden, total calm
leisure, relaxation
tennis 1 km, horse-riding 5 km

Visa ● Diners ● MASTER CARD

Road map p. 619

D703 between Souillac and Sarlat
(road of "Vallée de la Dordogne")

Brive: 55 km

Hostellerie de Meysset

Sarlat-la-Caneda
www.chateauxhotels.com/meysset | reservation service: 33 (0) 1.40.07.00.20

Route d'Argentouleau 24200 Sarlat-la-Caneda
Tel.: 33 (0) 5.53.59.08.29 – Fax: 33 (0) 5.53.28.47.61

meysset @chateauxhotels.com
Yvonne BROTTIER – Michel BROTTIER
20 rooms: 55 € / 78 €
2 flats: 100 € / 125 € - **4 suites:** 84 € / 108 €
Breakfast: 9,5 €
Menu(s): 18 € / 42 € - **1/2 board:** 55 € / 66 €

hotel annual closing
01/01 > 26/04•30/10 > 01/04
restaurant annual closing
01/01 > 26/04•30/10 > 01/04
equipments
telephone, T.V., safe
environment
architecture 20°, furniture
contemporain, park 1.2 ha,
garden, terrace 213 m², view
leisure, relaxation
tennis 5 km, golf course 6 km,
horse-riding 10 km

The hostellerie de Meysset is situated at the heart of Périgord Noir. 3 km from the living museum which is the beautiful city of Sarlat, an excellent centre for numerous excursions. Hotel is set in three acres of pine wood and garden, at the top of a hill overlooking two valleys.

Visa • Diners • MASTER CARD

Road map p. 619

After Sarlat, follow D6 dir. Les Eyzies

Brive: 52 km

L'Abbaye

Sarlat-la-Caneda I Saint-Cyprien

Rue de l'Abbaye des Augustins
24220 Saint-Cyprien
Tel.: 33 (0) 5.53.29.20.48 – Fax: 33 (0) 5.53.29.15.85
hotelabbaye@chateauxhotels.com
Yvette & Marcel SCHALLER
23 rooms: 76 € / 128 €
1 suite: 112,81 € / 115,86 €
Breakfast: 9,91 €

In the heart of the Périgord Noir, a house that inherited its name from the old Augustinian abbey, where the friendly atmosphere lives up to its promise. Old-world charm, elegant comfort, shaded patios, fragrant garden all complement a certain art of living.

hotel annual closing
01/01 > 19/04
restaurant annual closing
20/10 > 15/04
equipments
telephone, internet, T.V., safe
environment
architecture 18e, garden, terrace, view
leisure, relaxation
tennis 0.4 km, golf course 8 km

Visa ● Diners ● MASTER CARD

Road map p. 619

A10 exit Souillac then D703

Périgueux ou Bergerac: 50 km

L'Esplanade

Sarlat-la-Caneda I Domme

www.chateauxhotels.com/esplanade | reservation service: 33 (0) 1.40.07.00.20

Le Bourg 24250 Domme
Tel.: 33 (0) 5.53.28.31.41 – Fax: 33 (0) 5.53.28.49.92
esplanade@chateauxhotels.com
René GILLARD

24 rooms: 61 € / 122 €
1 suite: 138 € / 170 €
Breakfast: 11 €
Menu(s): 33 € / 69 € - **Carte:** 91 €

hotel annual closing
11/11 > 01/03
restaurant annual closing
11/11 > 01/03
restaurant weekly closing
mon(lun), wen(lun)
31/03 > 30/09
mon, wen(lun)
31/01 > 31/03
equipments
telephone, T.V., safe
environment
garden, terrace 80 m², view
leisure, relaxation
tennis 1 km, golf course 5 km,
horse-riding 8 km

In a mediaeval city overlooking the Dordogne, a refined gastronomy where foie gras, truffes, mushrooms, seafood go hand-in-hand, fillet of lamb on a skewer, fish. Charming rooms, some with view over the valley, others into old country residences. All the pleasures of Périgord. Golf 5 km away.

Visa ● Diners ● MASTER CARD

Road map p. 619

A20 exit Souillac dir. Sarlat

Brive-Périgueux: 80 km

La Ferme Lamy 241
Sarlat-la-Caneda I Meyrals
www.chateauxhotels.com/lamy | reservation service: 33 (0) 1.40.07.00.20

24220 Meyrals
Tel.: 33 (0) 5.53.29.62.46 – Fax: 33 (0) 5.53.59.61.41
lamy@chateauxhotels.com
Nelly & Michel BOUGON
12 rooms: 80 € / 160 €
Breakfast: 9 €

In the heart of the Perigord, just outside Sarlat, a lovely 17th c. farmhouse perched on a hillside offers tranquillity and rest. Set in the country, the hotel is still close to the major tourist sights. Comfortable rooms, shaded patios and flowering gardens contribute to give the hotel its authentic charm.

Open all year

equipments
telephone, internet, T.V., minibar, baby-sitting

environment
architecture 18e, furniture 18e, park 3 ha, garden, terrace 250 m², view, total calm

leisure, relaxation
tennis 3.5 km, golf course 15 km, horse-riding 10 km, jacuzzi

Visa ● Diners ● MASTERCARD

Road map p. 619

By D47 between Sarlat and les Eyzies, road C3 to Bénivès.

Périgueux: 45 km

| Sud Ouest

Les Glycines

Sarlat-la-Caneda I Les Eyzies-de-Tayac-Sireuil

www.chateauxhotels.com/glycines I reservation service: 33 (0) 1.40.07.00.20

24620 Les Eyzies-de-Tayac-Sireuil
Tel.: 33 (0) 5.53.06.97.07 – Fax: 33 (0) 5.53.06.92.19
glycines@chateauxhotels.com
Pascal LOMBARD
23 rooms: 60 € / 113 €
Breakfast: 10 €
Menu(s): 22 € / 46 € - **Carte:** 30,49 €
1/2 board: 67 € / 87 €

hotel annual closing
15/11 > 15/03
restaurant annual closing
15/11 > 15/03
restaurant weekly closing
mon(lun)
01/07 > 15/09
mon(lun), sat(lun)
15/03 > 15/11
equipments
telephone, T.V. Satellite
environment
architecture 19ᵉ, park 3 ha,
garden, terrace, view,
vegetable garden, total calm
leisure, relaxation
golf course 15 km, horse-riding
5 km

All of the charms of residences from the past are rediscovered in this former Post house located along the banks of the Vézère. The ageold grounds and restful rooms are harmonious reflections of the creations of the chef who draws his inspiration from local products and his organic vegetable garden.

Visa ● MASTER CARD

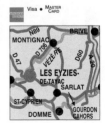

Road map p. 619
Périgueux D47 dir. Sarlat

 Périgueux Bassillac: 40 km

Manoir de Bellerive

243

Sarlat-la-Caneda ı Le Buisson-de-Cadouin
www.chateauxhotels.com/bellerive | reservation service: 33 (0) 1.40.07.00.20

Route de Siorac 24480 Le Buisson-de-Cadouin
Tel.: 33 (0) 5.53.22.16.16 – Fax: 33 (0) 5.53.22.09.05
bellerive@chateauxhotels.com
Marcel CLEVENOT

15 rooms: 98 € / 155 €
5 suites: 160 € / 244 €
Breakfast: 16,75 €
Menu(s): 34 € / 85 € - **Carte:** 70 € -
1/2 board: 99 € / 114,5 €

Located in the golden triangle of the Périgord Noir, in the heart of hikking trails between Bergerac and Sarlat, this 1830 Napoléon III château is taste-fully decorated. The early co-lours reflect those of the 8 acres park bordering on the Dordogne river. Gourmet res-taurant: "Les Délices d'Hortense".

hotel annual closing
03/01 > 01/03

restaurant annual closing
01/01 > 03/03

equipments
telephone, internet, T.V. Satellite, minibar, safe, baby-sitting

environment
architecture 19e, park 4 ha, garden, terrace 70 m², view, vegetable garden, total calm

leisure, relaxation
golf course 7 km, horse-riding 3 km, sauna, hammam, jacuzzi, horse-riding (3 km)

Visa ● Diners ● MASTER CARD

Road map p. 619

Exit Paris A20 dir. Toulouse exit Souil-lac then dir. Sarlat

✈ Périgueux: 40 km

Relais de Moussidière

Sarlat-la-Caneda

www.chateauxhotels.com/moussidiere | reservation service: 33 (0) 1.40.07.00.20

Lieu-dit Moussidière Basse
24200 Sarlat-la-Caneda
Tel.: 33 (0) 5.53.28.28.74 – Fax: 33 (0) 5.53.28.25.11
moussidiere@chateauxhotels.com
M. DUCOURET
35 rooms: 90 € / 140 €
Breakfast: 10 €

hotel annual closing
01/11 > 12/04

equipments
lift, telephone, T.V., minibar, safe

environment
architecture 18e, park 7 ha, garden, terrace 200 m², view, total calm

leisure, relaxation
tennis 0.8 km, golf course 10 km, horse-riding 3 km

This lovely restored house, full of character and well located is built against a large boulder in the heart of a landscaped 18-acre park, two steps from the medieval town centre. Refined charm and elegance. Cuisine in the fine gastronomic tradition. Sample the gentle life of the Périgord.

Visa • MASTER CARD

Road map p. 619

Exit Sarlat South, dir. Bergerac, turn left to the garage "Citroën"

 Brive: 60 km

Lacave 46200 Souillac
Tel.: 33 (0) 5.65.37.87.04 – Fax: 33 (0) 5.65.32.77.41
ouysse@chateauxhotels.com
Marinette & Daniel CHAMBON
12 rooms: 122 € / 130 €
2 flats: 138 € / 153 €
Breakfast: 13 €
Menu(s): 28 € / 92 € - **Carte:** 31 € -
1/2 board: 130 € / 138 €

Seduced by the charm of the house, you will think of nothing but strolling on the banks of the Ouysse. Enchanted by the light air of blue Quercy, you will discover the gastronomic secrets revealed to you by Daniel Chambon: truffles, foie gras, cepes, crayfish, chickens from Adrienne's farm, etc.

hotel annual closing
11/11 > 01/03
restaurant annual closing
11/11 > 01/03
restaurant weekly closing
mon(lun), tue(lun)
01/05 > 30/09
mon, tue(lun)
01/03 > 30/04 ● 01/10 > 10/11
equipments
telephone, internet, T.V., minibar, safe
environment
furniture contemporain, garden, terrace, total calm
leisure, relaxation
heated pool, tennis 6 km, golf course 20 km, horse-riding 5 km

Visa ● Diners ● JCB ● MasterCard

Road map p. 619

On D43 between Souillac and Rocamadour

Brive: 40 km

Château Lalande

Vielleneuve-sur-Lot I Saint-Sylvestre-sur-Lot
www.chateauxhotels.com/chateaulalande | reservation service: 33 (0) 1.40.07.00.20

47140 Saint-Sylvestre-sur-Lot
Tel.: 33 (0) 5.53.36.15.15 – Fax: 33 (0) 5.53.36.15.16
chateaulalande@chateauxhotels.com
Yves PRENAT
18 rooms: 130 € / 200 €
4 suites: 214 € / 310 €
Breakfast: 14 €
Menu(s): 37 € / 61 € - **1/2 board:** 109 € / 144 €

Open all year
equipments
lift, telephone, internet, T.V.,
minibar, safe, baby-sitting,
valet parking
environment
architecture, park 9 ha,
garden, terrace, total calm
leisure, relaxation
golf course 15 km, horse-riding
4 km, beauty salon, balneo,
hammam, solarium, fitness

*This luxury hotel/restaurant
set like a jewel and the green
splendour, was built between
the XIIIth and XVIIIth centuries.
In every one of the 22 bedrooms, the past has been
imaginatively reconstructed.
Two restaurants are able to
satisfy your every gourmet desire (from light cooking to
haute cuisine).*

Visa • Diners • MASTER CARD

Road map p. 619

A62 exit 6 or 7, dir. Villeneuve/Lot,
D911 dir. Fumel/Cahors

 Agen: 35 km

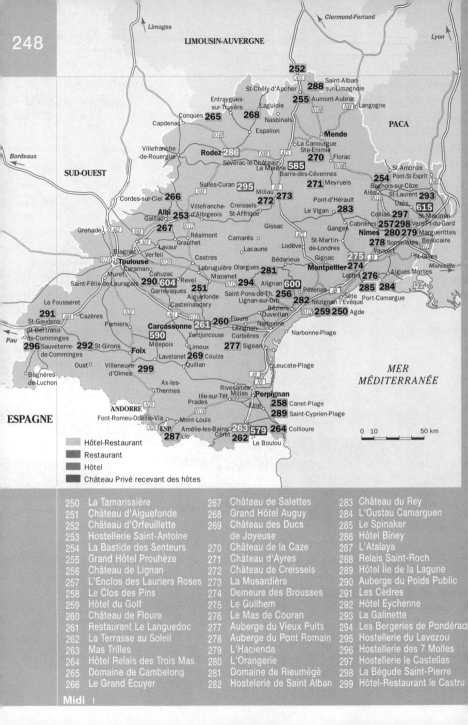

MER MÉDITERRANÉE

ESPAGNE

LIMOUSIN-AUVERGNE

SUD-OUEST

PACA

ANDORRE

0   10   50 km

Hôtel-Restaurant
Restaurant
Hôtel
Château Privé recevant des hôtes

How to book ?

→ At the Châteaux & Hôtels reservation centre:
- Tél : 00 33 (0) 1 40 07 00 20
- Fax : 00 33 (0) 1 40 07 00 30

→ By Internet:
- www.chateauxhotels.com
- resa@chateauxhotels.com

→ Directly with the establishement required

La Tamarissière

Agde

www.chateauxhotels.com/tamarissiere | reservation service: 33 (0) 1.40.07.00.20

Lieu-dit La Tamarissière 34300 Agde
Tel.: 33 (0) 4.67.94.20.87 – Fax: 33 (0) 4.67.21.38.40
tamarissiere@chateauxhotels.com
Nicolas ALBANO

24 rooms: 63 € / 112 €
2 suites: 118 € / 244 €
Breakfast: 11,45 €
Menu(s): 27,50 € / 39,50 € - **Carte:** 61 €

hotel annual closing
02/11 > 10/03
restaurant annual closing
02/11 > 10/03
restaurant weekly closing
mon, tue(lun)
15/06 > 15/09
sun(ev), mon
16/09 > 14/06

equipments
telephone, T.V. Satellite,
minibar, safe

environment
garden, terrace, view

leisure, relaxation
tennis 8 km, golf course 8 km,
horse-riding 0.5 km,
thalassotherapy 8km

Very near Agde, close to the beach, on the Hérault's picturesque estuary, a nice house, between the river and the sea ...Pretty rooms, terrace upon the water, and a cuisine like an hymn to the Mediterranean and Languedoc regions.

Visa ● Diners ● MasterCard

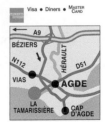

Road map p. 619

A9 Exit Agde/Pezenas, dir. Agde/La Tamarissière, embankment Hérault (right bank)

✈ Béziers-Vias: 15 km

www.chateauxhotels.com/aiguefonde | reservation service: 33 (0) 1.40.07.00.20

81200 Aiguefonde
Tel.: 33 (0) 5.63.98.13.70 – Fax: 33 (0) 5.63.98.69.90
aiguefonde@chateauxhotels.com
Henk GOENS
5 rooms: 120 € / 155 €
3 suites: 195 €
Breakfast: 15 €
Menu(s): 40 € / 40 €

In the heart of Cathar country, near the Black Mountain, a magnificently restored 14th century chateau. Inside 16th, 17th and 18th century tapestries and paintings, and period furniture in the 8 rooms. French garden, English park, with romantic waterfalls and fountains...

hotel annual closing
01/10 > 25/05
restaurant annual closing
01/10 > 25/05
equipments
telephone, internet
environment
architecture 14º, furniture 18º, park 8 ha, garden, terrace, view, total calm
leisure, relaxation
tennis 5 km, golf course 5 km, horse-riding 2 km

Visa ● Diners ● MASTER CARD

Road map p. 619

A50 exit Carcassonne or A9 exit Béziers, dir. Mazamet

Castres-Mazamet: 9 km

Château d'Orfeuillette

Albaret Sainte-Marie

www.chateauxhotels.com/orfeuillette | reservation service: 33 (0) 1.40.07.00.20

La Garde 48200 Albaret Sainte-Marie
Tel.: 33 (0) 4.66.42.65.65 – Fax: 33 (0) 4.66.42.65.66

orfeuillette@chateauxhotels.com
Philippe GARDEREAU

23 rooms: 75 € / 105,5 €
4 suites: 105,5 €
Breakfast: 9,15 €
Menu(s): 25,92 € / 36,59 € - **Carte:** 5,4 €
1/2 board: 69,5 € / 85,5 €

restaurant annual closing
07/01 > 31/01
restaurant weekly closing
wen(lun)
01/07 > 31/08
wen
01/09 > 30/06
equipments
lift, telephone, T.V. Canal+, minibar
environment
architecture 19e, furniture contemporain, park 12 ha, garden, terrace, view, total calm
leisure, relaxation
heated pool, tennis 8 km, golf course 25 km, horse-riding 8 km, thermal baths, mountain bikes for hire

In Haute-Lozere, at the foot of the Tarn gorges, this magnificent 19th c residence grandly overlooking a 5 acre park graced by hundred-year-old trees provides guests with a warm welcome. Vast, luxuriously decorated rooms and exquisite country cooking are a testament to the French art of living.

Visa ● Diners ● MASTER CARD

Road map p. 619

A75 exit 32 (aire de Lozere) dir. Montpellier ou Clermont-Ferrand, à 200m dir. La Garde

Clermont-Ferrand: 120 km

17, rue Saint-Antoine 81000 Albi
Tel.: 33 (0) 5.63.54.04.04 – Fax: 33 (0) 5.63.47.10.47
saintantoine@chateauxhotels.com
J.F. RIEUX
36 rooms: 100 € / 160 €
8 suites: 160 € / 220 €
Breakfast: 10 €
Menu(s): 22 € / 45 € - **Carte:** 48 €

The Hostellerie, located on an interior garden in the heart of Albi, is just 5 minutes from the Cathedral and the Toulouse-Lautrec Museum. Founded in 1734 and rebuilt in 1971, an exclusive place, with the expert service, the antique furniture, including the fine local cuisine...

Open all year
restaurant weekly closing
mon(lun), sat(lun), sun
01/04 > 31/10
mon, sat(lun), sun
01/11 > 31/03
equipments
lift, telephone, internet, T.V.
Satellite, minibar, safe,
baby-sitting, valet parking
environment
garden, total calm
leisure, relaxation
tennis 2 km, golf course 3 km,
horse-riding 5 km, solarium,
private swimming pool 3km

Visa ● Diners ● JCB ● MASTER CARD

Road map p. 619
A68 from TOULOUSE exit Albi

Toulouse: 78 km

| Midi

La Bastide des Senteurs

Ales I Saint-Victor-de-Malcap

www.chateauxhotels.com/senteurs I reservation service: 33 (0) 1.40.07.00.20

Le village 30500 Saint-Victor-de-Malcap
Tel.: 33 (0) 4.66.60.24.45 – Fax: 33 (0) 4.66.60.26.10
senteurs@chateauxhotels.com
Franck SUBILEAU
9 rooms: 55 € / 67 €
: 57 € / 87 €
Breakfast: 7 €
Menu(s): 26 € / 65 €

hotel annual closing
26/10 > 04/11

restaurant annual closing
26/10 > 04/11

restaurant weekly closing
mon(lun), tue(lun), wen(lun),
thi(lun), fri(lun), sat(lun)
01/07 > 31/08
wen, sun(ev)
01/09 > 30/06

equipments
telephone, T.V.

environment
architecture contemporaine,
furniture contemporain,
terrace, view

leisure, relaxation
tennis 0.2 km, horse-riding
5 km

La Bastide is a group of typical village houses restored in 1996, overlooking a splendid Cevenol landscape. Your hosts will guide you through the region's delights: imaginative dishes of chef Frank Subileau, no newcomer to famous restaurants, and wines selected by his wife Roselyne.

Visa ● Diners ● MASTER CARD

Road map p. 619

A7 exit Bollène or Nîmes dir. Ambroix

Nîmes: 60 km

Aumont-Aubrac

www.chateauxhotels.com/prouheze | reservation service: 33 (0) 1.40.07.00.20

2, route du Languedoc 48130 Aumont-Aubrac

Tel.: 33 (0) 4.66.42.80.07 – Fax: 33 (0) 4.66.42.87.78

prouheze@chateauxhotels.com

M. & Mme. Guy PROUHEZE

24 rooms: 61 € / 87 €
Breakfast: 13 €
Menu(s): 29 € / 89 € - **Carte:** 17 € -
1/2 board: 95 € / 120 €

Between the gates of Langue-doc and Auvergne, at the bend of a real village, a large and beautiful century-old house.. Wishing to share the quiet rooms, and the exquisit discoveries of an instinctive cuisine, with flowers and co-lours of this unforgettable country.

hotel annual closing
01/01 > 23/03
restaurant annual closing
01/01 > 23/03
hotel weekly closing
mon(ev), sun(ev)
01/09 > 30/06
restaurant weekly closing
mon(lun)
01/07 > 31/08
mon, tue(lun), sun(ev)
01/09 > 30/06
equipments
telephone, T.V. Canal+,
minibar, safe
environment
architecture 19ᵉ, furniture
contemporain, garden
leisure, relaxation
tennis 1 km, horse-riding 5 km,
thermal baths

Visa ● Diners ● MASTER CARD

Road map p. 619

A75. From Paris, exit 35. From Mont-pellier, exit 36

Rodez: 90 km

Château de Lignan

Béziers I Lignan-sur-Orb

www.chateauxhotels.com/lignan | reservation service: 33 (0) 1.40.07.00.20

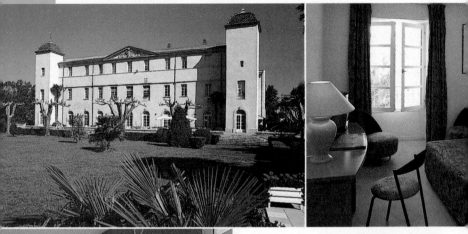

Place de l'église 34490 Lignan-sur-Orb
Tel.: 33 (0) 4.67.37.91.47 – Fax: 33 (0) 4.67.37.99.25
lignan@chateauxhotels.com
Monique DZIERWA & Jean BIZET
47 rooms: 91,47 € / 121,96 €
Breakfast: 12,96 €
Menu(s): 28,2 € / 64,79 €
1/2 board: 114,34 € / 175,32 €

Open all year
equipments
lift, telephone, internet, T.V.
Satellite, minibar
environment
architecture 17e, park 6.5 ha,
garden, terrace, total calm
leisure, relaxation
golf course 6 km, horse-riding
7 km, hammam, jacuzzi

The chateau and its estate stroll in a 15-acres of grounds bordered by the Orb river. Stay in one of the 49 air conditioned guest rooms and suites. Swimming pool, hammam and jacuzzi. In the restaurant, local dishes and regional specialities. Helicopter pad. Room service. Mountainbikes for hire.

Visa ● Diners ● MASTER CARD

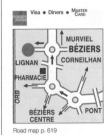

Road map p. 619

A9 Béziers east, dir. Bédarieux then St-Pons then Lignan

Vias-Béziers: 15 km

L'Enclos des Lauriers Roses
Pont du Gard ı Cabrières
www.chateauxhotels.com/lauriersroses ı reservation service: 33 (0) 1.40.07.00.20

257

71, rue du 14 Juillet 30210 Cabrières
Tel.: 33 (0) 4.66.75.25.42 – Fax: 33 (0) 4.66.75.25.21
lauriersroses@chateauxhotels.com
M. & Mme. BARGETON
10 rooms: 68,6 € / 121,96 €
2 flats: 129,58 € / 182,94 € - **2 suites:** 129,58 € / 182,94 €
Breakfast: 9,91 €
Menu(s): 18,29 € / 38,11 € - **Carte:** 45,73 € -
1/2 board: 67,08 € / 129,58 €

Sun-drenched houses with old red tiles and stone walls bathe in the southernlight. The longed-for coolness of the swimming-pools, warm colours in the restful guestrooms, luscious food tasting of the sun, and a friendly welcome from Bargeton family.

hotel annual closing
06/01 > 15/03•03/11 > 14/12
restaurant annual closing
06/01 > 15/03•03/11 > 14/12
equipments
telephone, T.V., minibar
environment
architecture 17e, furniture 17e, garden, terrace 300 m², total calm
leisure, relaxation
tennis 0.25 km, golf course 15 km, horse-riding 3 km

Visa ● Diners ● MASTER CARD

Road map p. 619

A9 exit Remoulins - N86 dir. Nîmes

Nîmes-Arles-Camargue: 15 km

Le Clos des Pins

Canet-en-Roussillon

www.chateauxhotels.com/pins | reservation service: 33 (0) 1.40.07.00.20

34, rue du Roussillon
66140 Canet-en-Roussillon
Tel.: 33 (0) 4.68.80.32.63 – Fax: 33 (0) 4.68.80.49.19
pins@chateauxhotels.com
Famille DELCROS

15 rooms: 92 € / 135 €
1 flat: 155 € / 185 €
1 suite: 125 € / 145 €
Menu(s): 27 € - **Carte:** 40 € - **1/2 board:** 84 € / 123 €

hotel annual closing
02/01 > 01/03

restaurant annual closing
02/01 > 01/03

equipments
telephone, T.V. Satellite, minibar, safe

environment
park 0.4 ha, garden, terrace, total calm

leisure, relaxation
heated pool, tennis 1 km, golf course 5 km, horse-riding 4 km, thalassotherapy, balneo, thermal baths, sauna, hammam

A large Catalan-style house, 200 m from the beach, in the heart of an extraordinary garden with the scents of the south. Near the Cathares châteaux and vineyards. And all the pleasures of the great outdoors.

Visa ● MASTER CARD

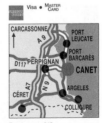

Road map p. 619

A10 exit 12 Perpignan north. dir. Canet-en-Roussillon

 Perpignan: 10 km

Île des Loisirs 34300 Cap-d'Agde

Tel.: 33 (0) 4.67.26.87.03 – Fax: 33 (0) 4.67.26.26.89
hotelgolf@chateauxhotels.com
Cécile MALORTIGUE & Pascal SEGUIER

46 rooms: 77 € / 129 €
4 suites: 154 € / 258 €
Breakfast: 13 €
Menu(s): 20 € / 30 € - **Carte:** 41,92 € -
1/2 board: 106 € / 115 €

300 yards from the finest beach in Cap d'Agde and 18-hole golf course, an entirely renovated hotel nestling among trees and shrubs, fragrant with rose laurel, lavender and broom. Colorfully decorated rooms, fitness center, good food at the restaurant, terrace, wine cellar. The Mediterranean adds the finishing touch.

Visa ● Diners ● MASTER CARD

Road map p. 619
A9 exit Agde, dir. Cap-d'Agde

hotel annual closing
02/01 > 30/01
restaurant annual closing
02/01 > 01/03
restaurant weekly closing
thi(lun), sat(lun)
01/07 > 01/09
equipments
telephone, internet, T.V.
Satellite/Canal+, minibar, safe,
baby-sitting
environment
architecture contemporaine,
furniture contemporain,
garden, terrace 200 m², view
leisure, relaxation
tennis 1 km, golf course
0.3 km, horse-riding 1 km,
thalassotherapy, balneo,
sauna, hammam, fitness,
jacuzzi, 18-hole golf course

Béziers-Vias: 15 km

Château de Floure

Carcassonne I Floure

www.chateauxhotels.com/floure | reservation service: 33 (0) 1.40.07.00.20

1, allée Gaston Bonheur 11800 Floure
Tel.: 33 (0) 4.68.79.11.29 – Fax: 33 (0) 4.68.79.04.61

floure@chateauxhotels.com
Dominique & Jerry ASSOUS
9 rooms: 100 € / 150 €
4 flats: 170 € - **3 suites:** 230 €
Breakfast: 12 €
Menu(s): 35 € / 55 € - **Carte:** 58 €
1/2 board: 92 € / 127 €

hotel annual closing
01/01 > 22/03 ● 31/10 > 22/03
restaurant annual closing
01/01 > 22/03 ● 31/10 > 22/03
equipments
telephone, T.V., minibar
environment
architecture 13°, garden,
terrace 250 m², view
leisure, relaxation
heated pool, golf course 9 km,
horse-riding 9 km

Located 9 km from Carcassonne, a former Roman abbey at the foot of Mont Alaric. The writer, Gaston Bonheur, lived there. A peaceful haven with comfortable rooms, the friendly atmosphere of the restaurant Le Poète Disparu. Relaxation at the bar in the 12th century wing.

Visa ● Diners ● MASTER CARD

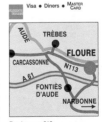

Road map p. 619

A61 exit Carcassonne-Est n° 24, then
RN113 direction Narbonne

Toulouse: 100 km

27-32 allée d'Iéna 11000 Carcassonne
Tel.: 33 (0) 4.68.25.22.17 – Fax: 33 (0) 4.68.25.04.14
montsegur@chateauxhotels.com
Lucien & Didier FAUGERAS
Breakfast: 21,80 €
Menu(s): 38,87 € / 38,87 €

The Languedoc in Carcassonne, Isabelle Faugeras' smile is as striking as her husband Didier's talent. He is a fourth generation master cook, and delights in offering an exquisite variety of inspiring dishes made with fresh, lush country produce. Excellent wine-cellar with more than 130 local wines. Rooms with standard facilities at the montsegur hotel.

restaurant annual closing
22/12 > 22/03 • 23/06 > 03/07
restaurant weekly closing
mon(lun)
03/07 > 25/08
environment
architecture 19^e, garden,
terrace 70 m^2
leisure, relaxation
tennis 1 km, golf course 2 km,
horse-riding 6 km, beauty
salon

Visa ● Diners ● JCB ● MASTER CARD

Road map p. 619

A61 exit West Carcassonne N113

La Terrasse au Soleil

Céret
www.chateauxhotels.com/terrassesoleil | reservation service: 33 (0) 1.40.07.00.20

Route de Fontfrede 66400 Céret
Tel.: 33 (0) 4.68.87.01.94 – Fax: 33 (0) 4.68.87.39.24
terrassesoleil@chateauxhotels.com
Pascal LEVEILLE-NIZEROLLE
14 rooms: 98 € / 241 €
7 suites: 129 € / 272 €
Breakfast: 13 €
Menu(s): 43 € / 60 € - **Carte:** 53 €
1/2 board: 110 € / 163 €

Open all year
equipments
telephone, internet, T.V.
Satellite, minibar, safe,
baby-sitting
environment
architecture 19e, park 4 ha,
garden, terrace, view, total
calm
leisure, relaxation
heated pool, golf course 8 km,
horse-riding 2 km

Between the sea and the mountains, two adjacent villas command spectacular views. Bright rooms with splendid panorama. Decor with colours of the south. Cuisine with Mediterranean influence. In summer, meals on the terrace facing Mont Canigou, under an 100-year old olive tree.

Visa ● Diners ● MASTER CARD

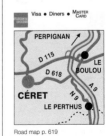

Road map p. 619
A9 exit Le Boulou, D115 dir. Céret

Perpignan-Rivesaltes: 30 km

Le Pont de Reynès 66400 Céret
Tel.: 33 (0) 4.68.87.38.37 – Fax: 33 (0) 4.68.87.42.62
mastrilles@chateauxhotels.com
Marie-France LASZLO BUKK
8 rooms: 90 € / 195 €
2 suites: 125 € / 205 €
Breakfast: included

English spoken. Hotel open for Paques. In the heart of Romanesque Roussillon, superb 17th century traditional Catalan residence, overlooking the river Tech. Warm welcome, spacious personalised rooms with private terrace. Light meals. Recently renovated. Closed parking. Heated pool.

Visa • MASTER CARD

hotel annual closing
07/10 > 29/03
equipments
telephone, T.V., safe
environment
architecture 17e, park 5 ha, garden, terrace, view, calm
leisure, relaxation
heated pool, tennis 2 km, golf course 4 km, horse-riding 2 km

Road map p. 619

A9 exit Le Boulou or D115 dir. Amélie-les-Bains

Road map p. 619

Hôtel Relais des Trois Mas

Collioure

www.chateauxhotels.com/troismas | reservation service: 33 (0) 1.40.07.00.20

Route de Port-Vendres 66190 Collioure
Tel.: 33 (0) 4.68.82.05.07 – Fax: 33 (0) 4.68.82.38.08
troismas@chateauxhotels.com
Jean-Pierre de GELDER
19 rooms: 96 € / 190 €
4 suites: 220 € / 430 €
Breakfast: 16 €
Menu(s): 34 € / 68 € - **Carte:** 60 €

hotel annual closing
11/11 > 20/12
restaurant annual closing
11/11 > 20/12
equipments
telephone, internet, T.V.
Satellite, minibar, safe
environment
garden, terrace, view, total
calm
leisure, relaxation
heated pool, tennis 2 km, golf
course 12 km, horse-riding
2 km, balneo, thermal baths,
solarium, jacuzzi

Located at a site immortalized by Matisse, Picasso and Dufy, 23 rooms and suites each personalised with the name of a painter, with air conditioning, balneotherapy pool, satellite TV, minibar, electronic safe, sea views. Direct access to the beach. Renowned gourmet restaurant La Balette.

Visa ● MASTER CARD

Road map p. 619

A9 exit Le Boulou, D618 then N114
dir. Port-Vendres

Perpignan: 30 km

Le Moulin 12320 Conques
Tel.: 33 (0) 5.65.72.84.77 – Fax: 33 (0) 5.65.72.83.91
cambelong@chateauxhotels.com
Hervé BUSSET
10 rooms: 99 € / 145 €
Breakfast: 11 €
Menu(s): 30 € / 40 € - **Carte:** 53 € -
1/2 board: 90 € / 115 €

At the foot of the listed village of Conques, a "World Heritage site", Le Moulin de Cambelong is one of the last water mills along the Dourdou. Here the discrete charm of the rooms, the family-style welcome and the audacious cuisine of the chef have taste that make you want to return for more.

Visa ● Diners ● MASTER CARD

Road map p. 619

A20 to Cressensac, then N140 by Figeac (or A71 or N7) then A75

hotel annual closing
04/03 > 15/03●04/11 > 14/12
restaurant annual closing
04/03 > 15/03●04/11 > 14/12
restaurant weekly closing
mon(lun), tue(lun), wen(lun), thi(lun), fri(lun), sat(lun)
01/01 > 14/07
mon(lun), tue(lun), wen(lun), thi(lun), fri(lun), sat(lun)
31/08 > 31/12

equipments
telephone, T.V.
environment
architecture 18°, furniture 18°, park 8 ha, garden, terrace 100 m², view, vegetable garden, total calm
leisure, relaxation
tennis 5 km, golf course 30 km, horse-riding 10 km, thermal baths, canoeing

 Rodez-Marcillac: 35 km

Le Grand Ecuyer

Cordes-sur-Ciel

www.chateauxhotels.com/grandecuyer | reservation service: 33 (0) 1.40.07.00.20

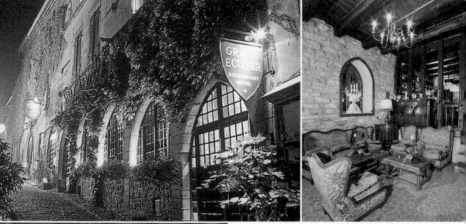

Grand Rue Raymond VII 81170 Cordes-sur-Ciel
Tel.: 33 (0) 5.63.53.79.50 – Fax: 33 (0) 5.63.53.79.51
grandecuyer@chateauxhotels.com
Colette & Yves THURIES
12 rooms: 77 € / 151 €
1 suite: 200 €
Breakfast: 11 €
Menu(s): 26 € / 72 € - **Carte:** 26 €
1/2 board: 220 €

hotel annual closing
13/10 > 20/03
restaurant annual closing
13/10 > 20/03
restaurant weekly closing
mon(lun), tue(lun), wen(lun),
thi(lun), fri(lun), sat(lun)
equipments
telephone, internet, T.V.
Satellite, minibar
environment
architecture 13e, furniture 13e,
view, total calm
leisure, relaxation
tennis 0.5 km, golf course
25 km, horse-riding 25 km

This magnificent 13th century residence, former home of Raymond VII, count of Toulouse, is located in one of France's most beautiful mediaeval villages. Rooms are decorated with period furniture. Taste the Chef's wild strawberry gratin. The wine cellar boasts over 1000 different wines.

Visa • Diners • JCB • MASTER CARD

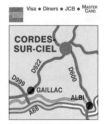

Road map p. 619

A68 exit Albi-Gaillac then 22 km

Toulouse-Blagnac: 70 km

Lieu dit Salettes 81140 Cahuzac-sur-Vere
Tel.: 33 (0) 5.63.33.60.60 – Fax: 33 (0) 5.63.33.60.61
salettes@chateauxhotels.com
Yorrick PELLEGRI
13 rooms: 99,09 € / 144,83 €
5 suites: 236,3 € / 266,79 €
Breakfast: 13,72 €
Menu(s): 21,34 € / 79,27 € - **Carte:** 21,34 € -
1/2 board: 102,9 € / 125,77 €

Between Toulouse and Albi, in the heart of the Gaillac vineyards, this fine château steeped in history stands amidst the vines. A subtle contrast between contemporary spirit and old stonework. Period-furnished rooms, friendly service and conviviality. The inventive cuisine follows the seasons.

hotel annual closing
04/02 > 24/02
restaurant annual closing
04/02 > 24/02
equipments
telephone, internet, T.V., baby-sitting
environment
architecture 13e, furniture contemporain, park 3 ha, garden, terrace 300 m^2, view, total calm
leisure, relaxation
tennis 5 km, golf course 16 km, horse-riding 10 km, balneo

Visa ● Diners ● MASTER CARD

Road map p. 619

A68 exit Gaillac, D922 dir. Cahuzac s/Vère

Toulouse-Blagnac: 60 km

Grand Hôtel Auguy

Laguiole

www.chateauxhotels.com/auguy | reservation service: 33 (0) 1.40.07.00.20

2, allée de l'Amicale 12210 Laguiole
Tel.: 33 (0) 5.65.44.31.11 – Fax: 33 (0) 5.65.51.50.81
auguy@chateauxhotels.com
Isabelle & Jean-Marc MUYLAERT-AUGUY

19 rooms: 57 € / 80 €
1 suite: 115 € / 152 €
Breakfast: 8,5 €
Menu(s): 33,6 € / 61 € - **Carte:** 40 € -
1/2 board: 60 € / 71 €

hotel annual closing
12/11 > 30/03
restaurant annual closing
12/11 > 30/03
hotel weekly closing
sun(ev), mon, tue(lun)
01/09 > 30/06
restaurant weekly closing
sun(ev), mon, tue(lun)
01/09 > 30/06
equipments
lift, telephone, internet, T.V.
environment
architecture contemporaine,
furniture contemporain,
garden, total calm
leisure, relaxation
tennis 0.5 km, golf course
9 km, horse-riding 8 km

For three generations, the Auguy family has delighted in running this charming inn. Isabelle's original recipes do her local area proud, blending tradition with fresh seasonal produce and hearty country cooking. Every room has its own distinctive style.

Visa ● Diners ● MASTER CARD

Road map p. 619

D921 Rodez/St-Flour, A75 exit St-Flour or Aumont-Aubrac

 Rodez: 55 km

B.P. 45 11190 Couiza
Tel.: 33 (0) 4.68.74.23.50 – Fax: 33 (0) 4.68.74.23.36
joyeuse@chateauxhotels.com
Dominique AVELANGE
26 rooms: 75 € / 120 €
10 suites: 120 € / 175 €
Breakfast: 11 €
Menu(s): 27 € / 43 € - **Carte:** 30 € -
1/2 board: 72,5 € / 122,5 €

In the heart of the Cathar country, in a park on the banks of the Aude, this fine castle is a listed monument where you will find the legendary hospitality of a fascinating region. Modern comforts blend discreetly with the splendor of a medieval past. Fine cuisine. Altogether a different world.

hotel annual closing
01/01 > 22/03●16/12 > 31/12
restaurant annual closing
01/01 > 22/03●16/12 > 31/12
equipments
telephone, internet, T.V. Satellite
environment
architecture 16e, garden, terrace 400 m², total calm
leisure, relaxation
golf course 30 km, horse-riding 2 km, hydrospeed

Visa ● Diners ● MASTER CARD

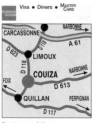

Road map p. 619

A61 exit 23 dir. Limoux then Couiza, Quillan

Carcassonne: 40 km

| Midi

Château de la Caze
Mende I Sainte-Enimie
www.chateauxhotels.com/lacaze | reservation service: 33 (0) 1.40.07.00.20

Route des Gorges du Tarn
48210 Sainte-Enimie
Tel.: 33 (0) 4.66.48.51.01 – Fax: 33 (0) 4.66.48.55.75
lacaze@chateauxhotels.com
Sandrine & Jean-Paul LECROQ
7 rooms: 92 € / 160 €
1 flat: 200 € / 260 € - **8 suites:** 130 € / 200 €
Breakfast: 12 €
Menu(s): 27 € / 65 € - **1/2 board:** 83 € / 117 €

hotel annual closing
01/01 > 15/03•11/11 > 15/03
restaurant annual closing
01/01 > 15/03•11/11 > 15/03
hotel weekly closing
wen
15/03 > 16/05•10/09 > 11/11
restaurant weekly closing
thi(lun)
15/03 > 11/11
wen
15/03 > 16/05•10/09 > 11/11

equipments
telephone, internet, T.V.
Satellite, minibar, safe

environment
architecture 15e, park 5 ha,
garden, terrace 56 m², view,
total calm

leisure, relaxation
heated pool, tennis 7 km, golf
course 20 km

In the heart of the Gorges du Tarn, there is a legendary château protected by a universe of golden cliffs. In the leaving room as well as in the distinguished bedrooms, time stops in front of an unforgettable panorama. Back on earth, the soul will appreciate the exquisite and traditional food.

Visa ● Diners ● MASTER CARD

Road map p. 619

A75 exit La Canourgue, road 907bis

Montpellier-Fréjorgue:
140 km

Château d'Ayres

Meyrueis

www.chateauxhotels.com/ayres | reservation service: 33 (0) 1.40.07.00.20

271

Ayres 48150 Meyrueis

Tel.: 33 (0) 4.66.45.60.10 – Fax: 33 (0) 4.66.45.62.26

ayres@chateauxhotels.com

J.F. de MONTJOU

21 rooms: 67 € / 124 €
3 flats: 138 € / 168 € - **3 suites:** 138 € / 168 €
Breakfast: 11 €
Menu(s): 17 € / 41 € - **Carte:** 20 € -
1/2 board: 63,5 € / 91,5 €

This Benedictine monastery converted in the XVIIIth century into a lordly residence, has been in the centre of Languedoc's history. Blanche de Castille lived there. The historic meeting between De Gaulle and Adenauer took place here. A gastronomic restaurant in the heart of the Cévennes.

hotel annual closing
15/12 > 15/03

equipments
telephone, T.V., minibar

environment
architecture 18ᵉ, park 6 ha, garden, terrace, total calm

leisure, relaxation
heated pool, horse-riding

Visa ● Diners ● MASTER CARD

Road map p. 619

A75 exit La Canourgue dir. Ste-Enimie - Gorges du Tarn

Montpellier: 120 km

| Midi

Château de Creissels

Millau

www.chateauxhotels.com/creissels | reservation service: 33 (0) 1.40.07.00.20

Route de St-Affrique Creissels 12100 Millau
Tel.: 33 (0) 5.65.60.16.59 – Fax: 33 (0) 5.65.61.24.63
creissels@chateauxhotels.com
Anne BALDET & Jean-François AUSTRUY
30 rooms: 46 € / 71 €
Breakfast: 7,5 €
Menu(s): 20,5 € / 40 € - **1/2 board:** 46 € / 60 €

hotel annual closing
31/12 > 01/03
hotel weekly closing
sun(lun)
01/11 > 30/03
restaurant weekly closing
mon(lun), sun(ev)
01/11 > 30/03
mon(lun), sun(ev)
30/09 > 30/04
equipments
telephone, internet, T.V., safe
environment
architecture 12e, garden,
terrace, view
leisure, relaxation
tennis 3 km, horse-riding
10 km

Located at the gates of Millau, in a calm, tranquil setting, this XIIth century château is surrounded by a shady park. Rooms with terrace or balcony with views of the old village. Restaurant in the former guardroom. In summer, dinner served on covered terraces. Regional cuisine.

Visa ● Diners ● MASTER CARD

Road map p. 619

A75 exit Millau - D992 dir. Albi

Rodez: 70 km

34, avenue de la République 12100 Millau
Tel.: 33 (0) 5.65.60.20.63 – Fax: 33 (0) 5.65.59.78.13
lamusardiere@chateauxhotels.com
Anne & Emmanuel ROUX

14 rooms: 55 € / 190 €
Breakfast: 10 €
Menu(s): 19 € / 61 € - **Carte:** 32 € -
1/2 board: 60 € / 123 €

In the centre of Millau, the hosts of this beautiful residence of a 19th c master glove-maker will charm you with their outstanding hospitality. Wander between luxurious rooms decorated in warm tones and an elegant dining-room where Emmanuel Roux invites you to taste his exquisite and inventive recipes.

Open all year

equipments
lift, telephone, internet, T.V., minibar, safe

environment
architecture 19e, garden, view

leisure, relaxation
tennis 2 km, horse-riding 3 km, jacuzzi, paragliding, hang-gliding, canoeing-kayak

Visa ● Diners ● MASTER CARD

Road map p. 619

A75 exit Millau

Montpellier: 110 km

Demeure des Brousses
Montpellier
www.chateauxhotels.com/brousses | reservation service: 33 (0) 1.40.07.00.20

Route de Vauguières 34000 Montpellier
Tel.: 33 (0) 4.67.65.77.66 – Fax: 33 (0) 4.67.22.22.17
brousses@chateauxhotels.com
Didier HUET
17 rooms: 62 € / 99 €
Breakfast: 9 €
Menu(s): 30 € / 42 € - **Carte:** 45 €

Open all year
equipments
telephone, internet, T.V.
environment
architecture 18ᵉ, park 1.5 ha, garden, terrace 150 m², calm
leisure, relaxation
golf course 8 km, thalassotherapy 8km, balneotherapy

Close to Montpellier is an authentic 18th century mas situated amidst peaceful and shaded grounds. It offers current comforts in rooms furnished in an old-style. A restful stopover for visiting the region.

Visa ● Diners ● Master Card

Road map p. 619

A9 exit 29 Montpellier East, dir. Odysseum Multiplexe

Fréjorgues: 7 km

18, rue Jean-Jacques Rousseau
34000 Montpellier
Tel.: 33 (0) 4.67.52.90.90 – Fax: 33 (0) 4.67.60.67.67
guilhem@chateauxhotels.com
Eric CHARPENTIER
33 rooms: 71 € / 115 €
Breakfast: 9 €

In the heart of this historical city, sublime comfort in a tastefully restored 16th century residence. Peaceful rooms. Spacious terrace commanding stunning views of the gardens, cathedral and 12th century medical college. Your hosts will be happy to help you discover the charm of the region.

Open all year
equipments
lift, telephone, internet, T.V., minibar, baby-sitting
environment
architecture 16ᵉ, terrace
leisure, relaxation
tennis 1 km, golf course 3 km

Visa ● Diners ● JCB ● MASTER CARD

MONTPELLIER EST
BD HENRY IV
R. FOCH
QUAI DU
VERDANSON
A 9
CORUM
BD V. HUGO
PLACE DE LA COMÉDIE

Road map p. 619

A9 exit Montpellier East, follow dir. Historical Centre

Montpellier: 5 km

Midi

Mas de Couran

Montpellier I Lattes

www.chateauxhotels.com/couran I reservation service: 33 (0) 1.40.07.00.20

Route de Fréjorgues 34970 Lattes
Tel.: 33 (0) 4.67.65.57.57 – Fax: 33 (0) 4.67.65.37.56
couran@chateauxhotels.com
Véronique GABELLIER
16 rooms: 61 € / 82 €
2 suites: 75 € / 82 €
Breakfast: 8 €
Menu(s): 17 € / 37,5 € - **1/2 board:** 59,5 € / 70 €

Open all year
restaurant weekly closing
mon(lun), sat(lun), sun(ev)
01/09 > 30/06
equipments
telephone, internet, T.V.
environment
architecture 19e, park 1 ha,
garden, terrace
leisure, relaxation
tennis 1 km, golf course
10 km, horse-riding 2 km

Long-standing residence in superb park, with very large pool. Discreet charm. Meals served in the dining room or in the park during summer. Nearby: beaches, golf club, airport and town. To the north, the unusual countryside of the Cévennes. To the south, the sea, horses and bulls of the Camargue.

Visa ● Diners ● MASTER CARD

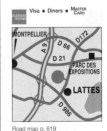

Road map p. 619
A9 exit Montpellier South

Montpellier: 3 km

Auberge du Vieux Puits

Narbonne | Fontjoncouse

www.chateauxhotels.com/vieuxpuits | reservation service: 33 (0) 1.40.07.00.20

Auberge du Vieux Puits Avn St-Victor
11360 Fontjoncouse
Tel.: 33 (0) 4.68.44.07.37 - Fax: 33 (0) 4.68.44.08.31
vieuxpuits@chateauxhotels.com
Gilles & Marie-Christine GOUJON

8 rooms: 91 € / 190 €
Menu(s): 52 € / 67 € - **Carte:** 70 €

The delight begins on the road through rocky hills and garrigue where crickets sing. Then the sunny and comfortable house, Marie-Christine's art of receiving, her flowers and dining room. Lastly, the inspired cooking, with award-winning Gilles Goujon's delicious accents of the Corbières region.

restaurant annual closing
01/01 > 02/10

equipments
telephone, T.V., minibar, safe, baby-sitting

environment
garden, total calm

leisure, relaxation
heated pool, golf course 50 km, horse-riding 15 km, jacuzzi

Visa • Diners • Master Card

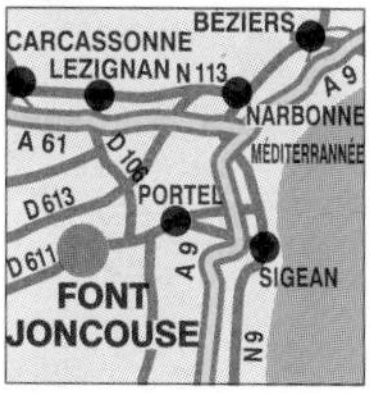

Road map p. 619

A61 exit 25 Lézignan, D106, D611 - A9 exit 38 Narbonne South, N9, D611-A9 exit 39 Sigean, D611

Perpignan: 40 km

Auberge du Pont Romain
Nîmes I Sommières
www.chateauxhotels.com/pontromain I reservation service: 33 (0) 1.40.07.00.20

2 rue Émile Jamais 30250 Sommières
Tel.: 33 (0) 4.66.80.00.58 – Fax: 33 (0) 4.66.80.31.52
pontromain@chateauxhotels.com
Monique MICHEL
16 rooms: 70 € / 99 €
Breakfast: 11 €
Menu(s): 30 € / 52 € - **Carte:** 40 €
1/2 board: 73 € / 110 €

hotel annual closing
15/01 > 15/03●01/11 > 01/12
restaurant annual closing
15/01 > 15/03●01/11 > 01/12
equipments
lift, telephone, internet, T.V.,
safe
environment
architecture 19e, garden,
terrace 300 m², view
leisure, relaxation
heated pool, tennis 1 km, golf
course 15 km, horse-riding
2 km

This former 19th century rug factory is truly a "must-stay" spot, thanks to chef Bernard Michel's culinary talent & Frédéric Michel's pastries, which can satisfy the most demanding sweet tooth. From the wooded park, guests can marvel at the Roman Bridge, built in 1 AD. Moderate temperature pool (Apr-Oct.)

Visa ● Diners ● MASTER CARD

Road map p. 619
A9 exit 27 then D34 dir. Sommières

Nîmes ou Montpellier: 25 km

Le Mas de Brignon 30320 Marguerittes
Tel.: 33 (0) 4.66.75.02.25 – Fax: 33 (0) 4.66.75.45.58
hacienda@chateauxhotels.com
M. & Mme. Jean-Jacques CHAUVIN
12 rooms: 75 € / 140 €
Breakfast: 11 €
Menu(s): 30 € / 55 € - **Carte:** 30 € -
1/2 board: 85 € / 120 €

Provençal farmhouse where comfort, refinement, awaits you. Gastronomic cuisine with the perfumes of the markets of Provence. Candlelight dinners. Ideal for seeing the Gard Bridge, the Camargue, the Ardèche Gorges. An enclosed park, helicopter pad. Swimming pool, sauna, bicycles rent, ping-pong.

Open all year
equipments
telephone, T.V. Satellite, minibar, safe
environment
garden, terrace 80 m^2, total calm
leisure, relaxation
tennis 2 km, golf course 10 km, horse-riding 0.5 km, sauna, solarium

Visa ● MASTER CARD

Road map p. 619

A9 exit n° 24 Nîmes East. N86. At Marguerittes, follow the red sign

Nîmes-Garons: 7 km

L'Orangerie
Nîmes
www.chateauxhotels.com/orangerie | reservation service: 33 (0) 1.40.07.00.20

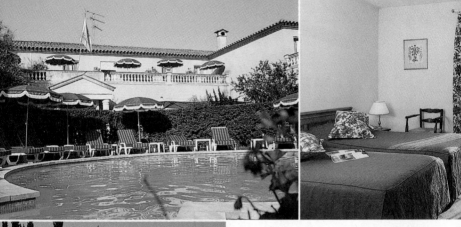

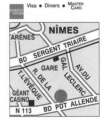

755, rue Tour-de-l'Evêque 30000 Nîmes
Tel.: 33 (0) 4.66.84.50.57 – Fax: 33 (0) 4.66.29.44.55
orangerie@chateauxhotels.com
Hervé PRINGALLE

25 rooms: 61 € / 99 €
2 flats: 158 € / 167 €
Breakfast: 9 €
Menu(s): 18 € / 25 € - **Carte:** 13,72 €
1/2 board: 61 € / 76 €

Open all year
equipments
telephone, internet, T.V.
Canal+, minibar, safe,
baby-sitting
environment
garden, terrace 25 m²
leisure, relaxation
tennis 3 km, golf course 4 km,
horse-riding 0.4 km, sauna,
fitness, jacuzzi

1 km from historic downtown, near a ravishing wooded park; l'Orangerie welcomes you in a decor personalised, with provencal colours. A warm welcome, the intimate style and other amenities guarantee a high-quality stay. Dining restaurant pleasures run a range of refined dishes, served on the terrace in summer.

Visa ● Diners ● Master Card

Road map p. 619

A9 exit west, east, centre of Nîmes,
N113 dir. Montpellier

Nîmes: 8 km

Route de Saint-Pons 34390 Olargues
Tel.: 33 (0) 4.67.97.73.99 – Fax: 33 (0) 4.67.97.78.52
rieumege@chateauxhotels.com
Hubert HENROTTE
11 rooms: 69 € / 122 €
2 suites: 141 € / 265 €
Breakfast: 11 €
Menu(s): 20 € / 33 € - **Carte:** 25,92 € -
1/2 board: 61 € / 153 €

Nestling at the foot of the Cévenes, in the southern sun, this comfortable and charming 17th century establishment, in the calm of a 35-acre estate, is a paradise of authenticity and nature. Warm welcome, famous cuisine, inspired by the sea and the sun. Dinner on terrace, 2 swimming pools.

Visa • Diners • MASTER CARD

Road map p. 619

A9 Béziers East, dir. Bédarieux then Lamalou

hotel annual closing
06/11 > 31/03
restaurant annual closing
06/11 > 31/03
restaurant weekly closing
mon(lun), tue(lun), wen(lun), thi(lun), fri(lun), sat(lun)
equipments
telephone, T.V., minibar, safe
environment
architecture 17e, park 3 ha, terrace 100 m^2, view
leisure, relaxation
heated pool, golf course 17 km, horse-riding 17 km

Hostellerie de Saint-Alban

Pézenas ı Nézignan-L'Evêque
www.chateauxhotels.com/saintalban | reservation service: 33 (0) 1.40.07.00.20

31, route d'Agde 34120 Nézignan-L'Evêque
Tel.: 33 (0) 4.67.98.11.38 – Fax: 33 (0) 4.67.98.91.63
saintalban@chateauxhotels.com
Hansruedi KEISER – Niklaus HURLIMANN
14 rooms: 67,08 € / 105,19 €
Breakfast: 9,15 €
Menu(s): 22,87 € - **1/2 board:** 63,27 € / 82,32 €

hotel annual closing
01/12 > 15/02
restaurant annual closing
01/12 > 15/02
restaurant weekly closing
mon(lun), tue(lun), wen(lun),
thi(lun), fri(lun), sat(lun), sun(lun)
16/06 > 15/09
wen, thi(lun)
15/02 > 15/06 • 16/09 > 30/11
equipments
telephone, internet, T.V.
Satellite
environment
garden, terrace 250 m²
leisure, relaxation
golf course 12 km, jacuzzi

A 19th century residence, in a peaceful village, not far from the sea and Pezenas. Ideal location for touring the Languedoc-Roussillon region. Make the most of our special low-season rates; as well as sunshine from April through October and tranquillity year round.

Visa ● Diners ● MASTER CARD

Road map p. 619
A9/A75 exit Pézenas, D13

Béziers: 25 km

30570 Pont-d'Hérault
Tel.: 33 (0) 4.67.82.40.06 – Fax: 33 (0) 4.67.82.47.79
rey@chateauxhotels.com
Guilhem CAZALIS de FONDOUCE
12 rooms: 57,93 € / 88,42 €
1 suite: 129,58 €
Breakfast: 7,62 €
Menu(s): 23,63 € / 44,97 € - **Carte:** 27,44 €

The Château du Rey, in the heart of the Cévennes in Languedoc, has been restored in the XIXth century by Viollet-le-Duc. A 5-acre park awaits you for leisure activities in the morning. Fishing day can be organised. Helicopter landing pad. The 13th vaulted restaurant features Cevennes-style cuisine.

Visa • MASTER CARD

Road map p. 619

A9 exit Montpellier - D999 dir. Ganges-Le-Vigan

Montpellier-Fréjorgues:
60 km

hotel annual closing
01/01 > 01/03
restaurant annual closing
01/01 > 01/03
restaurant weekly closing
mon, sun(ev)
01/03 > 01/07
equipments
telephone, T.V., minibar
environment
architecture 13e, park 3 ha, garden, terrace 80 m^2, total calm
leisure, relaxation
tennis 4 km, horse-riding 4 km

| Midi

L'Oustau Camarguen

Port Camargue

www.chateauxhotels.com/camarguen | reservation service: 33 (0) 1.40.07.00.20

3, route des Marines 30240 Port Camargue
Tel.: 33 (0) 4.66.51.51.65 – Fax: 33 (0) 4.66.53.06.65
camarguen@chateauxhotels.com
Pascale TEISSEDRE-DÄWERITZ
36 rooms: 68 € / 90 €
2 flats: 102 € / 135 € - **1 suite:** 141 €
Breakfast: 9 €
Menu(s): 25 € / 29,5 € - **1/2 board:** 61 € / 74 €

hotel annual closing
13/10 > 28/04
restaurant annual closing
01/10 > 09/05
restaurant weekly closing
01/07 > 31/08
for lunch
01/09 > 12/10•28/03 > 30/06
for lunch and wen(ev)
equipments
telephone, T.V. Satellite,
minibar, safe
environment
architecture contemporaine,
garden, terrace 8 m²
leisure, relaxation
golf course 15 km, horse-riding
2 km, thalassotherapy,
hammam, jacuzzi

This superb residence in typical Camargue architecture, is situated in the heart of a large pleasure port. Everything necessary for a wonderful holiday is at your disposal: spacious rooms, hammam, jacuzzi, Provincial cooking and the mysterious, yet welcoming Camargue to explore.

Visa • Diners • MASTER CARD

Road map p. 619

A9 exit 26 Gallargues, D979 dir. Aimargues, Aigues-Mortes, Le Grau du Roi

Fréjorgues: 20 km

Le Spinaker

Pointe de la Presqu'île 30240 Port Camargue
Tel.: 33 (0) 4.66.53.36.37 – Fax: 33 (0) 4.66.53.17.47
spinaker@chateauxhotels.com
Famille CAZALS

21 rooms: 105 € / 125 €
5 suites: 166 € / 227 €
Breakfast: 11 €
Menu(s): 30 € / 76 € - **Carte:** 50 € -
1/2 board: 137 € / 164 €

Le Spinaker is an oasis of tranquillity cradled by the Mediterranean. Sun-drenched pretty white bungalows overlook lawn-terraces and an inviting swimming-pool. Flavours from the South abound in Jean-Pierre Cazals' cooking which is a tribute to the delights of fresh sea-food. Pure bliss!

hotel annual closing
11/11 > 14/02
restaurant annual closing
11/11 > 14/02
equipments
telephone, T.V., minibar, safe
environment
architecture contemporaine, furniture contemporain, garden, terrace
leisure, relaxation
, game of bowls, sea-trips, safari photos, sailing

Visa ● MASTER CARD

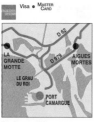

Road map p. 619

A9 exit Gallargues-Les-Plages

Montpellier-Fréjorques: km

Hôtel Biney
Rodez
www.chateauxhotels.com/biney | reservation service: 33 (0) 1.40.07.00.20

7, bld Gambetta -7, rue Massol 12000 Rodez
Tel.: 33 (0) 5.65.68.01.24 – Fax: 33 (0) 5.65.75.22.98
biney@chateauxhotels.com
Didier BAYZELON & Jean ASTIC
28 rooms: 68 € / 135 €
1 suite: 183 €
Breakfast: 9 €

Open all year
equipments
lift, telephone, internet, T.V.
TPS, minibar, safe
environment
architecture contemporaine,
furniture contemporain,
garden, view, total calm
leisure, relaxation
tennis 5 km, golf course 5 km,
horse-riding 5 km, sauna,
hammam

*In the center of historic Rodez,
this hotel of character, with
opulent rooms and attentive
service, offers a setting of calm
and serenity to appreciate the
wealth of the town's past. Povençal bar and drawing-room,
business center, breakfast
looking out on the garden.*

Road map p. 619

from Paris: A75 exit 42 Severac le
Château, N88 - from Toulouse: N88

Rodez-Marcillac: 10 km

66800 Llo
Tel.: 33 (0) 4.68.04.70.04 – Fax: 33 (0) 4.68.04.01.29
atalaya@chateauxhotels.com
M. TOUSSAINT
12 rooms: 79,27 € / 120,43 €
1 suite: 120,43 €
Breakfast: 10,37 €
Menu(s): 25,61 € / 51,07 € - **Carte:** 21 €

Near the Spanish and Andorran border lies a sun-drenched landscape, the Cerdagne, and Llo is one of its most typical villages. L'Atalaya is a house of character where the hallmarks of authentic living are cultivated, inviting you to partake in the roots of a region where life is lived to the full.

Visa ● MASTER CARD

Road map p. 619

A9 exit Perpignan or N120, N116 dir. Bourg-Madame/Andorre

Open all year
equipments
T.V.

environment
architecture 18°, terrace, view, total calm

leisure, relaxation
tennis 3 km, golf course 10 km, horse-riding 5 km

Perpignan: 90 km

Relais Saint-Roch

Saint-Alban-sur-Limagnole

www.chateauxhotels.com/saintroch | reservation service: 33 (0) 1.40.07.00.20

Château de la Chastre
48120 Saint-Alban-sur-Limagnole
Tel.: 33 (0) 4.66.31.55.48 – Fax: 33 (0) 4.66.31.53.26

saintroch@chateauxhotels.com
Christian CHAVIGNON
9 rooms: 98 € / 148 €
Breakfast: 12 €
Menu(s): 18 € / 56 € - **Carte:** 40 €
1/2 board: 86 € / 110 €

hotel annual closing
01/01 > 27/03 • 04/11 > 31/03
restaurant annual closing
01/01 > 27/03 • 04/11 > 31/03
restaurant weekly closing
mon(lun), tue(lun)
01/07 > 31/08
equipments
telephone, internet, T.V.
Satellite, minibar, valet parking
environment
architecture 19ᵉ, furniture
contemporain, garden, view,
total calm
leisure, relaxation
heated pool, Fly-fishing
workshop

*A 19th century manor house
in Lozère, a jewel of pink granite set in wooded grounds.
Attractive and restful rooms,
warm and attentive service,
authentic and generous fare.
For lovers of quiet dreamy surroundings, fresh air and good
living. Cellar boasting 250
whiskies.*

Visa • Diners • JCB • MASTER CARD

Road map p. 619

A75 exit 34 or RN9 dir. Clermont-
Montpellier

Midi |

✈ Clermond-Ferrand: 150 km

Hôtel Île de la Lagune

Saint-Cyprien Sud

www.chateauxhotels.com/lagune | reservation service: 33 (0) 1.40.07.00.20

Boulevard de L'Almandin
66750 Saint-Cyprien Sud
Tel.: 33 (0) 4.68.21.01.02 – Fax: 33 (0) 4.68.21.06.28
lagune@chateauxhotels.com
Jean-Paul HARTMANN – Famille LORMAND
18 rooms: 114 € / 180 €
4 suites: 171 € / 235 €
Breakfast: 13 €
Menu(s): 37 € / 67 € - **Carte:** 60 € -
1/2 board: 117 € / 140 €

*In the far south of France, on a
leafy, flowered island, bathed
in Mediterranean sunshine, a
dream holiday awaits you. No
sooner do you cross the
wooden bridge than you feel
you are in another world. Spacious rooms with terrace, attentive service and southern-
flavoured food.*

hotel annual closing
11/02 > 25/02 • 28/10 > 05/11
restaurant annual closing
11/02 > 25/02 • 28/10 > 05/11
restaurant weekly closing
mon, tue
01/10 > 30/04
equipments
lift, telephone, T.V.
Satellite/Canal+, minibar, safe
environment
garden, terrace, view, total
calm
leisure, relaxation
golf course 2 km, horse-riding
1 km, tennis, sailing harbour,
boat access to the beach, free
shuttle

Visa ● Diners ● MASTER CARD

Road map p. 619

A9 exit 42 Perpignan Souh, dir.
Argelés, dir. St-Cyprien then Les
Capellans

Perpignan-Rivesaltes: 20 km

Auberge du Poids Public

Saint-Félix-Lauragais

www.chateauxhotels.com/poidspublic | reservation service: 33 (0) 1.40.07.00.20

Faubourg Saint-Roch
31540 Saint-Félix-Lauragais
Tel.: 33 (0) 5.62.18.85.00 – Fax: 33 (0) 5.62.18.85.05
poidspublic@chateauxhotels.com
Claude TAFFARELLO

8 rooms: 45 € / 55 €
2 suites: 88 € / 122 €
Breakfast: 10 €
Menu(s): 22 € / 57 € - **Carte:** 45 €
1/2 board: 103 € / 113 €

hotel annual closing
01/11 > 09/11 ● 01/01 > 01/02
restaurant annual closing
01/11 > 09/11 ● 01/01 > 01/02
equipments
telephone, T.V., minibar
environment
terrace, view, total calm
leisure, relaxation
horse-riding 25 km

This magnificent inn set in the calm of the Lauragais countryside, near Toulouse. Comfortable bedrooms combining good taste and fine living. Experience the delicious goose-liver terrine or the local speciality, Cassoulet in the stately dining room or terrace, open in the summer.

Visa ● MasterCard

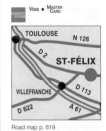

Road map p. 619

dir. Revel at the exit of the A61

 Blagnac: 40 km

Villeneuve de Rivière 31800 Saint-Gaudens
Tel.: 33 (0) 5.61.89.36.00 – Fax: 33 (0) 5.61.88.31.04
cedres@chateauxhotels.com
Christophe COUTON – Claude TAFFARELLO
20 rooms: 53,36 € / 91,47 €
Breakfast: 9 €
Menu(s): 21,34 € / 53,36 € - **Carte:** 38,11 €

30 minutes from the Spanish border and an hour from Toulouse, this 17th century manor is the ultimate in hopitality and calm. The former residence of the Marquise de Montespan, this hotel is steeped in history and retains a discreet charm. An ideal stop-over on the Compostelle route.

Visa ● MASTER CARD

Road map p. 619

A64 exit 17/18 Montréjeau-N117 dir.Villeneuve-de-Rivière or St Gaudens

 Toulouse-Blagnac: 100 km

Open all year
restaurant weekly closing
mon(lun)
01/11 > 01/04
equipments
telephone, T.V. Canal+
environment
architecture 17e, park, garden, terrace
leisure, relaxation
tennis 0.3 km, golf course 30 km, horse-riding 5 km, thalassotherapy, thermal baths

Hôtel Eychenne
Saint-Girons
www.chateauxhotels.com/eychenne | reservation service: 33 (0) 1.40.07.00.20

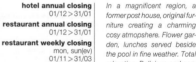

8, avenue Paul-Laffont 09200 Saint-Girons
Tel.: 33 (0) 5.61.04.04.50 – Fax: 33 (0) 5.61.96.07.20
eychenne@chateauxhotels.com
Michel BORDEAU

35 rooms: 45,80 € / 122 €
Breakfast: 7,93 €
Menu(s): 22 € / 50,35 € - **Carte:** 30,50 €
1/2 board: 57,90 € / 90 €

hotel annual closing
01/12 > 31/01
restaurant annual closing
01/12 > 31/01
restaurant weekly closing
mon, sun(ev)
01/11 > 31/03
equipments
telephone, internet, T.V.,
minibar, baby-sitting
environment
architecture 19°, garden,
terrace 200 m²
leisure, relaxation
heated pool, tennis 1 km, golf
course 25 km, horse-riding
1 km, thermal baths,
canoening and kayak,
paragliding, flight tour

In a magnificent region, a former post house, original furniture creating a charming cosy atmopshere. Flower garden, lunches served beside the pool in fine weather. Total relaxation. Delicious and generous fare, wine lovers will love bottles from Michel Bordeau's excellent cellar.

Visa • Diners • MASTER CARD

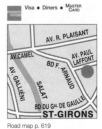

Road map p. 619

Bram-Foix   N117   D117   dir.
Carcassonne/A64 Toulouse-Biarritz

Blagnac: 100 km

1, place de l'Arbre
30126 Saint-Laurent-des-Arbres
Tel.: 33 (0) 4.66.50.14.14 – Fax: 33 (0) 4.66.50.46.30
galinette@chateauxhotels.com
Azélie HAUSTRATE
10 rooms: 80 € / 195 €
3 suites: 122 € / 164 €
Breakfast: 10 €
Menu(s): 15 € / 35 € - **Carte:** 34,3 €

20 kilometers from Avignon, set in a wonderful medieval village, La Galinette offers everything in comfort, between terrace, pool, and sunshine which go together so well in the south of France. The new gourmet restaurant completes the picture for a delightful stay far from the madding crowd.

hotel annual closing
10/01 > 11/02

equipments
T.V. Satellite, minibar, safe, baby-sitting

environment
architecture 14e, terrace 30 m², total calm

leisure, relaxation
tennis 0.8 km, golf course 15 km, horse-riding 2 km

Visa ● Diners ● MASTER CARD

Road map p. 619

A9 exit Roquemaure-Tavel, N580 dir. Bagnols s/Cèze

✈ Avignon: 22 km

❄ P ≈

| Midi

Les Bergeries de Pondérach

Saint-Pons-de-Thomières

www.chateauxhotels.com/ponderach | reservation service: 33 (0) 1.40.07.00.20

Route de Pondérach
34220 Saint-Pons-de-Thomières
Tel.: 33 (0) 4.67.97.02.57 – Fax: 33 (0) 4.67.97.29.75

ponderach@chateauxhotels.com
Gilles LENTIN
7 rooms: 62 € / 92 €
Breakfast: 9 €
Menu(s): 16 € / 41 € - **Carte:** 22 €
1/2 board: 64 € / 80 €

hotel annual closing
30/11 > 01/03
restaurant annual closing
30/11 > 01/03
equipments
telephone, T.V., baby-sitting
environment
architecture 17e, park 7 ha,
garden, terrace, view, total
calm
leisure, relaxation
tennis 0.3 km, golf course
35 km, horse-riding 5 km

*Set amidst lush greenery, this
17th century farmhouse offers
unmatchable beauty. Your
host is a former art gallery
owner who has decorated
each room with subtle taste
and elegance. The cooking,
like the place itself, is delicate
and flavourful, featuring fresh
products from this fertile region.*

Visa ● Diners ● MASTER CARD

Road map p. 619

A9 exit Béziers West or Narbonne
West, N112 dir. Saint-Pons/Mazamet

Montpellier-Toulouse:
125 km

Salles-Curan

www.chateauxhotels.com/levezou | reservation service: 33 (0) 1.40.07.00.20

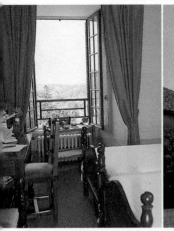

Rue du Château 12410 Salles-Curan
Tel.: 33 (0) 5.65.46.34.16 – Fax: 33 (0) 5.65.46.01.19
levezou @chateauxhotels.com
Christine MICHEL
Menu(s): 15,24 € / 45,73 € - **Carte:** 20,58 €

A charming place to stay in the heart of the Levezou. Step inside the former residence of the bishops of Rodez. Exquisite meals, enhanced by a touch of flavours from the Aveyron. After these culinary treats, retire to a luxuriously comfortable room.

restaurant annual closing
10/10 > 20/04

restaurant weekly closing
mon(lun), tue(lun)
30/06 > 15/09
mon, tue(lun), sun(ev)
20/04 > 30/06

environment
architecture 14e, garden, terrace, view, vegetable garden, total calm

leisure, relaxation
tennis 0.2 km, horse-riding 5 km

Visa ● Diners ● MASTER CARD

Road map p. 619

A75 exit Séverac-le-Château or Millau, follow "Les Lacs du Lévezou"

 Rodez-Marcillac: 40 km

Hostellerie des 7 Molles

Saint-Gaudens | Sauveterre-de-Comminges

www.chateauxhotels.com/septmolles | reservation service: 33 (0) 1.40.07.00.20

31510 Sauveterre-de-Comminges
Tel.: 33 (0) 5.61.88.30.87 – Fax: 33 (0) 5.61.88.36.42

septmolles@chateauxhotels.com
Gilles FERRAN

16 rooms: 80 € / 128 €
1 flat: 140 € / 187 € - **1 suite:** 140 € / 187 €
Breakfast: 12 €
Menu(s): 29 € / 47 € - **Carte:** 38 €
1/2 board: 90 € / 114 €

hotel annual closing
15/02 > 15/03
restaurant annual closing
15/02 > 15/03
equipments
lift, telephone, internet, T.V.
Satellite, minibar
environment
garden, terrace, view, total
calm
leisure, relaxation
golf course 12 km, horse-riding
10 km

At the foot of the Pyrenees, this beautiful residence is a soothing stopover for discovering the beauty of the mountains. The peaceful rooms and the cuisine with pronounced rural accents of Gilles Ferran's country are a treat for the eyes and palate. A choice break in the journey.

Visa ● Diners ● MASTER CARD

Road map p. 619

A64 exit 18 St-Gaudens, D8 dir. St-Bertrand, Valentine, D9, Sauveterre

 Toulouse: 100 km

Grand Rue 30210 Collias
Tel.: 33 (0) 4.66.22.88.88 – Fax: 33 (0) 4.66.22.84.28
castellas@chateauxhotels.com
Chantal & Raymond APARIS
15 rooms: 93 € / 141 €
2 suites: 188 €
Breakfast: 14 €
Menu(s): 32 € / 76 € - **Carte:** 38 € -
1/2 board: 102,5 € / 122,5 €

Charming house of character with unusual and unforgettable rooms, in the heart of an old village. The gentle life, relax in the swimming pool. Creative cuisine rich in flavours. Canoeing, hiking, climbing. Cultural sites: the Gard Bridge, Nîmes, Arles.

hotel annual closing
06/01 > 10/03

restaurant annual closing
06/01 > 10/03

restaurant weekly closing
mon(lun), wen(lun), fri(lun)
30/06 > 31/08
mon(lun), wen, fri(lun)
10/03 > 31/05

equipments
telephone, internet, T.V.
Satellite, minibar, safe

environment
architecture 17ᵉ, garden,
terrace, total calm

leisure, relaxation
tennis 0.3 km, golf course
5 km, horse-riding 2 km,
canoeing

American Express • Visa • Diners • MASTER CARD

Road map p. 619

A9 exit Remoulins - Pont-du-Gard,
D981 dir. Uzès

Nîmes-Garons: 35 km

La Bégude Saint-Pierre

Vers-Pont-du-Gard

www.chateauxhotels.com/saintpierre | reservation service: 33 (0) 1.40.07.00.20

CD 981 30210 Vers-Pont-du-Gard
Tel.: 33 (0) 4.66.63.63.63 – Fax: 33 (0) 4.66.22.73.73

saintpierre@chateauxhotels.com
Bruno GRIFFOUL – Pierre GRIFFOUL
26 rooms: 53,50 € / 114,50 €
3 suites: 152,50 € / 213,50 €
Breakfast: 11,5 €
Menu(s): 29 € / 49 € - **Carte:** 50 €
1/2 board: 67,25 € / 97,75 €

Open all year
hotel weekly closing
sun(ev), mon(ev)
01/11 > 01/04
restaurant weekly closing
sun(ev), mon
01/11 > 01/04
equipments
telephone, internet, T.V.
Satellite, minibar, safe
environment
architecture 17e, furniture 19e,
park 3 ha, garden, terrace
350 m², view
leisure, relaxation
tennis 2 km, golf course
10 km, horse-riding 5 km,
Introductory lesson in
one-seater car-racing

A short distance from the Pont du Gard, the old walls of this former XVIIth century Post house shelter peace of mind and enchantment. The rooms are modern and comfortable and the cuisine of Bruno Griffoul is imaginative and colourful. The 14 ha estate stretches out as far as the gorges of Gardon.

Visa ● Diners ● JCB ● MasterCard

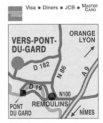

Road map p. 619

A9 exit Remoulins, D981

✈ Nîmes-Arles-Camargue:
30 km

Le Castrum

Villeneuve-d'Olmes

www.chateauxhotels.com/castrum | reservation service: 33 (0) 1.40.07.00.20

Le Laouzet 09300 Villeneuve-d'Olmes
Tel.: 33 (0) 5.61.01.35.24 – Fax: 33 (0) 5.61.01.22.85
castrum@chateauxhotels.com
Jean-Jacques BENET
7 rooms: 69 € / 99 €
1 suite: 107 € / 122 €
Breakfast: 11 €
Menu(s): 21 € / 91 € - **Carte:** 46 € -
1/2 board: 64 € / 88 €

At the foot of the Pyrenees, not far from Montségur, a lovely house with a magnificent view. Warm and comfortable rooms, attentive service and delectable food prepared by Jean-Jacques Bénet make this a memorable base to explore one of France's most beautiful regions.

Open all year
equipments
telephone, internet, T.V. Satellite, minibar
environment
park 1 ha, garden, terrace 140 m², view, total calm
leisure, relaxation
heated pool, tennis 0.5 km, golf course 30 km, horse-riding 5 km

Visa ● Diners ● JCB ● MASTER CARD

Road map p. 619

From "Foix" RN28 or from "Perpignan" RN29, exit Lavelanet and direction Villeneuve d'Olmes

Blagnac: 120 km

| Midi

A book to devour!

117 recipes presented by their chefs,
to be followed or savoured,
Not in moderation !

CHÂTEAUX & HÔTELS
DE FRANCE²

To order this book, see conditions page 23.

www.chateauxhotels.com

Provence-Alpes-Côte-d'Azur

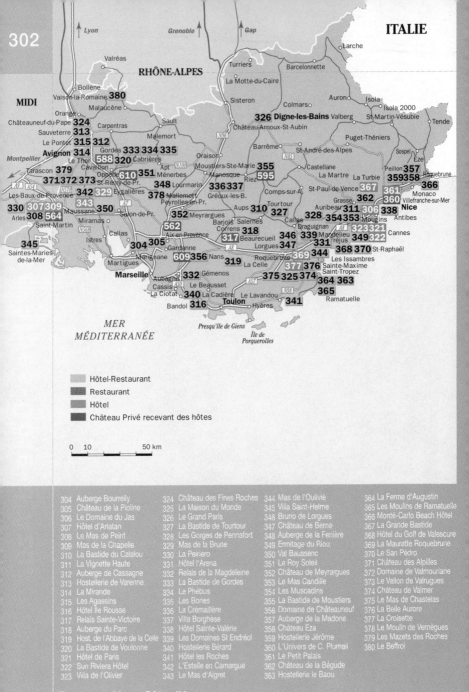

MER
MÉDITERRANÉE

Hôtel-Restaurant

Restaurant

Hôtel

Château Privé recevant des hôtes

0   10   50 km

How to book ?

➔ At the Châteaux & Hôtels reservation centre:
- Tél : 00 33 (0) 1 40 07 00 20
- Fax : 00 33 (0) 1 40 07 00 30

➔ By Internet:
- www.chateauxhotels.com
- resa@chateauxhotels.com

➔ Directly with the establishement required

CHÂTEAUX & HÔTELS
DE FRANCE®

Auberge Bourrelly
Calas

www.chateauxhotels.com/bourrelly | reservation service: 33 (0) 1.40.07.00.20

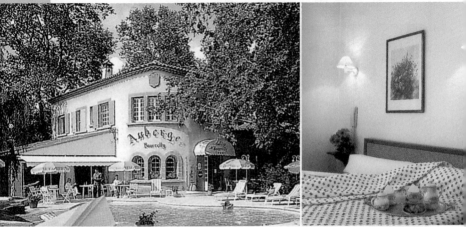

Place Albert Florent 13480 Cabriès
Tel.: 33 (0) 4.42.69.13.13 – Fax: 33 (0) 4.42.69.13.40
bourrelly@chateauxhotels.com
Roger BOURRELLY
15 rooms: 67 € / 122 €
1 suite: 152 € / 182,94 €
Breakfast: 8,5 €
Menu(s): 31 € / 42 € - **Carte:** 46 €
1/2 board: 72 € / 100 €

hotel annual closing
03/02 > 18/02
restaurant annual closing
03/02 > 18/02
equipments
internet, T.V. Satellite, minibar,
safe
environment
architecture 18º, terrace
leisure, relaxation
golf course 5 km, horse-riding
5 km, thalassotherapy, thermal
baths, tourist trail to main
places of interest

*5 mn from Aix-en-Provence, at
the heart of a charming village,
is this beautiful provencal family estate. For over 4 generations the Bourrelly family has
maintained the refined taste of
a by-gone era. Hundred year
old trees and terraces sur-
round this auberge creating a
truly splendid setting.*

Visa ● Diners ● MasterCard

Road map p. 619

A7 exit Plan de Campagne, D9 dir.
Calas

 Marignane: 9 km

260, rue Guillaume du Vair
13546 Aix-en-Provence
Tel.: 33 (0) 4.42.52.27.27 – Fax: 33 (0) 4.42.52.27.28
pioline@chateauxhotels.com
Véronique CHICHEPORTICHE
29 rooms: 136 € / 280 €
4 suites: 290 € / 300 €
Breakfast: 19 €
Menu(s): 30 € / 60 € - **1/2 board:** 125 € / 197 €

Located 5 km from Aix en Provence, the elegant XVIth century château classed as a historic monument is set against a background of yellow ochre and pink marble. The beautiful park with its French gardens onto which spacious rooms open out is as outstanding as the provençal cuisine. A refined stay.

hotel annual closing
01/02 > 27/02

restaurant annual closing
01/02 > 27/02

restaurant weekly closing
sat(lun), sun
01/11 > 31/03

equipments
telephone, internet, T.V. Satellite/Canal+, minibar, safe, baby-sitting, valet parking

environment
architecture 16e, furniture 17e, park 4 ha, garden, terrace 700 m²

leisure, relaxation
tennis 5 km, golf course 3 km, horse-riding 1 km, balneo

Visa ● Diners ● JCB ● MASTER CARD

Road map p. 619

D9 exit A1 La Pioline

Marseille Provence: 25 km

Le Domaine du Jas

Antibes I Biot

www.chateauxhotels.com/jas | reservation service: 33 (0) 1.40.07.00.20

625, route de la Mer 06410 Biot
Tel.: 33 (0) 4.93.65.50.50 – Fax: 33 (0) 4.93.65.02.01
jas@chateauxhotels.com
Christine MASCELLA – Chérif TORGOMAN
19 rooms: 115 € / 240 €
Breakfast: 10 €

hotel annual closing
15/11 > 01/03

equipments
telephone, internet, T.V.
Satellite

environment
architecture contemporaine,
furniture contemporain,
garden, terrace 150 m², view,
total calm

leisure, relaxation
heated pool, tennis 0.5 km,
golf course 0.5 km,
horse-riding 10 km, beauty
salon, thalassotherapy, thermal
baths

Splendid Mediterranean property halfway between Nice and Cannes, close to Biot, listed as one of France's most beautiful villages. Rooms with patio sheltered by palm trees, rose laurels and cypresses, heated swimming pool. A truly peaceful haven only a few minutes from the beach.

Visa ● MASTER CARD

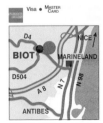

Road map p. 619

A8 exit Villeneuve-Loubet- N7 dir.
Antibes/Marineland.

Nice - Côte d'Azur: 20 km

26, rue du Sauvage 13631 Arles
Tel.: 33 (0) 4.90.93.56.66 – Fax: 33 (0) 4.90.49.68.45
arlatan@chateauxhotels.com
Yves DESJARDIN
41 rooms: 77 € / 137 €
7 suites: 157 € / 227 €
Breakfast: 10 €

In the ancient townhouse of the Counts d'Arlatan de Beaumont (15th century), a lovely hotel in a beautifully preserved area. Antique furnishing, refined comfort, patio and garden.

hotel annual closing
05/01 > 04/02

equipments
lift, telephone, internet, T.V. Satellite, minibar, safe, valet parking

environment
architecture 15e, garden, total calm

leisure, relaxation
heated pool, golf course 20 km, horse-riding 2 km, thalassotherapy, hammam, fitness

Visa ● Diners ● MASTER CARD

Road map p. 619

A9-A54 exit Arles

Nîmes: 20 km

Le Mas de Peint

Arles

www.chateauxhotels.com/maspeint | reservation service: 33 (0) 1.40.07.00.20

Le Sambuc 13200 Arles
Tel.: 33 (0) 4.90.97.20.62 – Fax: 33 (0) 4.90.97.22.20
maspeint@chateauxhotels.com
Lucille & Jacques BON
8 rooms: 197 € / 246 €
3 suites: 313 € / 358 €
Breakfast: 17 €
Menu(s): 30 € / 43 € - **1/2 board:** 158 € / 239 €

hotel annual closing
07/01 > 07/03 ● 18/11 > 19/12
restaurant annual closing
07/01 > 07/03 ● 18/11 > 19/12
equipments
telephone, T.V. Satellite,
minibar, safe
environment
architecture 17°, park 500 ha,
garden, terrace 70 m²,
vegetable garden, total calm
leisure, relaxation
horse-riding, 4 wheel drive to
discover the cattle

*In the centre of the wild and
secret Camargue, this elegant
XVIIth century residence is a
subtle compromise between
the conviviality of a guesthouse and a charming hotel.
The rooms are comfortable,
the cuisine authentic and the
welcome is exceptional. And
500 ha for galloping in full
liberty.*

Visa ● Diners ● MASTER CARD

Road map p. 619
A54 exit n° 4, dir. Salin de Giraud, D36

Provence-Alpes-Côte-d'Azur |

 Nîmes-Garons: 50 km

Petite route de Tarascon 13200 Arles
Tel.: 33 (0) 4.90.93.00.45 – Fax: 33 (0) 4.90.18.86.11
chapelle@chateauxhotels.com
Dominique GERARD
13 rooms: 75 € / 150 €
Breakfast: 8,93 €

Memories, memories... Provence, cicadas, lavender, colored skies, market scents, Van Gogh, férias, "L'Arlésienne", bareback riders in the Camargue, gipsy pilgrims at Saintes-Maries, sand dunes, siestas, "Norma" at the amphitheatre, aperitifs, riveting music in the Mas chapel... bliss.

Open all year
equipments
telephone, internet, T.V.
Satellite, minibar
environment
architecture 16ᵉ, furniture 19ᵉ,
park 6 ha, garden, terrace
60 m²
leisure, relaxation
golf course 13 km, horse-riding
2 km, solarium

Visa ● JCB ● MASTER CARD

Road map p. 619

Ring road Arles dir. Avignon,
N570, Z.I. North, Turn of the left

✈ Nîmes-Garons: 25 km

| Provence-Alpes-Côte-d'Azur

La Bastide du Calalou
Aups
www.chateauxhotels.com/calalou | reservation service: 33 (0) 1.40.07.00.20

Moissac-Bellevue 83630 Aups
Tel.: 33 (0) 4.94.70.17.91 – Fax: 33 (0) 4.94.70.50.11
calalou@chateauxhotels.com
Famille VANDEVYVER
32 rooms: 83,85 € / 190,94 €
Breakfast: 12,95 €
Menu(s): 22,87 € / 38,11 € - **Carte:** 19,06 €
1/2 board: 82,40 € / 135,90 €

hotel annual closing
04/01 > 28/03●17/11 > 28/12
restaurant annual closing
04/01 > 28/03●17/11 > 28/12
equipments
telephone, T.V. Satellite,
minibar, safe
environment
park 4 ha, garden, terrace
40 m², view, total calm
leisure, relaxation
horse-riding 10 km

Overlooking the valley, nestling in leafy gardens on a hillside Templar village, this country house offers thoughtful service and fine food inspired by a local tradition as venerable as the shade of the olive trees. The antique furniture accentuates the air of Provençal serenity.

Visa ● JCB ● MASTER CARD

Road map p. 619

A8 exit Le Muy. Route d'Aups dir.
Moissac-Bellevue

Nice: 120 km

370, route du Village
06810 Auribeau-sur-Siagne
Tel.: 33 (0) 4.93.42.20.01 – Fax: 33 (0) 4.93.42.31.16
vignettehaute@chateauxhotels.com
J.J. MEYER – E. REVEL
15 rooms: 185 € / 280 €
1 suite: 275 € / 325 €
Breakfast: 14,5 €
Menu(s): 77 € / 90 €

A romantic auberge on a hill, with an original, medieval and also cosy atmosphere. Antique furnitures, rooms with a personnal touch, gastronomic restaurant lit by oil lamps, with a view on the animal pen... An enchanting place, unique in France.

restaurant annual closing
12/11 > 15/12
restaurant weekly closing
mon, tue(lun), wen(lun)
15/12 > 01/05
equipments
telephone, internet, T.V.
Canal+, minibar, safe,
baby-sitting
environment
architecture 17e, garden,
terrace, view
leisure, relaxation
heated pool, tennis 5 km, golf
course 6 km, horse-riding
8 km, jacuzzi

Visa ● MASTER CARD

Road map p. 619

A8 exit 40 Mandelieu. D109 dir.
Pégomas/Auribeau

✈ Nice - Côte d'Azur: 29 km

Auberge de Cassagne

Avignon / Le Pontet

www.chateauxhotels.com/cassagne | reservation service: 33 (0) 1.40.07.00.20

450, allée de Cassagne
84130 Le Pontet / Avignon
Tel.: 33 (0) 4.90.31.04.18 – Fax: 33 (0) 4.90.32.25.09
cassagne@chateauxhotels.com
J.M.GALLON, A.TRESTOUR & Ph. BOUCHER

19 rooms: 100 € / 290 €
1 flat: 350 € - **1 suite:** 460 €
Breakfast: 17 €
Menu(s): 30 € / 80 € - **Carte:** 60 €
1/2 board: 132 € / 227 €

Open all year

equipments
telephone, internet, T.V.
Satellite/Canal+, minibar, safe,
baby-sitting, valet parking

environment
architecture 19e, furniture 19e,
park 3 ha, garden, terrace
300 m², view, total calm

leisure, relaxation
golf course 2 km, horse-riding
5 km, beauty salon, balneo,
sauna, solarium, fitness,
jacuzzi, bowling, mountain
bike, caves

*Old Provençal residence in a
magnificent leafy setting.
Luxury air-conditionned
rooms with local decoration,
terraces, gardens. Internationally famous gastronomic restaurant. Wine list contains a
selection of more than 600
items.*

Road map p. 619

A7 exit Avignon north then follow the
sign "Golf Grand Avignon"

Avignon: 5 km

91 PLACE ST JEAN 30150 Sauveterre

Tel.: 33 (0) 4.66.82.59.45 – Fax: 33 (0) 4.66.82.84.83

varenne@chateauxhotels.com

Robert BOYTHIAS

12 rooms: 69 € / 130 €
2 suites: 106 € / 137 €
Breakfast: 10 €
Menu(s): 30 € / 55 € - **Carte:** 21,34 € -
1/2 board: 69 € / 100 €

Superb XVIIIth century residence dominating the Rhône valley. Complete tranquility, exceptionally lush green setting. Midway between Orange and Avignon, near Châteauneuf-du-Pape, Nîmes , The Gard Bridge, the Baux de Provence, the supreme Côtes du Rhône vineyard. Lovely gastronomic stop-over.

Visa ● Diners ● MASTER CARD

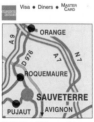

Road map p. 619

A7 exit Orange-centre - D976/D480
Avignon-Orange

Avignon: 20 km

hotel annual closing
01/02 > 28/02 ● 01/11 > 15/11

restaurant annual closing
01/02 > 28/02 ● 01/11 > 15/11

restaurant weekly closing
wen(lun)
01/06 > 30/09
wen
01/10 > 31/05

equipments
telephone, T.V., minibar, baby-sitting

environment
architecture 18e, park 3 ha, garden, terrace 120 m^2, view

leisure, relaxation
tennis 1 km, golf course 20 km, horse-riding 5 km

La Mirande

Avignon

www.chateauxhotels.com/mirande | reservation service: 33 (0) 1.40.07.00.20

4, place de la Mirande 84000 Avignon
Tel.: 33 (0) 4.90.85.93.93 – Fax: 33 (0) 4.90.86.26.85

mirande@chateauxhotels.com
Achim STEIN

19 rooms: 260 € / 430 €
1 flat: 640 € / 830 € - **1 suite:** 570 € / 640 €
Breakfast: 25 €
Menu(s): 38 € / 75 €
Table d'hôte (sur rés.): 95 €

Open all year
equipments
lift, telephone, internet, T.V.
Satellite, minibar, safe,
baby-sitting, valet parking
environment
architecture 17e, garden,
terrace, view, total calm
leisure, relaxation
, cooking school "Le
Marmiton"

In the heart of Avignon, this former cardinal residence converted to mansion in the XVIIth century is a prestigious witness of the past. The exceptional quality of the interior decoration, the secret garden, the tranquillity of the terraces and a true gourmand cuisine give direct access to ecstasy.

Visa ● Diners ● JCB ● MASTER CARD

Road map p. 619
A7 exit Avignon North

Provence-Alpes-Côte-d'Azur |

Avignon: 8 km

Lieu-dit Le Pigeonnier 84130 Le Pontet
Tel.: 33 (0) 4.90.32.42.91 – Fax: 33 (0) 4.90.32.08.29
agassins@chateauxhotels.com
Famille MARIANI

16 rooms: 90 € / 245 €
2 suites: 190 € / 426 €
Breakfast: 17 €
Menu(s): 23 € / 73 € - **Carte:** 45 € -
1/2 board: 105 € / 199 €

On the outskirts of Avignon, the Latin charm of a Provençal house enhanced by the subtle blend of colors and textures. Enchanting breakfast on flowered balconies. The beguiling warmth of the South, raised to a fine art by the subtle flavors of the food. Impressive wine list.

Visa ● Diners ● MASTER CARD

Road map p. 619

A7 exit Avignon north. N107 dir. Le Pontet/Avignon 4 km

✈ Avignon-Caumont: 7 km

hotel annual closing
01/01 > 01/03
restaurant annual closing
01/01 > 01/03
equipments
lift, telephone, internet, T.V. Satellite/Canal+, minibar, safe, baby-sitting, valet parking
environment
architecture 19e, park 3 ha, garden, terrace 1000 m², view, vegetable garden, total calm
leisure, relaxation
tennis 1 km, horse-riding 5 km, solarium, swimming pool, 3 golf nearby, excursions, visit of wine cellars, cookery classes

Hôtel Île Rousse
Bandol
www.chateauxhotels.com/rousse | reservation service: 33 (0) 1.40.07.00.20

25, boulevard Louis Lumière 83150 Bandol
Tel.: 33 (0) 4.94.29.33.00 – Fax: 33 (0) 4.94.29.49.49
rousse@chateauxhotels.com
Jean-Pierre GHIRIBELLI
54 rooms: 102 € / 320 €
2 suites: 290 € / 515 €
Breakfast: 17 €
Menu(s): 37 € / 49 € - **Carte:** 70 €
1/2 board: 49 € / 51 €

Open all year
equipments
lift, telephone, internet, T.V.
Satellite/Canal+, minibar, safe,
baby-sitting, valet parking
environment
architecture contemporaine,
garden, terrace 125 m², view
leisure, relaxation
tennis 2 km, golf course 4 km,
horse-riding 4 km, beauty
salon, thalassotherapy,
hammam, fitness, jacuzzi, sea

*A hotel of character, just a
short walk from the center of
Bandol, with sunlit rooms and
a splendid view over Rénécros
bay. With amenities including
a beauty center, sea-water
treatment, 4 restaurants (2
gourmet and 2 beachside),
you will find everything you
need to unwind in luxurious
comfort.*

Visa ● Diners ● JCB ● Master Card

Road map p. 619

A50 dir. Toulon exit Bandol

 Toulon-Hyères: 35 km

13100 Beaurecueil
Tel.: 33 (0) 4.42.66.94.98 – Fax: 33 (0) 4.42.66.85.96
saintevictoire@chateauxhotels.com
Danièle, René & Natacha JUGY BERGES
Menu(s): 34,3 € / 60,98 € - **Carte:** 53,36 €

In the land of Cézanne, this coaching house has perpetuated the highest culinary tradition since 1952. René Bergès is an inspired chef who loves the Provence to the point of extracting the savours. The result is fabulous.

restaurant annual closing
03/02 > 10/02●27/10 > 05/11
restaurant weekly closing
mon, fri(lun), sun(ev)
01/03 > 31/10
mon, fri, sun(ev)
01/11 > 28/02
environment
park 3 ha, garden, terrace,
view, total calm

leisure, relaxation
golf course 10 km, horse-riding
2 km

Visa ● MASTER CARD

Road map p. 619

A7 exit Aix en Provence-3 Sautets,
then N7

Marseille Provence: 35 km

| Provence-Alpes-Côte-d'Azur

Auberge du Parc

Brignoles I Correns

www.chateauxhotels.com/aubergeparc | reservation service: 33 (0) 1.40.07.00.20

Place Général de Gaulle 83570 Correns
Tel.: 33 (0) 4.94.59.53.52 – Fax: 33 (0) 4.94.59.53.54
aubergeparc@chateauxhotels.com
Bruno CLEMENT
5 rooms: 99,09 € / 129,58 €
1 suite: 175,32 €
Breakfast: 10,67 €
Menu(s): 28,97 € / 41,16 €

Open all year
equipments
telephone, T.V.
environment
park, terrace, total calm
leisure, relaxation
tennis 1 km, golf course 20 km

In Correns, a unique village, Bruno Clément has revived the old inn. A fountain pool, terrace and lovers' cask adorn the park. The house has 5 guest rooms, one suite, a conservatory dining room and a salon with a Louis XIV fireplace. Sumptuous decor, wood-panelled walls and frescos.

Visa ● MASTER CARD

Road map p. 619
A8 exit Brignoles

Hyères: 70 km

Place du Général de Gaulle 83170 La Celle
Tel.: 33 (0) 4.98.05.14.14 – Fax: 33 (0) 4.98.05.14.15
abbayecelle@chateauxhotels.com
Laurence JEANVOINE
9 rooms: 175 € / 260 €
1 suite: 245 € / 290 €
Breakfast: 14 €
Menu(s): 33 € / 55 € - **Carte:** 12 € / 29 €

In the heart of the Var region, the Hostellerie de l'Abbaye de la Celle greets you with a history-filled setting whose architecture is in perfect harmony with the Southern French countryside. Comfortable rooms, a natural park, and genuine cuisine which honours the flavours of the region's gastronomy.

Open all year
equipments
telephone, internet, T.V. Satellite/Canal+, minibar, safe, baby-sitting, valet parking
environment
architecture 18^e, garden, terrace 300 m^2, view, vegetable garden, total calm
leisure, relaxation
heated pool, tennis 0.5 km, golf course 10 km, horse-riding 10 km

Visa • Diners • MASTER CARD

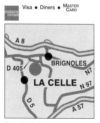

Road map p. 619
A8 exit Brignoles. D405

Hyères-Toulon: 60 km

La Bastide de Voulonne

Cabrières-d'Avignon
www.chateauxhotels.com/voulonne | reservation service: 33 (0) 1.40.07.00.20

84220 Cabrières-d'Avignon
Tel.: 33 (0) 4.90.76.77.55 – Fax: 33 (0) 4.90.76.77.56
voulonne@chateauxhotels.com
Sophie & Alain REBOURG
8 rooms: 122 € / 145 €
2 suites: 153 € / 236 €
Breakfast: 11 €
Table d'hôtes (sur rés.): 26 €
4 evenings by week

hotel annual closing
15/11 > 15/12

restaurant annual closing
15/11 > 15/12

restaurant weekly closing
mon(lun), tue(lun), wen(lun),
thi(lun), fri(lun), sat(lun), sun(lun)
01/01 > 15/11

equipments
no smoker bedroom,
telephone, T.V.

environment
architecture 18e, park 5 ha,
garden, terrace 50 m², view

leisure, relaxation
heated pool, tennis 5 km, golf
course 8 km, horse-riding 6 km

Charm, warmth and hospitality characterise this small country house, at the heart of the Luberon. This former 18th century farm and its 12-acre park offer discovery and relaxation for the seasoned traveller. In summer, meals are served near the fountain and, in winter, in the vast dining-room.

Visa ● MASTER CARD

Road map p. 619

A7 exit Cavaillon dir. Apt - In Coustellet
dir. Gordes-les-Imberts D2, 2 km after,
follow signs

Avignon: 20 km

34, bd d'Alsace 06400 Cannes
Tel.: 33 (0) 4.93.38.30.89 – Fax: 33 (0) 4.93.39.04.61
hotelparis@chateauxhotels.com
Didier LAZZARI
43 rooms: 55 € / 120 €
7 suites: 120 € / 250 €
Breakfast: 11 €

The Hotel de Paris, considered as one of the best in the region, is a genuine 19th c. period town house, decorated in medieval style, with 50 guest rooms and elegant suites, all fully airconditioned and soundproofed. A haven of peace right in the center of Cannes.

hotel annual closing
16/11 > 26/12

equipments
lift, telephone, internet, T.V. Satellite, safe

environment
architecture 19e, furniture 16e, garden, terrace 90 m²

leisure, relaxation
tennis 0.5 km, golf course 10 km, horse-riding 5 km, hammam, jacuzzi

Visa ● Diners ● JCB ● MASTER CARD

Road map p. 619

A8 exit Cannes-Mougins

Nice: 25 km

Sun Riviera Hôtel

Cannes

www.chateauxhotels.com/sunriviera | reservation service: 33 (0) 1.40.07.00.20

138, rue d'Antibes 06400 Cannes
Tel.: 33 (0) 4.93.06.77.77 – Fax: 33 (0) 4.93.38.31.10
sunriviera@chateauxhotels.com
Nadine BRUNO
40 rooms: 110 € / 210 €
2 suites: 220 € / 410 €
Breakfast: 14 €

hotel annual closing
16/11 > 27/12

equipments
lift, telephone, internet, T.V.
Satellite/Canal+, minibar, safe,
baby-sitting

environment
garden, terrace 45 m², total
calm

leisure, relaxation
golf course 5 km, horse-riding
7 km, beauty salon,
thalassotherapy, balneo,
solarium

*In the Rue d'Antibes, right
near the Croisette, this hotel
matches the modern comfort
of the rooms with the serenity
of the surroundings. Warm
welcome. Original paintings.
An invitation to lounge on the
terrace in the shade of the
bougainvillea, or in the garden
around the pool.*

Visa ● Diners ● JCB ● MASTER CARD

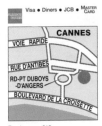

Road map p. 619
A8 exit Cannes-centre

Provence-Alpes-Côte-d'Azur |

Nice: 30 km

5-7, rue des Tambourinaires 06400 Cannes

Tel.: 33 (0) 4.93.39.53.28 – Fax: 33 (0) 4.93.39.55.85

olivier@chateauxhotels.com

Joseph SCHILDKNECHT

23 rooms: 74 € / 120 €

1 suite: 244 €

Breakfast: 9 €

Overlooking the old town, in the Suquet district, in a leafy setting, the hotel is located 300 meters from the Midi beach, the new municipal casino, the old yacht basin, the Festival and Congress Center. You will be seduced by its luxury. Pleasant lounge with bar, covered terrace, swimming-pool.

hotel annual closing
01/12 > 22/12

equipments
telephone, T.V., safe

environment
garden, terrace 90 m², view

leisure, relaxation
tennis 2 km, golf course 5 km

Visa ● Diners ● JCB ● MASTER CARD

LA BOCCA
AV. DR PICAUD
AV. DES ANCIENS CO
R. CLEMENCEAU
LE SUC
SQ. MISTRAL
BOUL. J. HIBERT

Road map p. 619

A8 exit Cannes centre. N7 dir. Suquet area

Nice: 30 km

324

Château des Fines Roches
Châteauneuf-du-Pape
www.chateauxhotels.com/finesroches | reservation service: 33 (0) 1.40.07.00.20

84230 Châteauneuf-du-Pape
Tel.: 33 (0) 4.90.83.70.23 – Fax: 33 (0) 4.90.83.78.42
finesroches@chateauxhotels.com
André CHABERT
6 rooms: 150 € / 192 €
Breakfast: 14 €
Menu(s): 43 € / 69 € - **Carte:** 22,87 €

hotel annual closing
02/01 > 01/03
restaurant annual closing
02/01 > 01/03
equipments
telephone, T.V., minibar
environment
architecture 19e, garden,
terrace, view, total calm
leisure, relaxation
golf course 8 km, horse-riding
8 km

The former residence of the Marquise Folco de Baroncelli Javo, a wellknown Provincial poet, this château is situated in the heart of the Chateauneuf du Pape vineyard. Perched on the summit of a hill it offers rooms with a view over the vineyards, the Rhône valley. Excellent Provincial cuisine.

Visa ● MASTER CARD

Road map p. 619

A7 exit Avignon north. dir. Sorgues-Chateauneuf du Pape

Provence-Alpes-Côte-d'Azur |

Avignon: 15 km

63, rue Carnot 83310 Cogolin

Tel.: 33 (0) 4.94.54.77.54 – Fax: 33 (0) 4.94.54.77.55

maisondumonde@chateauxhotels.com

Marie-Pierre GIAIME

12 rooms: 80 € / 145 €
Breakfast: 12,3 €
Menu(s): 15 € / 40 €

A couple of miles from the beach, La Maison du Monde invites you to enjoy the peaceful beauty of its hundred-year-old park and pastel-hued, sunny rooms. The restaurant "La Carte de Clarisse" does justice to a creative cuisine mingling French style with the taste of travel.

hotel annual closing
01/02 > 28/02

restaurant annual closing
01/02 > 28/02

equipments
telephone, internet, T.V. Satellite

environment
park, terrace

Road map p. 619

A8 exit "Le Luc / La Garde Freinet", then dir. "La Garde Freinet / Grimaud / Cogolin" by the road D558

✈ Nice, Toulon-Hyères, La Môle: 80 km

Le Grand Paris

Digne-les-Bains

www.chateauxhotels.com/grandparis | reservation service: 33 (0) 1.40.07.00.20

19, boulevard Thiers 04000 Digne-les-Bains
Tel.: 33 (0) 4.92.31.11.15 – Fax: 33 (0) 4.92.32.32.82
grandparis@chateauxhotels.com
Noémi RICAUD

16 rooms: 79 € / 107 €
3 flats: 120 € / 150 € - **1 suite:** 114 € / 135 €
Breakfast: 10 €
Menu(s): 23 € / 67 € - **Carte:** 16 €
1/2 board: 86 € / 99 €

hotel annual closing
01/12 > 01/03
restaurant annual closing
01/12 > 01/03
equipments
lift, telephone, internet, T.V.,
minibar, safe, baby-sitting
environment
architecture 17ᵉ, garden,
terrace 200 m²
leisure, relaxation
tennis 1 km, golf course 3 km,
horse-riding 3 km, beauty
salon, thermal baths, sauna,
hammam, solarium, fitness,
jacuzzi

Located in a former Trinitarian monastery right in the center of the old thermal resort, this hotel welcomes you to an unspoilt natural environment. The Ricaud family will offer you a taste of superlative food with a regional flavor. Comfortable rooms, private salons, shaded terrace.

Visa ● Diners ● JCB ● MASTER CARD

Road map p. 619

A51 Marseille-Gap exit 20 Peyruis-Les
Mees -N85 (road Napoléon:
Grenoble-Nice)

Provence-Alpes-Côte-d'Azur |

 Marseille-Marignane: 130 km

Route de Flayosc 83690 Tourtour
Tel.: 33 (0) 4.98.10.54.20 – Fax: 33 (0) 4.94.70.54.90
tourtour@chateauxhotels.com
Pascal LODDO
25 rooms: 62,5 € / 241 €
Breakfast: 14,5 €
Menu(s): 24,5 € / 49 € - **Carte:** 57,17 € -
1/2 board: 107 € / 173 €

The Bastide de Tourtour, an oasis of tranquillity, illustrates how nature sometimes achieves what no magician would dare to attempt: imagine a place as fragrant and vivid as Provence, as vibrant as the Côte d'Azur – here is a carefree place made for those who love to wander as their fancy takes them.

Open all year

restaurant weekly closing
mon(lun), tue(lun), wen(lun), thi(lun), fri(lun)
01/09 > 03/07

equipments
lift, telephone, T.V. Satellite, minibar, safe

environment
park 4 ha, garden, terrace, view, total calm

leisure, relaxation
heated pool, golf course 30 km, horse-riding 15 km, jacuzzi

Visa ● Diners ● MASTER CARD

Road map p. 619
A8 exit Le Luc or Le Muy

Nice 110 km / Marseille: 125 km

Les Gorges de Pennafort

Draguignan I Callas

www.chateauxhotels.com/pennafort | reservation service: 33 (0) 1.40.07.00.20

D25 83830 Callas

Tel.: 33 (0) 4.94.76.66.51 – Fax: 33 (0) 4.94.76.67.23

pennafort@chateauxhotels.com

Philippe Da SILVA

11 rooms: 110 € / 145 €

1 flat: 260 € / 290 € - **4 suites:** 160 € / 185 €

Breakfast: 15 €

Carte: 76 €

hotel annual closing
15/01 > 15/03

equipments
T.V. Canal+, minibar, safe

environment
garden, terrace, view, total calm

leisure, relaxation
golf course 7 km, horse-riding 15 km

Opposite the majestic gorges of Pennafort and a short distance from the Gulf of St Tropez is a residence that has the scents of nature for rendez-vous. The comfort is modern and the cuisine at the service of local savours. For the lovers of a preserved South of France.

Visa ● MASTER CARD

Road map p. 619

A8 exit Le Muy, D25 dir. Callas

Provence-Alpes-Côte-d'Azur |

Nice: 80 km

Mas de la Brune
Eygalières-en-Provence
www.chateauxhotels.com/brune | reservation service: 33 (0) 1.40.07.00.20

329

13810 Eygalières-en-Provence

Tel.: 33 (0) 4.90.90.67.77 – Fax: 33 (0) 4.90.95.99.21

brune@chateauxhotels.com

Marie de LAROUZIERE

11 rooms: 155 € / 230 €
1 suite: 325 € / 355 €
Breakfast: 13 €

A charming 16th century mansion hidden away in its big landscaped park featuring a heated Roman swimming pool. Guests are received like friends in cosy rooms. Near the Alpilles, Arles and Avignon, a historic monument, evidence of the Provençal art of living during the Renaissance.

Visa ● MASTER CARD

Road map p. 619

A7 exit Cavaillon. D99 dir. St-Rémy-de-Provence

hotel annual closing
10/12 > 21/01

equipments
telephone, internet, T.V. Satellite, minibar, safe, valet parking

environment
architecture 16°, furniture 16°, park 5 ha, garden, terrace 30 m², vegetable garden, total calm

leisure, relaxation
tennis 3 km, golf course 25 km, horse-riding 2 km, visit the alchemist's garden

✈ Marseille: 45 km

La Peiriero
Fontvieille
www.chateauxhotels.com/peiriero | reservation service: 33 (0) 1.40.07.00.20

34 Avenue des Baux 13990 Fontvieille
Tel.: 33 (0) 4.90.54.76.10 – Fax: 33 (0) 4.90.54.62.60
peiriero@chateauxhotels.com
Frédéric JACQUEMIN
42 rooms: 75 € / 130 €
Breakfast: 9 €
Menu(s): 20 € - **1/2 board:** 65,70 € / 93,20 €

hotel annual closing
01/01 > 30/03●03/11 > 19/04
restaurant annual closing
01/01 > 30/03●03/11 > 19/04
equipments
lift, telephone, internet, T.V.
Satellite
environment
park 4 ha, garden, terrace
300 m², view
leisure, relaxation
heated pool, tennis 1.5 km,
golf course 5 km, horse-riding
2 km, sauna, solarium, giant
chess set, mini-golf course,
game of bowls

*At the foot of the Alpilles, this
Southern country house built
on ancient stone quarries,
hums with the buzz of cicadas.
Huge rooms decorated in rich
Provencal colours and fabrics.
Authentic, delicious meals
served on the terrace evoke
glimmers of a life beloved by
Alphonse Daudet.*

Visa ● MASTER CARD

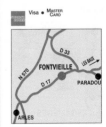

Road map p. 619

Exit Arles N° 7 (direction Fontvieille)

 Nîmes: 30 km, Marseille:
75 km

145, rue Gal. de Gaulle 83600 Fréjus
Tel.: 33 (0) 4.94.17.09.40 – Fax: 33 (0) 4.94.52.01.52
arena@chateauxhotels.com
M. BLUNTZER & Mme. BOUCHOT
33 rooms: 73 € / 150 €
Breakfast: 8,5 €
Menu(s): 23 € / 43 € - **Carte:** 48,02 € -
1/2 board: 74 € / 99 €

*Attractive Provençal resi-
dence in the historic centre of
Fréjus. Bright and air-
conditioned rooms around a
patio. Seductive gastronomic
repertory, with a seafood or
Provençal market menus. Fréjus also means 2,000 years of
history, fine sandy beaches,
the Maures, l'Estérel.*

hotel annual closing
01/01 > 15/01

restaurant annual closing
01/01 > 15/01

equipments
lift, telephone, internet, T.V.
Satellite, safe

environment
garden, terrace 200 m²

leisure, relaxation
tennis 2 km, golf course 3 km,
horse-riding 4 km

Visa ● Diners ● MASTER CARD

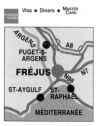

Road map p. 619
A8 exit Frejus then city centre

Nice: 60 km

Relais de la Magdeleine

Gémenos

www.chateauxhotels.com/magdeleine | reservation service: 33 (0) 1.40.07.00.20

Rond Point de la Fontaine 13420 Gémenos
Tel.: 33 (0) 4.42.32.20.16 – Fax: 33 (0) 4.42.32.02.26

magdeleine@chateauxhotels.com
Daniel MARIGNANE

24 rooms: 90 € / 140 €
1 suite: 190 €
Breakfast: 13 €
Menu(s): 40,50 € / 49 € - **Carte:** 45 €

hotel annual closing
01/12 > 15/03

restaurant annual closing
01/12 > 15/03

equipments
lift, internet, T.V.

environment
architecture 18e, furniture 18e,
park 2 ha, terrace

leisure, relaxation
tennis 1 km, golf course
20 km, horse-riding 2 km

At the foot of the Sainte-Baume mountain, half-way between the Aix country and the sea, 24 rooms with character set in an 18th century farmhouse. Restaurant under the plane trees. Cassis beach and creeks nearby. Near the village of Gémenos, the Saint-Pons Park. Riding, tennis, golf.

Visa ● Master Card

Road map p. 619

A52 exit Pont-de-l'Étoile, D80 then D2
dir. Gémenos

Provence-Alpes-Côte-d'Azur |

 Marseille: 40 km

Le Village 84220 Gordes

Tel.: 33 (0) 4.90.72.12.12 – Fax: 33 (0) 4.90.72.05.20

gordes@chateauxhotels.com

Jacques MAZET

27 rooms: 140 € / 453 €
2 suites: 330 € / 364 €
Breakfast: 21 €
Menu(s): 56 € / 91 € - **Carte:** 77 €

You have to stop to contemplate this splendid edifice and admire the sober and majestic facade rising proudly above the lovely terraces. The rooms and suites are superb, the cuisine refined, the staff attentive and friendly - all the ingredients for happy memories.

Open all year

equipments
lift, telephone, internet, T.V., minibar, safe

environment
architecture 12°, garden, terrace, view, total calm

leisure, relaxation
heated pool, tennis 4 km, golf course 8 km, horse-riding 15 km, sauna

Visa ● **MASTER CARD**

Road map p. 619

A7 Cavaillon or Avignon south. N100 dir. Gordes

Marignane-Marseille: 40 km

Le Phébus

Gordes I Joucas

www.chateauxhotels.com/phebus | reservation service: 33 (0) 1.40.07.00.20

Route de Murs 84220 Joucas-Gordes
Tel.: 33 (0) 4.90.05.78.83 – Fax: 33 (0) 4.90.05.73.61

phebus@chateauxhotels.com
Xavier MATHIEU

18 rooms: 117,39 € / 228,67 €
7 suites: 212,67 € / 533,57 €
Breakfast: 16,01 €
Menu(s): 33,54 € / 66,32 € - **Carte:** 70 €
1/2 board: 105,19 € / 169,99 €

hotel annual closing
01/11 > 15/03
restaurant annual closing
01/11 > 15/03
equipments
telephone, internet, T.V.
Satellite, minibar, safe,
baby-sitting
environment
architecture 16e, furniture 18e,
park 4 ha, garden, terrace
250 m², view, total calm
leisure, relaxation
heated pool, golf course
12 km, horse-riding 1 km,
fishing and kayak (12 km)

Overlooking the Lubéron, this drystone traditional Provençal residence dominates the valley. The hosts offer a truly hearty welcome. Rooms and apartments fitted out in refined taste, sun-drenched terraces. Renowned cuisine, with a distinctly Provençal flavor. Heated pool. Air-conditioning.

Visa ● JCB ● MasterCard

Road map p. 619

A7 exit Cavaillon. dir. Joucas/Gordes

Avignon: 35 km

Route de l'Abbaye de Sénanque 84220 Gordes
Tel.: 33 (0) 4.90.72.00.51 – Fax: 33 (0) 4.90.72.01.22
bories@chateauxhotels.com
Françoise GALLON
26 rooms: 150 € / 310 €
1 flat: 400 €
Breakfast: 17 €
Menu(s): 30 € / 80 € - **Carte:** 85 € -
1/2 board: 157 € / 237 €

Bories are dry stone structures used in former times by shepherds. Built with respect of this tradition, this hotel, hidden amongst the garrigue scrubland, is conducive to glorious idleness by the charm of the rooms and the quality of the cuisine. Health and fitness centre, beauty farm pools inside and outside.

hotel annual closing
02/01 > 01/03
restaurant annual closing
02/01 > 01/03
equipments
lift, telephone, internet, T.V. Satellite, minibar, safe, baby-sitting, valet parking
environment
park 6 ha, garden, terrace, view, total calm
leisure, relaxation
heated pool/covered, golf course 15 km, beauty salon, sauna, hammam, fitness, jacuzzi, SPA & beauty

Visa ● Diners ● MasterCard

Road map p. 619

A7 exit Cavaillon. N100 dir. Apt then D2

✈ Avignon: 40 km

Provence-Alpes-Côte-d'Azur

La Crémaillère
Gréoux-les-Bains
www.chateauxhotels.com/cremaillere | reservation service: 33 (0) 1.40.07.00.20

Route de Riez 04800 Gréoux-les-Bains
Tel.: 33 (0) 4.92.70.40.04 – Fax: 33 (0) 4.92.78.19.80
cremaillere@chateauxhotels.com
Nathalie DUBOIS
51 rooms: 67 € / 72 €
Breakfast: 9 €
Menu(s): 16 € / 30 € - **1/2 board:** 63 € / 90 €

hotel annual closing
21/12 > 01/03
restaurant annual closing
21/12 > 01/03
equipments
lift, telephone, T.V.
Satellite/Canal+, safe
environment
furniture contemporain, park
4 ha, garden
leisure, relaxation
tennis 0.2 km, golf course
25 km, horse-riding 2 km,
beauty salon, thermal baths,
sauna, hammam, jacuzzi

A farmhouse in the pure Provençal tradition, with rooms in those colours. Restaurant formula thought out according to your stay: different set menu each day and/or à la carte Provençal menu, with the flavours of the south. Swimming-pool, golf practice range. Escapade stay with water treatments.

Visa ● Diners ● MASTER CARD

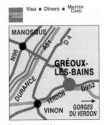

Road map p. 619

A51 exit St-Paul-les-Durance or exit Manosque

 Marseille-Provence: 70 km

Avenue des Thermes 04800 Gréoux-les-Bains
Tel.: 33 (0) 4.92.78.00.91 – Fax: 33 (0) 4.92.78.09.55
borghese@chateauxhotels.com
Jean-Claude REDOLFI
66 rooms: 66 € / 114 €
Breakfast: 10 €
Menu(s): 26 € / 38 € - **Carte:** 30 € -
1/2 board: 66 € / 90 €

A charming residence, at the doors to the Gorges du Verdon, welcoming you for pleasant relaxing stays: bedrooms with bath, colour TV, park, heated swimming-pool, sauna, etc. A sun-filled restaurant offers slimming menus. Bridge club with lessons and tournaments. Health and Beauty centre.

Visa ● Diners ● MASTER CARD

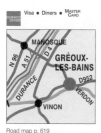

Road map p. 619

A51 exit St Paul-les-Durance / 50 km
from TGV station Aix-en-Provence

Marseille: 80 km

hotel annual closing
01/01 > 22/03 ● 11/11 > 25/03
restaurant annual closing
01/01 > 22/03 ● 11/11 > 25/03
equipments
lift, telephone, internet, T.V. Satellite/Canal+, minibar, baby-sitting
environment
architecture contemporaine, furniture contemporain, garden, terrace 350 m^2
leisure, relaxation
heated pool, golf course 20 km, horse-riding 2 km, beauty salon, balneo, thermal baths, sauna, fitness, jacuzzi

Hôtel Sainte-Valérie
Juan les Pins
www.chateauxhotels.com/saintevalerie | reservation service: 33 (0) 1.40.07.00.20

Rue de l'Oratoire 06160 Juan les Pins
Tel.: 33 (0) 4.93.61.07.15 – Fax: 33 (0) 4.93.61.47.52
saintevalerie@chateauxhotels.com
Christophe RIGOTTI
27 rooms: 114 € / 183 €
Breakfast: 11,5 €
Menu(s): 27,50 € - **Carte:** 25 €
1/2 board: 96 € / 130,50 €

hotel annual closing
01/01 > 28/03•01/10 > 31/12
restaurant annual closing
01/01 > 28/03•01/10 > 31/12
restaurant weekly closing
thi
15/04 > 15/10
equipments
lift, telephone, internet, T.V.
Satellite/Canal+, minibar, safe
environment
garden, terrace, total calm
leisure, relaxation
tennis 1 km, golf course 8 km,
beauty salon, sauna, solarium,
fitness

An oasis of shady calm in the heart of Juan-les-Pins, close to the casino and the beach. Dream Mediterranean holidays: a beautiful sunny villa bedecked with flowers, comfortable and stylish decor, and ample, delicious cuisine.

Road map p. 619

A8 Antibes, direction Juan les Pins
centre, La Pinède

 Nice Côte-d'Azur: 15 km

La Motte en Provence

www.chateauxhotels.com/endreol | reservation service: 33 (0) 1.40.07.00.20

Route de Bagnols en Forêt
83920 La Motte en Provence
Tel.: 33 (0) 4.94.51.89.80 – Fax: 33 (0) 4.94.51.89.81
endreol@chateauxhotels.com
Bernard LOMBARD
35 suites: 124 € / 175 €
Breakfast: 13 €
Menu(s): 30 € / 53 €

Between Provence and the Cote d'Azur, on an internationally reputed golf-course, in true provencal style, this hotel offers 35 luxury suites, complete with outdoor swimming-pool and jacuzzi. Sophisticated service. The Saint Endreol, in a country house with Mediterranean charm, also provides delicious regional cuisine.

Visa ● MASTER CARD

Road map p. 619

Motorway A8 exit N° 36 - Le Muy

Open all year
restaurant weekly closing
mon, sun(ev)
15/11 > 15/03
equipments
telephone, internet, T.V.
Satellite, minibar, safe,
baby-sitting
environment
terrace, view, total tranquillity
on golf course
leisure, relaxation
tennis 2 km, horse-riding 5 km,
jacuzzi, golf, swimming-pool

Nice - Côte d'Azur: 70 km

Hostellerie Bérard

La Cadière-d'Azur

www.chateauxhotels.com/berard | reservation service: 33 (0) 1.40.07.00.20

rue Gabriel Peri 83740 La Cadière-d'Azur
Tel.: 33 (0) 4.94.90.11.43 – Fax: 33 (0) 4.94.90.01.94
berard@chateauxhotels.com
Danièle & René BERARD
32 rooms: 84 € / 145 €
1 flat: 171 € / 182 €
Breakfast: 17 €
Menu(s): 26 € / 100 € - **Carte:** 25 €
1/2 board: 98 € / 129 €

hotel annual closing
04/01 > 14/02
restaurant annual closing
04/01 > 14/02
equipments
telephone, internet, T.V.
Canal+, minibar, safe
environment
architecture 11e, garden,
terrace, view
leisure, relaxation
heated pool, tennis 3 km, golf
course 3 km, horse-riding
4 km, sauna, solarium, fitness,
water-color painting course

Dominating the vineyards of Bandol, this provençal domain is perfect osmosis between the welcome of a successful stay and the quintessence of a luminous cuisine orchestrated by René Bérard who enjoys sharing in the discovery of his region, its products and its lively wines. A quality stopover!

Visa ● Diners ● JCB ● MASTER CARD

Road map p. 619
A50 exit 11 dir. La Cadière d'Azur

Marseille Provence: 60 km

1, avenue des trois Dauphins
83980 Le Lavandou
Tel.: 33 (0) 4.94.71.05.07 – Fax: 33 (0) 4.94.71.08.40
lesroches@chateauxhotels.com
Jean-Michel GALLON

34 rooms: 240 € / 490 €
5 flats: 540 € / 600 € - **1 suite:** 840 € / 990 €
Breakfast: 17 €
Menu(s): 50 € / 80 € - **Carte:** 70 € -
1/2 board: 202 € / 327 €

Close to St Tropez, the hotel is in a coveted position on the shore of the Mediterranean. Luxury bedrooms with sea-view and terraces running right to the private beach. Gastronomic cuisine in the panoramic restaurant in the evening. For lunch, grilled fish on the beach. Ferry-boat to St Tropez.

hotel annual closing
01/01 > 15/03
restaurant annual closing
01/01 > 15/03
equipments
telephone, internet, T.V. Satellite/Canal+, minibar, safe, baby-sitting, valet parking
environment
terrace, view, total calm
leisure, relaxation
golf course 30 km, sauna, hammam, jacuzzi, shuttle bus, boats for hire with skipper

Visa ● Diners ● JCB ● MASTER CARD

Road map p. 619
A8/A57 exit Cuers North or Hyères

marseille: 60 km

Le Mas d'Aigret

Les Baux de Provence

www.chateauxhotels.com/aigret | reservation service: 33 (0) 1.40.07.00.20

D27A 13520 Les Baux de Provence
Tel.: 33 (0) 4.90.54.20.00 – Fax: 33 (0) 4.90.54.44.00
aigret@chateauxhotels.com
Frédéric LALOY & Vincent MISSISTRANO
15 rooms: 95 € / 170 €
1 flat: 190 €
Breakfast: 12 €
Menu(s): 40 € / 40 € - **1/2 board:** 92,5 € / 130 €

Open all year
restaurant weekly closing
mon, tue
01/10 > 01/03
equipments
telephone, T.V.
Satellite/Canal+, minibar, safe
environment
architecture 17e, park 3.4 ha,
garden, terrace, view
leisure, relaxation
tennis 0.8 km, golf course
5 km, horse-riding 5 km,
swimming pool

In the shelter of a cliff in les Baux de Provence, this beautiful residence proposes spacious rooms, of which certain ones are troglodytic, with balcony or terrace. The gardens inspire tranquillity and peace and with the beauty of the setting make Mas d'Aigret a favoured holiday place.

Visa ● JCB ● MASTER CARD

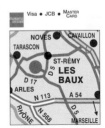

Road map p. 619

A7 exit Avignon south, dir. St-Rémy
D27A

 Nîmes-Garons: 25 km

Les Arcoules 13520 Les Baux de Provence
Tel.: 33 (0) 4.90.54.35.78 – Fax: 33 (0) 4.90.54.44.31
oulivie@chateauxhotels.com
Emmanuel ACHARD
22 rooms: 95 € / 230 €
1 suite: 280 € / 360 €
Breakfast: 10 €

At the heart of an olive grove, in the idyllic setting of a marvelous typical village, a charming hotel with its stunning swimming pool landscaped with rocks and jacuzzi. Provençal style outside and inside. Grilled meats and salads seasoned with hotel olive oil are served around the pool.

hotel annual closing
11/11 > 21/03

equipments
telephone, internet, T.V.
Satellite, minibar, safe,
baby-sitting

environment
architecture contemporaine,
furniture contemporain,
garden, terrace 200 m^2, view

leisure, relaxation
golf course 2 km, horse-riding
1 km, beauty salon, jacuzzi,
hiking, mountain bike

Visa ● Diners ● MASTER CARD

Road map p. 619

A7 exit Avignon South or A54 St
Martin de Crau, D78f dir. Fontvieille

Avignon: 30 km

Villa Saint-Elme

Les Issambres

www.chateauxhotels.com/saintelme | reservation service: 33 (0) 1.40.07.00.20

Corniche des Issambres 83380 Les Issambres
Tel.: 33 (0) 4.94.49.52.52 – Fax: 33 (0) 4.94.49.63.18
saintelme@chateauxhotels.com
Kery CHBIB
3 rooms: 114,34 € / 297,28 €
13 suites: 243,92 € / 701,27 €
Menu(s): 22,87 € / 67,08 €

Open all year
equipments
lift, telephone, T.V., minibar
environment
architecture 10ᵉ, terrace, view
leisure, relaxation
covered pool, golf course
10 km, horse-riding 10 km,
thalassotherapy, sauna

In the Bay of Isssambres, op-posite St-Tropez, this luxuri-ous pink seaside building built in the 30's offers visitors calm rooms, all different from one another, the enjoyment of its pine grove and the quality of its cuisine. Beach and seawa-ter pool.

Road map p. 619

A8 exit Le Muy. N98 dir. Ste Maxime

Provence-Alpes-Côte-d'Azur |

Nice: 70 km

Route du petit Rhône (D38)
13460 Saintes-Maries-de-la-Mer
Tel.: 33 (0) 4.90.97.89.01 – Fax: 33 (0) 4.90.97.80.36
camargue@chateauxhotels.com
Philippe & Laure GENNER – Sven FUHRMANN
19 rooms: 130 € / 300 €
1 suite: 150 € / 300 €
Breakfast: included
Menu(s): 25 € / 85 € - **Carte:** 35 € -
1/2 board: 100 € / 205 €

In an unspoilt area of the Camargue, 2 km from the sea, this hotel offers charm, comfort and a friendly atmosphere. The sunny rooms, decorated in the colors of Provence, overlook the landscape or the private terraces. A rare and enchanting setting perfectly in tune with the food.

hotel annual closing
06/01 > 22/03•01/12 > 20/12
restaurant annual closing
06/01 > 22/03•01/12 > 20/12
equipments
telephone, internet, T.V.
Satellite, minibar, safe
environment
park 3 ha, garden, terrace
200 m², view
leisure, relaxation
heated pool, horse-riding 1 km,
4x4 tour to see herds of wild
horses, natural reserve

Visa • Diners • JCB • MASTER CARD

Road map p. 619

A7, A9, A54 dir.Arles exit 4 Stes-
Maries-de-la-Mer, D570, D38

Garons/Nîmes/Arles: 45 km

Provence-Alpes-Côte-d'Azur

Bruno de Lorgues

Lorgues
www.chateauxhotels.com/bruno | reservation service: 33 (0) 1.40.07.00.20

Campagne Mariette Route des Arcs
83510 Lorgues
Tel.: 33 (0) 4.94.85.93.93 – Fax: 33 (0) 4.94.85.93.99
bruno@chateauxhotels.com
Clément BRUNO

3 rooms: 83,85 € / 129,58 €
1 flat: 205,81 €
Breakfast: 12,2 €
Menu(s): 52 € / 99,09 €

Open all year
hotel weekly closing
mon, sun
15/09 > 15/06
restaurant weekly closing
mon, sun(ev)
15/09 > 15/06
equipments
telephone, T.V., valet parking
environment
garden, terrace
leisure, relaxation
golf course 40 km, horse-riding
5 km, thalassotherapy

Outside of the attractive provençal village of Lorgues this pleasant country house is one of the most popular places in the South of France. In his kitchen with an open heart, Bruno is inciting a following entirely devoted to him. The result is, of course, incomparable! A few delightful rooms.

Visa • Diners • MASTER CARD

Road map p. 619

A8 exit Le Luc/Le Muy

 Nice: 100 km

Chemin de Berne 83510 Lorgues
Tel.: 33 (0) 4.94.60.48.88 – Fax: 33 (0) 4.94.60.48.89
berne@chateauxhotels.com
Christine MONTEIL & Vanessa GRINGET
13 rooms: 168 € / 290 €
2 suites: 328 € / 488 €
Breakfast: 18 €
Menu(s): 16,39 € / 58 € - **1/2 board:** 168 € / 213 €

Here is one of the most beautiful estates of Provençe with its 520 ha of garrigue scrubland and 85 ha of vineyard. All has been designed for the benefit of the wine, from the cellars as far as the table in passing by the restful and spacious rooms. For the lovers of gustative thrills and preserved nature.

hotel annual closing
07/01 > 01/03●04/11 > 26/12
restaurant annual closing
07/01 > 01/03●04/11 > 26/12
equipments
lift, telephone, internet, T.V. Satellite, minibar, safe
environment
park 550 ha, garden, terrace, view, vegetable garden, total calm
leisure, relaxation
heated pool, golf course 25 km, horse-riding 5 km, beauty salon, sauna, fitness, jacuzzi

Visa ● Diners ● JCB ● MasterCard

Road map p. 619
A8 exit Le Muy, dir. Les Arcs-Lorgues

Nice: 100 km

Provence-Alpes-Côte-d'Azur

Route de Cadenet 84160 Lourmarin
Tel.: 33 (0) 4.90.68.11.79 – Fax: 33 (0) 4.90.68.18.60

feniere@chateauxhotels.com
Reine & Guy SAMMUT
6 rooms: 100 € / 138 €
1 suite: 168 €
Breakfast: 13 €
Menu(s): 40 € / 95 € - **Carte:** 68,60 €
1/2 board: 127 € / 161 €

hotel annual closing
17/11 > 14/01
restaurant annual closing
17/11 > 14/01
restaurant weekly closing
mon, tue(lun)
07/02 > 17/11
equipments
telephone, T.V.
environment
park 6 ha, garden, terrace,
view, vegetable garden
leisure, relaxation
tennis 2 km, golf course
15 km, horse-riding 4 km,
mountain bike hire at the hotel

On a hill between Durance and Lubéron, this traditional inn cultivates conviviality with affection. Seven character-filled rooms offer one of the most beautiful views of the region and Reine Sammut tenderly prepares outstanding cuisine from the heart with savour and emotion.

Visa ● Diners ● MASTER CARD

Road map p. 619

Direction Avignon, D943 direction Lourmarin

Marseille-Marignane: 60 km

Avenue Henri Clews
06210 Mandelieu-La Napoule
Tel.: 33 (0) 4.93.49.95.56 – Fax: 33 (0) 4.92.97.69.05
riou@chateauxhotels.com
Anne-Sophie HOUILLON – Famille SUMEIRE

37 rooms: 120 € / 287 €
4 suites: 325 € / 504 €
Breakfast: 15 €
Menu(s): 39 € / 74,7 € - **Carte:** 25 € -
1/2 board: 95 € / 143,5 €

In the Bay of Cannes, on La Napoule harbor, you'll find l'Ermitage du Riou, a charming house elegantly renovated. The rooms all personalized with seaside or golf course view combine antique furniture and engravings with all the modern refinement. The chef will welcome you at the restaurant Le Riou.

Open all year
equipments
telephone, internet, T.V., minibar, safe, baby-sitting
environment
architecture, garden, terrace, view
leisure, relaxation
tennis 1 km, golf course 1 km, horse-riding 3 km, beauty salon, thalassotherapy, sauna, fitness, guided tour of La Napoule château and gardens

Visa ● Diners ● JCB ● Master Card

Road map p. 619

A8 exit 40 Mandelieu la Napoule

Cannes-Mandelieu: 5 km

Val Baussenc

Maussane-les-Alpilles

www.chateauxhotels.com/valbaussenc | reservation service: 33 (0) 1.40.07.00.20

122, av. de la vallée des Baux
13520 Maussane-les-Alpilles
Tel.: 33 (0) 4.90.54.38.90 – Fax: 33 (0) 4.90.54.33.36
valbaussenc@chateauxhotels.com
Isabelle & Philippe AUZIAS
21 rooms: 89 € / 106 €
1 flat: 197 € / 231 €
Breakfast: 11 €
Menu(s): 28 € / 35 € - **1/2 board:** 69 € / 81 €

hotel annual closing
01/01 > 01/03●15/11 > 16/12
restaurant annual closing
01/01 > 01/03●15/11 > 01/03
equipments
telephone, T.V. Satellite,
minibar
environment
garden, terrace 60 m², view,
total calm
leisure, relaxation
tennis 0.5 km, golf course
7 km, horse-riding 1 km

In the heart of Provence, quiet, typical and sunny rooms, offering real Provençal harmony and modern comfort: the brightness of Provençal cottons stand out against the pale walls and enhance the Baux stone. You'll enjoy the local cuisine in the restaurant beside the garden and the swimming pool.

Visa ● Diners ● MASTER CARD

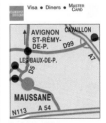

Road map p. 619
A7 exit Salon or Cavaillon

Nîmes: 35 km

Le Fort 84560 Ménerbes

Tel.: 33 (0) 4.90.72.25.61 – Fax: 33 (0) 4.90.72.36.55
roysoleil@chateauxhotels.com
Josyane DERINE

18 rooms: 119 € / 258 €
1 flat: 320 €
Breakfast: 14,5 €
Menu(s): 36,5 € / 72 € - **Carte:** 53 € -
1/2 board: 128 € / 197 €

In the heart of the Luberon region, amidst vines and cherry trees, this authentic 17th c. Provençal manor features pleasant comfortable rooms, many with their own patio or private garden. Our chef invites you to share the love of fine country cooking displayed in his inventive and plentiful dishes.

Visa • MASTER CARD

Road map p. 619

A7 exit Avignon, N100 dir. Apt., D 103
South
TGV train from Paris 2h30

Avignon: 28 km

restaurant annual closing
30/10 > 15/03

equipments
telephone, internet, T.V.
Satellite, minibar, safe,
baby-sitting

environment
architecture 17°, park 3 ha,
garden, terrace 350 m², view,
total calm

leisure, relaxation
tennis 8 km, golf course
10 km, horse-riding 8 km, tour
of Châteauneuf-du-Pape
estates and wine-tasting

Provence-Alpes-Côte-d'Azur

Château de Meyrargues

Meyrargues
www.chateauxhotels.com/meyrargues | reservation service: 33 (0) 1.40.07.00.20

Traverse Saint-Pierre 13650 Meyrargues
Tel.: 33 (0) 4.42.63.49.90 – Fax: 33 (0) 4.42.63.49.92
meyrargues@chateauxhotels.com
Maurice BINET
8 rooms: 114 € / 208 €
3 suites: 305 €
Breakfast: 15,25 €
Menu(s): 64 € - **1/2 board:** 99 € / 146 €

hotel annual closing
01/11 > 30/11

restaurant annual closing
14/01 > 14/03●01/11 > 13/12

equipments
lift, telephone, T.V.
Satellite/Canal+, minibar,
baby-sitting

environment
architecture 10ᵉ, park 6 ha,
terrace 400 m², view

leisure, relaxation
horse-riding, thermal baths,
jacuzzi

The château of which the earliest construction dates to the 10th century has preserved all of the dignity of its long history. Refined rooms and cuisine of great tradition symbolise a prestigious sojourn a short distance from Aix en Provence. A stately stone stairway and medieval entranceway.

Visa ● Diners ● JCB ● MasterCard

Road map p. 619

A7 exit Senas, N7 then N561 untill
Charleval-Meyrargues

Provence-Alpes-Côte-d'Azur |

 Marignane: 40 km

Boulevard Clément Rebuffel 06250 Mougins
Tel.: 33 (0) 4.92.28.43.43 – Fax: 33 (0) 4.92.28.43.40
candille@chateauxhotels.com
Michaël HOLLAND

39 rooms: 260 € / 455 €
1 suite: 625 € / 745 €
Breakfast: 23 €
Menu(s): 38 € / 73 € - **Carte:** 83 €

An exceptionally individual hotel, offering a sense of informal luxury, exclusive tranquillity and classic elegance. Situated within 4 ha of landscaped Provencal parkland, Le Mas Candille is surrounded by cypress trees and old olive groves, with mesmerising views across the valley to the Pre-Alps.

Open all year

equipments
telephone, internet, T.V. Satellite/Canal+, minibar, safe, valet parking

environment
architecture 18e, park 4 ha, garden, terrace 100 m², view, vegetable garden, total calm

leisure, relaxation
balneo, fitness, jacuzzi, 2 heated swimming-pool, pitch and put, 3 greens

Visa ● Diners ● JCB ● MASTER CARD

Road map p. 619

A8 dir.Grasse exit 42, N85, first exit, dir. Mougins, D3

Nice: 25 km

| Provence-Alpes-Côte-d'Azur

Les Muscadins

Mougins

www.chateauxhotels.com/muscadins | reservation service: 33 (0) 1.40.07.00.20

18, bd Georges Courteline 06250 Mougins
Tel.: 33 (0) 4.92.28.28.28 – Fax: 33 (0) 4.92.92.88.23

muscadins@chateauxhotels.com
Christophe LEROY – Edward W. BIANCHINI

7 rooms: 160 € / 335 €
4 suites: 290 € / 535 €
Breakfast: 20 €
Menu(s): 29 € / 58 € - **Carte:** 25 €
1/2 board: 138 € / 300,5 €

Open all year
equipments
telephone, internet, T.V.
Satellite, minibar, safe
environment
architecture 19ᵉ, furniture 19ᵉ,
terrace 100 m², view
leisure, relaxation
tennis 3 km, golf course 2 km,
horse-riding 2 km,
thalassotherapy, sauna,
hammam, fitness 2 km

A breathtaking view of Cannes and the Lérins islands - against this wonderful movie backdrop every detail has been thoughtfully arranged. Elegant guestrooms, magnificent surroundings. The food served in the exquisite dining-groom bears the stamp of Christophe Leroy. This is it - pure heaven.

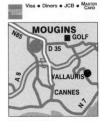

Visa ● Diners ● JCB ● MASTER CARD

Road map p. 619
A8 exit 42 Cannes-Mougins

Nice - Côte d'Azur: 30 km

Chemin de Quinson
04360 Moustiers-Sainte-Marie
Tel.: 33 (0) 4.92.70.47.47 – Fax: 33 (0) 4.92.70.47.48
moustiers@chateauxhotels.com
Dominique POTIER
11 rooms: 130 € / 260 €
1 suite: 235 € / 280 €
Breakfast: 13 €
Menu(s): 37 € / 49 €

Famous chef Alain Ducasse is the genius behind the magnificent restoration of this 17th century country house, pleasantly surrounded by gardens and fields of lavender and olive trees. The fine cooking takes on a southern accent: vegetables, herbs and fruit come fresh from the garden.

Open all year
restaurant weekly closing
wen, thi
15/12 > 01/03
equipments
telephone, internet, T.V.
Satellite/Canal+, minibar, safe
environment
architecture 17e, furniture 18e, park 4 ha, garden, terrace 100 m², view, vegetable garden, total calm
leisure, relaxation
heated pool, tennis 0.5 km, horse-riding 10 km, jacuzzi, paragliding, canyoning, hiking

Visa ● Diners ● MASTER CARD

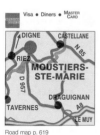

Road map p. 619

from Nice, A8 exit n° 36. from Marseille, A51 exit n° 17.

 Marseille: 118 km

| Provence-Alpes-Côte-d'Azur

Domaine de Châteauneuf

Nans-les-Pins

www.chateauxhotels.com/chateauneuf | reservation service: 33 (0) 1.40.07.00.20

N560 83860 Nans-les-Pins
Tel.: 33 (0) 4.94.78.90.06 – Fax: 33 (0) 4.94.78.63.30
chateauneuf@chateauxhotels.com
Georges CREMILLEUX & Alain BATTEUX
26 rooms: 108 € / 274 €
4 suites: 350 € / 474 €
Breakfast: 15 €
Menu(s): 37 € / 68 € - **Carte:** 45 €
1/2 board: 108 € / 191 €

hotel annual closing
03/01 > 02/03●04/11 > 21/12
restaurant annual closing
03/01 > 02/03●04/11 > 21/12
restaurant weekly closing
mon(lun), tue(lun), wen(lun),
thi(lun), fri(lun)
02/03 > 16/06
mon(lun), tue(lun), wen(lun),
thi(lun), fri(lun)
16/09 > 03/11

equipments
telephone, internet, T.V.
Satellite/Canal+, minibar, safe,
baby-sitting, valet parking

environment
architecture 18e, park 4 ha,
garden, terrace 150 m², view,
total calm

leisure, relaxation
horse-riding 2 km, drawing
lessons

*This 18th century fortified
dwelling was beautifully restored in 2000 in a spirit of
subdued elegance. Shaded
by magnificent centenary
trees, it remains a place for
rest, romantic strolls, memorable gourmet meals with
friends, hill-walking and, not to
forgotten, playing golf.*

Visa ● Diners ● MASTER CARD

Road map p. 619
A8 exit Saint Maximin, N560

✈ Marseille: 60 km

2, place Auguste Arnulf 06440 Peillon-Village
Tel.: 33 (0) 4.93.79.91.17 – Fax: 33 (0) 4.93.79.99.36
madone@chateauxhotels.com
Famille MILLO

14 rooms: 89 € / 151 €
3 suites: 190 € / 259 €
Breakfast: 11 €
Menu(s): 35 € / 58 € - **Carte:** 46 €

Between sea and sky, in the unspoint hinterland of Nice, this authentic and elegant house blends into a landscape of exuberant nature teeming with scents of the wild. The tasteful decor of the rooms and the exquisitely flavored dishes make for an unforgettable stay.

hotel annual closing
07/01 > 31/01 ● 20/10 > 20/12
restaurant annual closing
07/01 > 31/01 ● 20/10 > 20/12
equipments
telephone, internet, safe
environment
park 5 ha, garden, terrace, view, vegetable garden, total calm
leisure, relaxation
golf course 25 km, sea 17 km

Visa ● MASTER CARD

Road map p. 619

A8 exit 55 "Nice" East, D2204, D21, D121

Nice - Côte d'Azur: 24 km

Château Eza
Nice I Eze Village
www.chateauxhotels.com/eza I reservation service: 33 (0) 1.40.07.00.20

Rue de la Pise 06360 Eze Village
Tel.: 33 (0) 4.93.41.12.24 – Fax: 33 (0) 4.93.41.16.64
eza@chateauxhotels.com
Jesper JERRIK

7 rooms: 350 € / 600 €
3 suites: 600 € / 700 €
Menu(s): 45 € / 85 € - **Carte:** 90 €

hotel annual closing
01/11 > 01/04
restaurant annual closing
01/11 > 25/12
restaurant weekly closing
tue, wen
01/01 > 01/04
equipments
telephone, T.V. Satellite, safe,
valet parking
environment
architecture 15ᵉ, terrace
200 m², view, total calm
leisure, relaxation
tennis 2 km, golf course 5 km

Located above the Mediterranee, majestically overlooking the Côte d'Azur, the Château Eza is a cluster of small houses of exceptional character. The enchanting view from the restaurant is in perfect harmony with the superb gourmet cuisine. Such an abundance of pleasure assures an unforgettable stay.

Visa ● Diners ● JCB ● ᴹᴬˢᵀᴱᴿ CARD

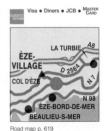

Road map p. 619

A8: from Nice, exit 57 - from Italy, exit 58. Then dir. Eze Village

 Nice - Côte d'Azur: 18 km

Monaco | La Turbie

www.chateauxhotels.com/jerome | reservation service: 33 (0) 1.40.07.00.20

20, rue Comte de Cessole 06320 La Turbie
Tel.: 33 (0) 4.92.41.51.51 – Fax: 33 (0) 4.92.41.51.50
jerome@chateauxhotels.com
Bruno CIRINO

4 rooms: 89 €
1 suite: 136 €
Breakfast: 12,50 €
Menu(s): 29 € / 45 € - **Carte:** 64,03 €

This old Provençal stone house in the medieval village of Turbie, within 5 km of Monaco, is an oasis of peace: Pergola, terrace, frescoes, and XVIIIth century furnishings pleasantly decorate the rooms and reception halls. The excellent cuisine is signed by Bruno Cirino.

Open all year
restaurant weekly closing
mon, tue
01/01 > 30/06
mon, tue
01/09 > 31/12
equipments
telephone, T.V., minibar
environment
architecture 13ᵉ, furniture 18ᵉ, terrace
leisure, relaxation
tennis 1 km, golf course 3 km

Visa ● MASTER CARD

Road map p. 619

A8 exit La Turbie, dir. Monaco, "Moyenne corniche"

Nice - Côte d'Azur: 15 km

L'Univers de Christian Plumail

Nice

www.chateauxhotels.com/plumail | reservation service: 33 (0) 1.40.07.00.20

54, boulevard Jean Jaurès 06300 Nice
Tel.: 33 (0) 4.93.62.32.22 – Fax: 33 (0) 4.93.62.55.69
plumail@chateauxhotels.com
Christian PLUMAIL
Menu(s): 16,77 € / 32,02 € - **Carte:** 38,11 €

Open all year

Christian Plumail is a cook who glorifies Southern gastronomy. The imagination does not give way with him, except before the truth of the product and the etherealness of the compositions. One must taste among others, his mullet and asparagus to measure at which point the talent transcends the technique.

Visa ● Diners ● MASTER CARD

Road map p. 619

50 m of the "place Masséna"

Nice - Côte d'Azur

17, avenue E. Bieckert 06000 Nice
Tel.: 33 (0) 4.93.62.19.11 – Fax: 33 (0) 4.93.62.53.60
petitpalais@chateauxhotels.com
Didier LENZI
25 rooms: 59,46 € / 123,48 €

Excellent comfort in the former residence of Sacha Guitry. Chagall and Matisse museums nearby, along with Cimiez monastery. Roman arena and Acropolis. Belle Epoque architecture, unique furnishings, floral terraces ans warm welcome. Rooms overlooking sea and Baie des Anges. Sea views.

Open all year

equipments
lift, telephone, T.V., safe, baby-sitting

environment
architecture 19^e, terrace 150 m^2, view, total calm

leisure, relaxation
tennis 2 km, golf course 20 km, horse-riding 10 km

Visa ● Diners ● JCB ● MASTER CARD

NICE

R. PASTORELLI	AV. E. BIECKST
DE GIOFFREDO	BD. CARABACEL
AV. F. FAURE	PALAIS DES CONGRÈS
BD. RISSO	ACROPOLIS

Road map p. 619

A8 exit 50 Nice, dir. Promenade des Anglais

Nice - Côte d'Azur: 6 km

Château de la Bégude
Opio
www.chateauxhotels.com/begude | reservation service: 33 (0) 1.40.07.00.20

Route de Roquefort les Pins 06650 Opio
Tel.: 33 (0) 4.93.12.37.00 – Fax: 33 (0) 4.93.12.37.13
begude@chateauxhotels.com
Sylvain JOANNARD – Andréa GANDET
31 rooms: 75 € / 142 €
2 suites: 183 € / 244 €
Breakfast: 12,2 €
Menu(s): 22,11 € / 27,44 € - **Carte:** 32,01 €
1/2 board: 72 € / 106 €

hotel annual closing
26/11 > 26/12
restaurant weekly closing
wen(ev)
15/10 > 31/03
equipments
telephone, internet, T.V.
Satellite, minibar, safe,
baby-sitting
environment
architecture 17ᵉ, park 10 ha,
garden, terrace 140 m², view,
total calm
leisure, relaxation
horse-riding 10 km

Located at Opio Valbonne, one of the oldest golf courses on the Côte d'Azur, a stately residence offering space, relaxation and tranquillity. At the restaurant overlooking Number 9 Hole, enjoy good food with colorful Provençal accents. Conferences and banquets for up to 150 guests.

Visa • MasterCard

Road map p. 619

A8 exit Villeneuve-Loubet D204 dir.
Valbonne

Nice - Côte d'Azur: 20 km

Avenue Gustave Etienne 83350 Ramatuelle
Tel.: 33 (0) 4.98.12.94.20 – Fax: 33 (0) 4.98.12.94.21
baou@chateauxhotels.com
Tancrède BARALE
39 rooms: 120 € / 280 €
1 flat: 400 € / 620 € - **2 suites:** 250 € / 340 €
Breakfast: 16 €
Menu(s): 37 € / 60 € - **Carte:** 50 € -
1/2 board: 110 € / 220 €

At the foot of the old village of Ramatuelle, the charm and comfort of a Provençal residence. Each room with terrace or balcony, and a commanding view of the sea. A few minutes from Saint-Tropez. Overlooking the Bay of Pamplona. Initiation into regional flavours at the Provençal restaurant.

hotel annual closing
01/01 > 22/03•20/10 > 31/03
restaurant annual closing
01/01 > 22/03•20/10 > 31/03
equipments
lift, telephone, internet, T.V. Satellite, minibar, safe, baby-sitting
environment
garden, terrace 120 m^2, view
leisure, relaxation
heated pool, tennis 0.1 km, golf course 15 km, horse-riding 6 km

Visa • Diners • MASTER CARD

Road map p. 619

A8 exit Le Muy/St Tropez, N98 dir. Saint-Tropez, D61 Ramatuelle

 Toulon-Hyères: 50 km

Provence-Alpes-Côte-d'Azur

La Ferme d'Augustin

Saint-Tropez I Ramatuelle
www.chateauxhotels.com/augustin | reservation service: 33 (0) 1.40.07.00.20

Plage de Tahiti St-Tropez 83350 Ramatuelle
Tel.: 33 (0) 4.94.55.97.00 – Fax: 33 (0) 4.94.97.40.30
augustin@chateauxhotels.com
Jacqueline VALLET
24 rooms: 95 € / 230 €
22 suites: 260 € / 450 €
Breakfast: 12 €

hotel annual closing
20/10 > 20/03
equipments
lift, telephone, internet, T.V., minibar, safe, baby-sitting
environment
garden, terrace, view, vegetable garden
leisure, relaxation
heated pool, tennis 0.2 km, golf course 10 km, horse-riding 8 km, balneo, hammam, solarium, jacuzzi

Only 5 minutes outside Saint-Tropez, near "Tahiti" beach, the rooms of the Ferme all overlook the sea or the countryside. Garde vegetables, fruit from the orchard and wines from our vineyard matured in our own cellar. What's more, breakfast served until noon! Enchanting terrace and pool.

Visa • MASTER CARD

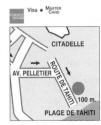

Road map p. 619

St-Tropez city centre, dir. "plage Tahiti"

Toulon: 40 km

www.chateauxhotels.com/lesmoulins | reservation service: 33 (0) 1.40.07.00.20

route des Plages Les Moulins
83350 Ramatuelle
Tel.: 33 (0) 4.94.97.17.22 – Fax: 33 (0) 4.94.97.72.70
lesmoulins@chateauxhotels.com
Christophe LEROY
5 rooms: 145 € / 222 €
Breakfast: 15 €
Menu(s): 50 € / 89 € - **1/2 board:** 126 € / 164 €

Among the vineyards of Ramatuelle, all of the gentleness of life awaits you in this peaceful character-filled house where time flows by in the nonchalant rhythm of the South of France. The beautifully decorated rooms in provençal cretonne couple with the succulent cuisine for a moment of magic.

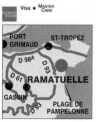

Visa ● MASTER CARD

PORT GRIMAUD — ST-TROPEZ
D 98ᴬ
D 93
D 61
RAMATUELLE
GASSIN
D 93
PLAGE DE PAMPELONNE

Road map p. 619

A8 exit Draguignan/St-Tropez, D98, D93, dir. Ramatuelle

hotel annual closing
15/11 > 15/03

restaurant annual closing
15/11 > 01/05

restaurant weekly closing
mon(lun), tue(lun), wen(lun), thi(lun), fri(lun), sat(lun), sun(lun)
01/06 > 30/09
mon(lun), tue(lun), wen, thi(lun), fri(lun), sat(lun), sun(lun)
15/03 > 31/05

equipments
telephone, internet, T.V. Satellite, minibar, safe, valet parking

environment
architecture 18ᵉ, garden, terrace 200 m², vegetable garden

leisure, relaxation
tennis 1 km, golf course 15 km, horse-riding 1 km

Nice: 115 km

Monté-Carlo Beach Hôtel

Roquebrune-Cap-Martin

www.chateauxhotels.com/beach | reservation service: 33 (0) 1.40.07.00.20

avenue Princesse Grace
06190 Roquebrune-Cap-Martin
Tel.: 33 (0) 4.93.28.66.66 – Fax: 33 (0) 4.93.78.14.18
beach@chateauxhotels.com
Danièle SIRI

41 rooms: 250 € / 460 €
1 flat: 950 € / 1495 € - **4 suites:** 375 € / 1035 €
Breakfast: 25 €
Menu(s): 50 € - **Carte:** 60 €

hotel annual closing
25/11 > 26/02

equipments
lift, telephone, internet, T.V.
Canal+, minibar, safe,
baby-sitting

environment
architecture, terrace 100 m²,
view, total calm

leisure, relaxation
heated pool, tennis 0.3 km,
golf course 15 km, jacuzzi,
SPA of Monté-Carlo

This splendid 1930's seaside house is a rendez-vous of elegance and comfort. Rooms with private loggias, looking out over the ocean waves, offer all the charm of the dolce vita. Gourmet food. Heated, Olympic-size sea-water pool. Luxury, tranquillity and lazy mornings!

Visa ● Diners ● MASTER CARD

Road map p. 619
A8 exit 56 Monaco

 Nice - Côte d'Azur: 25 km

Route de la colle 1350
06570 Saint-Paul-de-Vence
Tel.: 33 (0) 4.93.32.50.30 – Fax: 33 (0) 4.93.32.50.59
grandebastide@chateauxhotels.com
Johner HEINZ
12 rooms: 130 € / 206 €
2 suites: 183 € / 305 €
Breakfast: 15 €

An 18th century fortified house restored with loving care by amateurs of Saint-Paul-de-Vence, commanding an unrivalled view of the village and the sea on the horizon. Individually decorated rooms and suites display the colours of Provence. Bathrooms with jacuzzi and breakfast on the terrace.

hotel annual closing
25/11 > 20/12

equipments
telephone, internet, T.V. Satellite, minibar, safe, baby-sitting

environment
architecture 19ᵉ, garden, terrace 40 m², view

leisure, relaxation
heated pool, tennis 1 km, golf course 6 km, horse-riding 2 km

Visa • Diners • MASTER CARD

Road map p. 619

A8 exit Cagnes-sur-Mer dir. La Colle/ Loup and Saint-Paul

Nice: 14 km

Hôtel du Golf de Valescure

Saint-Raphaël

www.chateauxhotels.com/valescure | reservation service: 33 (0) 1.40.07.00.20

Avenue Paul L'hermite 83700 Saint-Raphaël
Tel.: 33 (0) 4.94.52.85.00 – Fax: 33 (0) 4.94.82.41.88

valescure@chateauxhotels.com
M. & Mme. PERCEPIED
40 rooms: 82 € / 154 €
Menu(s): 18 € / 33 € - **Carte:** 38 € -
1/2 board: 83 € / 100 €

hotel annual closing
06/01 > 31/01 • 15/11 > 21/12
restaurant annual closing
06/01 > 31/01 • 15/11 > 21/12
equipments
lift, telephone, T.V.
Satellite/Canal+, minibar, safe
environment
park 5 ha, garden, terrace,
view
leisure, relaxation
horse-riding 5 km

On the tee, hidden in its garden, the Golf Hotel welcomes you amidst a pinewood forest. Inside the property, you can enjoy the swimming-pool, the tennis courts and the open air archery. You will also enjoy charming and comfortables rooms, all with air-conditioned and private terrace.

Visa • Diners • MASTER CARD

Road map p. 619

A8 exit n° 38 ST-Raphaël, D37 dir.
Agay by Valescure

Nice - Côte d'Azur: 60 km

La Maurette 83520 Roquebrune-sur-Argens
Tel.: 33 (0) 4.98.11.43.53 – Fax: 33 (0) 4.98.11.43.52
maurette@chateauxhotels.com
Dr Christine SCHENKELBERG & Wolfgang BLUMBERG
11 rooms: 85 € / 120 €
Breakfast: 11 €

A house perched on its own private hillside surrounded by a forest of parasol pines and oaks, where nice rooms open wide onto shaded terraces; some of them have kitchenettes. Your only care is to indulge in the peace and serenity. The village and its restaurants are 2 km away.

hotel annual closing
01/11 > 28/02

equipments
telephone

environment
park, garden, terrace 500 m^2, view, total calm

leisure, relaxation
tennis 2 km, golf course 5 km, horse-riding 5 km, water ski 2 km

Visa • MASTER CARD

Road map p. 619

A8 exit Puget sur Argens or Le Muy, N7, D7, St-Tropez: 35 km

 Nice: 75 km

Le San Pédro
Saint-Raphaël
www.chateauxhotels.com/sanpedro | reservation service: 33 (0) 1.40.07.00.20

Av.du Colonel-Brooke 83700 Saint-Raphaël
Tel.: 33 (0) 4.94.19.90.20 – Fax: 33 (0) 4.94.19.90.21
sanpedro@chateauxhotels.com
Alain DONAT
27 rooms: 60 € / 135 €
1 flat: 121 € / 275 €
Breakfast: 12 €
Menu(s): 27,5 € / 45 € - **Carte:** 38 €
1/2 board: 64,5 € / 94,5 €

hotel annual closing
11/11 > 30/11
restaurant annual closing
11/11 > 30/11
equipments
lift, telephone, internet, T.V.
Satellite, minibar, safe,
baby-sitting
environment
garden, terrace 100 m^2,
vegetable garden, total calm
leisure, relaxation
tennis 0.8 km, golf course
0.8 km, horse-riding 3 km,
thalassotherapy, sauna,
solarium, fitness, jacuzzi,
nature and environment walk

A luxurious and refined country house (French bastide): medieval lounge, comfortable English bar. The greens of the golf course offer a pleasant view and calm surroundings. Comfortable rooms. 2 km far from the sea. Swimming-pool with jacuzzi and sauna.

Visa ● Diners ● JCB ● MASTER CARD

Road map p. 619

A8 exit Fréjus-St-raphaël dir. St-Raphaël then Valescure, N7 then D37 dir.Valescure/Agay

 Nice: 60 km

Rte D31 13210 Saint-Rémy-de-Provence
Tel.: 33 (0) 4.90.92.03.33 – Fax: 33 (0) 4.90.92.45.17
alpilles@chateauxhotels.com
Françoise BON & Catherine ROLLIN
15 rooms: 151 € / 214 €
1 flat: 252 € / 335 € - **4 suites:** 235 € / 267 €
Breakfast: 15,4 €
Menu(s): 33,6 € - **Carte:** 39,25 €

19th century manor house in a 4-acre park. A dream atmosphere, small gastronomic restaurant for hotel residents, grill in summer beside the swimming pool. Spacious rooms decorated with period furniture. Inclusive rates for cooking classes, gastronomic or sporting walks, cultural events.

hotel annual closing
01/01 > 15/02•15/11 > 27/12
restaurant weekly closing
wen(ev)
equipments
lift, telephone, internet, T.V. Canal+, minibar, safe, baby-sitting
environment
architecture 19ᵉ, park 4 ha, garden, terrace, total calm
leisure, relaxation
golf course 10 km, horse-riding 2 km, sauna, solarium

Visa ● Diners ● MASTER CARD

Road map p. 619

A7 exit Cavaillon, D99 dir. St-Rémy, D31 dir. Tarascon

Avignon: 17 km

Domaine de Valmouriane
Saint-Rémy-de-Provence
www.chateauxhotels.com/valmouriane | reservation service: 33 (0) 1.40.07.00.20

Petite route des Baux
13210 Saint-Rémy-de-Provence
Tel.: 33 (0) 4.90.92.44.62 – Fax: 33 (0) 4.90.92.37.32
valmouriane@chateauxhotels.com
Martina & Philippe CAPEL

10 rooms: 125 € / 305 €
1 suite: 230 € / 335 €
Breakfast: 15 €
Menu(s): 37 € / 65 € - **Carte:** 48 €
1/2 board: 117,5 € / 185 €

restaurant annual closing
17/11 > 03/12
restaurant weekly closing
mon(lun), tue(lun)
01/05 > 30/09
mon, tue(lun), sun(ev)
04/12 > 30/04
equipments
lift, telephone, minibar, safe
environment
architecture 18°, furniture 18°,
park 6 ha, garden, terrace,
view, total calm
leisure, relaxation
golf course 3 km, horse-riding
3 km, jacuzzi

Let our XVIIIth century Provençale mas become the heart of your stay in the beautiful region of Saint-Rémy-de-Provence. Traditional and flavoured food, olive trees, flowers, pine forest make a wonderful background for our swimming-pool with jacuzzi, tennis court and comfortable rooms.

Visa ● Diners ● MASTER CARD

MAILLANE
ST-RÉMY-DE-PROVENCE
D 571
D 27
D99
D 5
D 99
ARLES
MARSEILLE
LES BAUX-DE-PROVENCE

Road map p. 619

A7 exit Cavaillon, D99 and D27 dir.
Les Baux de Provence

 Marseille: 75 km

Chemin Canto Cigalo
13210 Saint-Rémy-de-Provence
Tel.: 33 (0) 4.90.92.04.40 – Fax: 33 (0) 4.90.92.44.01
valrugues@chateauxhotels.com
Françoise & Jean-Michel GALLON

38 rooms: 135 € / 270 €
10 flats: 460 € / 510 € - **5 suites:** 410 € / 880 €
Breakfast: 17 €
Menu(s): 30 € / 80 € - **Carte:** 83 € -
1/2 board: 149,5 € / 217 €

A temple of Provençal paradise and one of the finest restaurants in the Alpilles. Driving range, putting green, sauna, jacuzzi, billiards, children's garden, etc. Baux de Provence 5 minutes away, and within a 30 minutes radius: Arles, Roman Nîmes, Saintes-Maries de la Mer, Avignon, the Luberon.

hotel annual closing
27/01 > 23/02
restaurant annual closing
27/01 > 23/02
equipments
lift, telephone, internet, T.V. Satellite/Canal+, minibar, safe, baby-sitting, valet parking
environment
architecture, garden, terrace, view, total calm
leisure, relaxation
golf course 5 km, horse-riding 1 km, sauna, hammam, jacuzzi

Visa ● Diners ● JCB ● Master Card

Road map p. 619

A7 exit Cavaillon, D99 dir. St-Rémy de Provence/Tarascon

Avignon: 18 km

Château de Valmer

Saint-Tropez I La Croix-Valmer

www.chateauxhotels.com/valmer | reservation service: 33 (0) 1.40.07.00.20

Gigaro 83420 La Croix-Valmer
Tel.: 33 (0) 4.94.79.60.10 – Fax: 33 (0) 4.94.54.22.68
valmer@chateauxhotels.com
Graziella ROCCHIETTA
35 rooms: 162 € / 315 €
6 flats: 231 € / 472 € - **1 suite:** 338 € / 375 €
Breakfast: 16 €
Menu(s): 48 € - **Carte:** 48 €

hotel annual closing
15/10 > 30/04
restaurant annual closing
15/10 > 30/04
restaurant weekly closing
tue
01/06 > 15/09
tue
31/03 > 31/05
equipments
lift, telephone, internet, T.V.
Satellite, safe, baby-sitting
environment
architecture 19e, park 5 ha,
garden, terrace 40 m², view,
vegetable garden, total calm
leisure, relaxation
heated pool, golf course
15 km, horse-riding 10 km,
solarium, tennis, water sports,
kayak, pedal-boats,
windsurfing, private beach

The XIXth century Château de Valmer, set in a palm-tree filled park featuring a magnificent solarium-pool, has conserved all the charm of its origins. In addition to the lush botanical surroundings, a private beach awaits guests. The varied cooking conjures up fond memories or regional cooking

Visa ● Diners ● MASTER CARD

Road map p. 619

A8 exit Saint-Tropez/Le Muy then
N98 then N559 dir. La Croix-Valmer

Provence-Alpes-Côte-d'Azur |

Toulon-Hyères: 50 km

Quartier Bertaud 83580 Gassin
Tel.: 33 (0) 4.94.56.71.71 – Fax: 33 (0) 4.94.56.71.56
chastelas@chateauxhotels.com
Laurent JOUBERT
14 rooms: 99 € / 350 €
5 suites: 215 € / 735 €
Breakfast: 15 €
Menu(s): 26 € / 40 €

An 18th c. country house standing on 7 - acres of grounds planted with cork oaks and mimosas, redolent with the scent of Provence. There is a legendary feel to these serene old stone walls, where the guestrooms stretch lazily between the patios, two swimming pools and the garden.

Open all year
equipments
lift, telephone, internet, T.V. Satellite, minibar, safe
environment
architecture 18e, park 3 ha, garden, terrace 60 m², total calm
leisure, relaxation
golf course 10 km, jacuzzi, 2 tennis courts and 2 swimming-pool

Visa ● Diners ● MASTER CARD

Road map p. 619

from Port-Grimaud, follow St-Tropez - from St-Tropez, dir. Port-Grimaud

 Toulon-Hyères: 45 km

La Belle Aurore

Sainte-Maxime

www.chateauxhotels.com/belleaurore | reservation service: 33 (0) 1.40.07.00.20

5, bd Jean-Moulin 83120 Sainte-Maxime
Tel.: 33 (0) 4.94.96.02.45 – Fax: 33 (0) 4.94.96.63.87

belleaurore@chateauxhotels.com
Charles PITOLLET & Christophe ROUSTAN

16 rooms: 130 € / 314 €
1 suite: 350 € / 550 €
Breakfast: 15 €
Menu(s): 35 € / 49 € - **Carte:** 26,68 €
1/2 board: 115 € / 207 €

hotel annual closing
01/01 > 23/03 • 14/10 > 20/03
restaurant annual closing
01/01 > 23/03 • 14/10 > 20/03
restaurant weekly closing
wen
23/03 > 31/05
equipments
telephone, T.V. Satellite,
minibar, safe, baby-sitting
environment
terrace, view, total calm
leisure, relaxation
tennis 1 km, golf course 3 km,
horse-riding 5 km

Right on the seashore, 5 minutes from the centre of Sainte-Maxime, a hostelry with real Provençal charm. Guest rooms with terrace facing out to the sea, private beach. Gourmet restaurant overlooking the gulf of St Tropez, beach restaurant in summer, southern cuisine and seafood - here's to the holidays!

Visa • Diners • MASTER CARD

Road map p. 619

A8 exit Puget-sur-Argent or Le Muy,
N98 dir. St-Tropez

Provence-Alpes-Côte-d'Azur |

Hyères: 60 km

2, bd des Romarins 83120 Sainte-Maxime
Tel.: 33 (0) 4.94.96.17.75 – Fax: 33 (0) 4.94.96.52.40
croisette@chateauxhotels.com
Michèle LEANDRI
18 rooms: 57 € / 160 €
1 suite: 171 € / 279 €
Breakfast: 10 €

Facing the Gulf of Saint-Tropez, a small charming hotel just a few steps from the sea and 5 minutes from the town centre. 17 rooms decorated in the charming, colourful style of the South, some with private balconies providing a sea or a garden view. Shaded, tranquil terrace for lunch.

hotel annual closing
01/11 > 15/03

equipments
lift, telephone, internet, T.V. Satellite, minibar, safe

environment
architecture 19e, garden, terrace 40 m^2, view, total calm

leisure, relaxation
tennis 1 km, golf course 1.5 km, horse-riding 2 km, beauty salon, thalassotherapy, balneo, thermal baths, sauna, hammam, solarium, fitness, jacuzzi

Visa ● MASTER CARD

Road map p. 619

A8 exit 36 Le Muy - N98 dir. St-Tropez and Ste-Maxime

Toulon: 60 km

Provence-Alpes-Côte-d'Azur

Le Moulin de Vernègues

Aix-en-Provence **I** Mallemort

www.chateauxhotels.com/vernegue | reservation service: 33 (0) 1.40.07.00.20

Domaine et Golf de Pont-Royal
13370 Mallemort
Tel.: 33 (0) 4.90.59.12.00 – Fax: 33 (0) 4.90.59.15.90
vernegue@chateauxhotels.com
Olivier GERARD

36 rooms: 105 € / 185 €
2 suites: 185 €
Breakfast: 10 €
Menu(s): 29 € / 50 € - **Carte:** 30 €
1/2 board: 80 € / 120 €

hotel annual closing
10/02 > 03/03
restaurant annual closing
10/02 > 03/03
equipments
telephone, internet, T.V.
Satellite, safe, baby-sitting
environment
architecture 13ᵉ, park 7 ha,
terrace 150 m², view
leisure, relaxation
heated pool, horse-riding

Near the Gulf of Pont Royal in Provence, guests appreciate the warm atmosphere of country charm at the Moulin de Vernègues, an authentic 15th century house where the 36 rooms offer tasteful comfort. Enjoy a magnificent view of the park while you savour traditional dishes with Provençal accents.

Visa ● MASTER CARD

Road map p. 619

From Paris: A7 exit Senas, N7 dir.Aix-en-Provence -From Nice: A8 exit Aix West, N7 dir. Avignon

Marignane-Marseille: 50 km

Provence-Alpes-Côte-d'Azur |

Route de Fontvieille 13150 Tarascon

Tel.: 33 (0) 4.90.91.34.89 – Fax: 33 (0) 4.90.43.53.29

roches@chateauxhotels.com

Stéphane BALDACCIONI

37 rooms: 58 € / 130 €
1 suite: 137 €
Breakfast: 10 €
Menu(s): 15 € / 32 € - **1/2 board:** 57,50 € / 93 €

A charming hotel at the western end of the Alpilles, set in a 32 acre property. The restaurant nearly the large swimming pool offering attractive menus which highlight the flavors of Provence. A perfect place to explore various places of interest in Provence. Closed car park (access by TGV Méditerranée).

hotel annual closing
31/10 > 15/03
restaurant annual closing
20/12 > 20/01
equipments
telephone, internet, T.V.
Satellite, safe
environment
furniture contemporain, park
13 ha, garden, terrace 80 m^2,
total calm
leisure, relaxation
golf course 15 km, horse-riding
7 km

Visa ● Diners ● MASTER CARD

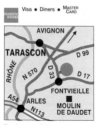

Road map p. 619

A7 exit Avignon North, dir. Arles, D33
dir. Fontvieille-les-Baux & A 54 exit
Arles dir D33

✈ Nîmes/Avignon: 25 km

Le Beffroi

Vaison-la-Romaine

www.chateauxhotels.com/beffroi | reservation service: 33 (0) 1.40.07.00.20

Rue de l'Evêché - Cité médiévale
84110 Vaison-la-Romaine
Tel.: 33 (0) 4.90.36.04.71 – Fax: 33 (0) 4.90.36.24.78
beffroi@chateauxhotels.com
Christine & Yann CHRISTIANSEN

22 rooms: 80 € / 120 €
Breakfast: 10 €
Menu(s): 25,50 € / 41 € - **Carte:** 13 €
1/2 board: 72 € / 86 €

hotel annual closing
27/01 > 22/03

restaurant annual closing
01/01 > 23/03 • 25/10 > 01/04

equipments
telephone, internet, T.V.
Satellite, minibar, safe

environment
architecture 16e, garden,
terrace 120 m², view

leisure, relaxation
heated pool, tennis 1 km, golf
course 25 km, horse-riding
5 km

At the foot of the chateau of the Counts of Toulouse, lordly residence of the 16th and 17th centuries joined together into a hotel, in the heart of the upper medieval village. Individually decorated rooms, tiling, waxed furniture. Provençal cuisine, wine cellar with local wines. Swimming pool.

Visa ● Diners ● JCB ● MASTER CARD

Road map p. 619

A7 exit Orange-Bollène

Avignon: 55 km

La Corse

MER MÉDITERRANÉE

Cap Corse

Rogliano

Nonza

Brando

386

Bastia

St-Florent

L'Île-Rousse

Belgodère

Murato

Calvi

Campitello

Borgo

Calenzana

Ponte Leccia

Vescovato

Asco

Morosaglia

Calacuccia

Omessa

Piedicroce

Corte

Corvione

Porto

Evisa

Piana

Venaco

Cargese

Vico

Vizzavona

Vezzani

Sari-d'Orcino

Aléria

Golfe de Sagone

Ghisoni

Bocognano

Ghisonaccia

Prunelli-di-Fiumorbo

Ajaccio

Zicavo

384

Santa-Maria-Siche

Solenzara

Golfe d'Ajaccio

Zonza

Olmeto

Levie

Propriano

Sartène

Porto-Vecchio

387

Figari

385 **Bonifacio**

Hôtel-Restaurant
Hôtel

0   10   20   30   40 km

EVADEZ-VOUS
EN WEEK-END
A CONDITIONS PRIVILEGIEES*

20% DE REMISE
SUR LA LOCATION
D'UN VEHICULE DE TOURISME*

10 agences Europcar en Corse
vous accueillent à Ajaccio,
Bastia, Bonifacio, Calvi, Porticcio,
Porto-Vecchio et Propriano.

www.europcar.fr

Information et Réservation :

▶ N° Indigo 0 825 358 358
9,15 € soit 0,98 Frs TTC/min

en précisant le code promotion : 806 43 905

*offre soumise à conditions. Nuit du samedi au dimanche obligatoire. Valable jusqu'au 31/12/2002

Europcar

VOUS LOUEZ PLUS QU'UNE VOITURE.

Le Maquis

Ajaccio I Porticcio

www.chateauxhotels.com/maquis I reservation service: 33 (0) 1.40.07.00.20

BP 94 20166 Porticcio
Tel.: 33 (0) 4.95.25.05.55 – Fax: 33 (0) 4.95.25.11.70
maquis@chateauxhotels.com
Catherine SALINI

19 rooms: 140 € / 450 €
2 flats: 350 € / 600 € - **1 suite:** 550 € / 900 €
Breakfast: 20 €
Menu(s): 45 € - **Carte:** 60 €
1/2 board: 150 € / 290 €

hotel annual closing
04/01 > 01/02
restaurant annual closing
04/01 > 01/02
equipments
lift, telephone, internet, T.V.
Satellite/Canal+, minibar, safe,
baby-sitting, valet parking
environment
architecture, garden, terrace,
view
leisure, relaxation
heated pool/covered, golf
course 5 km, horse-riding
5 km, beauty salon,
thalassotherapy, balneo,
solarium, coastal cruises on
sailing and sport motor boats

*The sun, the fine sand beach,
the luxurious vegetation, the
heady perfume of exotic fragrances, such is the paradise
setting of this hotel situated in
the Ajaccio gulf. The luxurious
rooms are only matched by
the skilful cuisine. Here, the
island of beauty truly deserves
its name.*

Visa ● Diners ● MASTER CARD

Road map p. 619

From Ajaccio, N196 dir. Bonifacio,
Propriano, then follow dir. Porticcio
(CD55)

Ajaccio - Campo Dell'Oro:
14 km

Route de Calalonga 20169 Bonifacio
Tel.: 33 (0) 4.95.73.14.13 – Fax: 33 (0) 4.95.73.04.82
marinadicavu@chateauxhotels.com
Anne & Jacques BERTIN
3 rooms: 91,50 € / 289,65 €
2 suites: 129,60 € / 533,60 €
Breakfast: 12,2 €
Menu(s): 33,54 € / 73,18 € -
1/2 board: 45,73 € / 85,38 €

Idyllic sea view, 400m from a beach of fine, white sand, Marina di Cavu gives you the opportunity to contemplate the best of what life has to offer. A charming arrangement of luxury rooms and suites with elegant patio in rich vibrant colours. Breathtaking view of the Isles of Lavezzo and Cavello.

restaurant annual closing
01/01 > 29/03•03/11 > 30/03
equipments
telephone, internet, T.V. Satellite, minibar, safe, baby-sitting
environment
park 6 ha, terrace 250 m^2, view, vegetable garden, total calm
leisure, relaxation
heated pool, tennis 6 km, golf course 3 km, horse-riding 3 km, jacuzzi

Visa ● Diners ● JCB ● MASTER CARD

Road map p. 619

Bonifacio, dir. "vallée de St-Julien", and "route de Calalonga"

Figari: 25 km

Castel Brando

Erbalunga ı Brando

www.chateauxhotels.com/castelbrando | reservation service: 33 (0) 1.40.07.00.20

B.P. 20 Erbalunga 20222 Brando
Tel.: 33 (0) 4.95.30.10.30 – Fax: 33 (0) 4.95.33.98.18
castelbrando@chateauxhotels.com
Jean-Paul & Joëlle PIERI
19 rooms: 69 € / 134 €
6 suites: 107 € / 160 €
Breakfast: 9,15 €

hotel annual closing
01/11 > 15/03

equipments
telephone, internet, T.V.
Satellite, safe, baby-sitting

environment
architecture 19^e, furniture 19^e,
garden, terrace 200 m^2

leisure, relaxation
heated pool, tennis 0.2 km,
golf course 25 km, horse-riding
1 km, solarium

19th century mansion in a park with hundred-year old trees. Charming, warm welcome. Air conditioning, swimming pool. Located in Erbalunga, the village of painters, a picturesque fishing village an Cape Corse. 8 km north Bastia, and 30 km from the airport. Kitchen facilities in the rooms for stays.

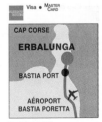

Visa ● MASTER CARD

CAP CORSE

ERBALUNGA

BASTIA PORT

AÉROPORT BASTIA PORETTA

Road map p. 619
On the road of Cap Corse

 Bastia-Poretta: 25 km

Bocca d'Oro 20137 Porto-Vecchio

Tel.: 33 (0) 4.95.70.45.20 – Fax: 33 (0) 4.95.70.47.61

rocefiori@chateauxhotels.com

Isabelle PROFIZI – Guy CIANCIONI

12 rooms: 145 € / 443 €
2 suites: 274 € / 527 €
Menu(s): 38 € / 60 € - **Carte:** 44 € -
1/2 board: 111 € / 260 €

Between sea and mountains, near the beaches of Santa Giulia and Palombaggia, a hotel of character that cultivates all the charm of its unspoilt surroundings. Luxurious rooms and suites. From the terrace and the swimming-pool, a breathtaking view of the gulf of Porto Vecchio. A magical place.

hotel annual closing
31/10 > 01/04

restaurant annual closing
31/10 > 01/04

equipments
telephone, T.V. Satellite, minibar, safe

environment
architecture contemporaine, furniture contemporain, garden, terrace 80 m^2, view, total calm

leisure, relaxation
tennis 2 km, golf course 25 km, horse-riding 5 km, beauty salon, solarium, jacuzzi, quad bike circuit

Visa ● Diners ● MASTER CARD

Road map p. 619

from Figari Airport: dir. Porto-Vecchio, N198 dir. Bonifacio then dir. Bocca d'Oro

 Figari - Sud Corse: 25 km

How to book ?

→ At the Châteaux & Hôtels reservation centre:

- Tél : 00 33 (0) 1 40 07 00 20
- Fax : 00 33 (0) 1 40 07 00 30

→ By Internet:

- www.chateauxhotels.com
- resa@chateauxhotels.com

→ Directly with the establishement required

CHATEAUX & HOTELS
DE FRANCE*

Rhône-Alpes

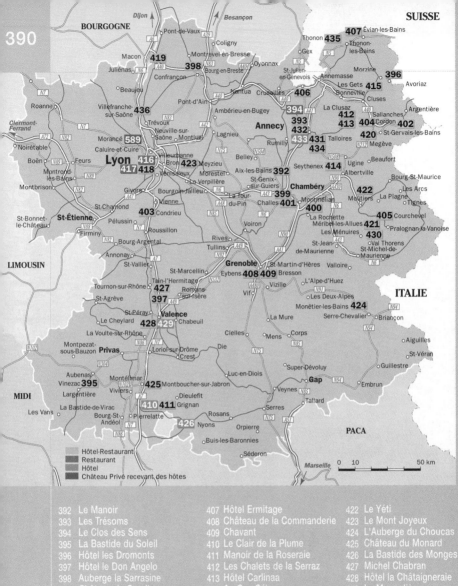

390

Rhône-Alpes

Le Manoir

Aix-les-Bains

www.chateauxhotels.com/manoir | reservation service: 33 (0) 1.40.07.00.20

37, rue Georges-1er 73100 Aix-les-Bains
Tel.: 33 (0) 4.79.61.44.00 – Fax: 33 (0) 4.79.35.67.67
manoir@chateauxhotels.com
Pierre PIRAT

73 rooms: 70 € / 140 €
2 suites: 150 € / 200 €
Breakfast: 10 €
Menu(s): 25 € / 50 € - **Carte:** 55 €
1/2 board: 65 € / 95 €

Open all year
equipments
telephone, internet, T.V.
Satellite/Canal+, safe
environment
architecture 19e, park, garden,
terrace, total calm
leisure, relaxation
heated pool/covered, tennis
2 km, golf course 3 km,
horse-riding 3 km, sauna,
hammam, fitness, jacuzzi

Close to the town and the casino, this charming hotel, formely a part of the famous Splendid Palace, offers the warmth of a country residence. Situated near the hot baths, an oasis of calm and greenery, with confortable rooms open onto the park or the country landscape.

Visa ● Diners ● MASTER CARD

Road map p. 619

A41 exit Aix-les-Bains south. Dir. town centre

 Chambéry-Aix: 8 km

3, boulevard de la Corniche 74000 Annecy

Tel.: 33 (0) 4.50.51.43.84 – Fax: 33 (0) 4.50.45.56.49

tresoms@chateauxhotels.com
Véronique & Pascal DROUX

50 rooms: 84 € / 183 €
Breakfast: 13 €
Menu(s): 23 € / 60 € - **Carte:** 15 € -
1/2 board: 79 € / 189 €

Nestled between the Annecy Lake and the Semnoz Mountain, this residence masjestically dominates a lush tree-filled environment. Top-comfort rooms overlook the Lake or the garden. The panoramic restaurant offers traditionnal gourmet cooking. In summer, lunch on the terrace.

Open all year

equipments
lift, telephone, internet, T.V. Satellite, minibar

environment
architecture, garden, terrace 200 m², view

leisure, relaxation
heated pool/covered, tennis 0.2 km, golf course 10 km, horse-riding 3 km, balneo, sauna, hammam, solarium, fitness

Visa ● Diners ● JCB ● Master Card

Road map p. 619

A41 exit South of Annecy dir. Albertville, Le Lac, Le Semnoz

Annecy: 10 km

Le Clos des Sens

Annecy-le-Vieux

www.chateauxhotels.com/sens | reservation service: 33 (0) 1.40.07.00.20

13, rue Jean Mermoz 74940 Annecy-le-Vieux
Tel.: 33 (0) 4.50.23.07.90 – Fax: 33 (0) 4.50.66.56.54
sens@chateauxhotels.com
Martine COIN & Laurent PETIT
Menu(s): 23 € / 60 € - **Carte:** 54 €

restaurant annual closing
08/09 > 27/09

restaurant weekly closing
mon, tue(lun)
01/07 > 31/08
mon, tue(lun), sun(ev)
01/09 > 30/06

equipments
lift

environment
architecture 11ᵉ, terrace
100 m², view, total calm

On the heights above the Lake of Annecy, near the residence of composer Gabriel Fauré, go in discovery of a savoyard restaurant where the cuisine has become an art entirely on its own. How can one remain unmoved to the char or the lamb of Aravis when they are so well prepared? Succulent!

Visa ● Diners ● MasterCard

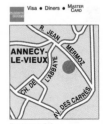

ANNECY-LE-VIEUX
R. JEAN MERMOZ
CH. DE L'ABBAYE
AV. DES CARRES

Road map p. 619
Annecy, dir. Annecy-Le-Vieux

 Annecy-Meythet: 3 km

L'ancien château 07110 Vinezac

Tel.: 33 (0) 4.75.36.91.66 – Fax: 33 (0) 4.75.36.91.59

bastidesoleil@chateauxhotels.com
Erick LABAUNE & Fabien CHATEL

4 rooms: 90 € / 128 €
1 suite: 150 €
Breakfast: 11 €
Menu(s): 22 € / 75 € - **Carte:** 56 € -
1/2 board: 85 € / 104 €

At the heart of this wonderful medieval village is a XVIIth château of which the renovation has scrupulously respected the old-style materials. Five rooms with discrete charm and a fragrant provençal cuisine are the guarantors of a peaceful stay harmonising with the past.

Visa ● Diners ● MASTER CARD

Road map p. 619

A7 exit Loriol. dir Aubenas, D104 dir Alès

hotel annual closing
12/11 > 14/03

restaurant annual closing
12/11 > 14/03

hotel weekly closing
tue(lun), wen(lun)
14/03 > 30/06
tue, wen
01/09 > 12/11

restaurant weekly closing
tue, wen
14/03 > 30/06
tue, wen
01/09 > 12/11

equipments
lift, telephone, internet, T.V., minibar

environment
architecture 17ᵉ, furniture contemporain, terrace 60 m², view, total calm

leisure, relaxation
tennis 0.5 km, golf course 30 km, horse-riding 6 km

✈ Lyon/St-Exupèry: 150 km

Hôtel des Dromonts

Avoriaz

www.chateauxhotels.com/dromonts | reservation service: 33 (0) 1.40.07.00.20

Quartier des Dromonts 74110 Avoriaz
Tel.: 33 (0) 4.50.74.08.11 – Fax: 33 (0) 4.50.74.02.79

dromonts@chateauxhotels.com
Christophe LEROY

24 rooms: 115 € / 229 €
1 flat: 298 € / 366 € - **6 suites:** 229 € / 336 €
Menu(s): 29 € / 64 € - **Carte:** 29 €
1/2 board: included in prices of rooms

hotel annual closing
22/04 > 15/12
restaurant annual closing
22/04 > 15/12
equipments
lift, telephone, internet, T.V.
Satellite, minibar, safe
environment
terrace 100 m², view, total
calm
leisure, relaxation
sauna, hammam, fitness,
jacuzzi, sleigh-rides with husky
dogs, ice-diving, skating rink

*For years a film stars' haunt,
this architectural jewel has
found new life under the direction of Christophe Leroy. A
gifted chef, he prepares delectable and inventive dishes
from excellent local produce.
Cheese and wine cellars, creative culinary art - the art of
living at its highest. (half board
only)*

Visa

Road map p. 619

A43 dir. Lyon-Chambéry, A41 dir.
Chamonix exit 18 Cluses, D902 dir.
Taninges, Les Gets, Morzinne

 Genève: 90 km

Avenue Alpes-Provence 26300 Bourg-de-Péage
Tel.: 33 (0) 4.75.72.44.11 – Fax: 33 (0) 4.75.72.20.01
donangelo@chateauxhotels.com
Bertrand ABRIAL
36 rooms: 93 € / 108 €
2 suites: 130 € / 160 €
Breakfast: 9,15 €
Menu(s): 20 € / 29 € - **Carte:** 12,96 € -
1/2 board: 113 € / 128 €

Once inside this hotel, you are in a different world. The Florentine architecture of this magnificent house highlights the graceful reception areas. Rooms and suites, with their own individual terraces, overlook an immense garden. Delicious menus, enhanced by great Cotes du Rhone wines, tickle your tastebuds.

Visa ● Diners ● MASTER CARD

Open all year
equipments
lift, telephone, internet, T.V. Satellite/Canal+, minibar, safe, baby-sitting, valet parking
environment
furniture contemporain, garden, terrace 300 m²
leisure, relaxation
tennis 1 km, golf course 15 km, horse-riding 10 km, beauty salon, sauna, hammam, solarium, jacuzzi, dog sleighing, canyoning, speleology, quad bike circuit, 4x4 trail

Road map p. 619

A7 exit Valence South, dir. Grenoble
A49 exit N° 6 Romans center

Saint-Exupéry: 100 km

Auberge la Sarrasine
Bourg-en-Bresse I Confrançon
www.chateauxhotels.com/lasarrasine I reservation service: 33 (0) 1.40.07.00.20

RN79 01310 Confrançon
Tel.: 33 (0) 4.74.30.25.65 – Fax: 33 (0) 4.74.25.24.23
lasarrasine@chateauxhotels.com
M. BEVY
9 rooms: 75 € / 138 €
1 flat: 152 € / 215 €
Breakfast: 11 €
Menu(s): 16 € / 30 €

hotel annual closing
15/10 > 15/03
except reservation
restaurant annual closing
15/10 > 15/03
except reservation
hotel weekly closing
wen
30/09 > 01/05
restaurant weekly closing
30/09 > 14/10 ● 15/03 > 01/05
for lunch
equipments
telephone, T.V. Satellite,
minibar
environment
architecture 17e, park 3 ha,
garden, terrace, view, total
calm
leisure, relaxation
heated pool, golf course
10 km, horse-riding 10 km

At 13 km from Bourg-en-Bresse, a peaceful and relaxing stopover at the gates of Burgundy. Former Bressane farm set amidst green parkland. Comfortable and quiet rooms. 6 golf courses within 40 km. Private parking closed at night. Restaurant for client only.

Visa ● Diners ● JCB ● MASTER CARD

Road map p. 619

A40 exit Vonnas. N79 between Mâcon and Bourg-en-Bresse

Lyon/Satolas: 70 km

Rue du Bois-de-Candie
73000 Chambéry-le-Vieux
Tel.: 33 (0) 4.79.96.63.00 – Fax: 33 (0) 4.79.96.63.10
candie@chateauxhotels.com
Didier LHOSTIS

15 rooms: 104 € / 198 €
5 suites: 213 € / 252 €
Breakfast: 13 €
Menu(s): 26 € / 61 € - **Carte:** 48 € -
1/2 board: 82 € / 120 €

History meets gastronomy at this 14th c. fortified Savoyard house built on the site of ancient Templar ruins. Aesthetically pleasing interior design, luxuriously comfortable guestrooms, and outstanding country cuisine selected by the Campanella brothers, talented young chiefs.

Open all year

equipments
lift, telephone, internet, T.V.

environment
architecture 10ᵉ, park 6 ha, garden, terrace 100 m², view, total calm

leisure, relaxation
tennis 10 km, golf course 10 km, horse-riding 10 km, thermal baths, fitness

Visa • JCB • MASTER CARD

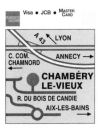

A43 LYON
C. COM. CHAMNORD
ANNECY →
CHAMBÉRY LE-VIEUX
R. DU BOIS DE CANDIE
AIX-LES-BAINS →

Road map p. 619

A43/A41 exit Chambéry, then speedway exit N° 15

 Chambéry-Aix: 10 km

Rhône-Alpes

Château de la Tour du Puits

Chambéry I Coise-St-Jean

www.chateauxhotels.com/tourpuits | reservation service: 33 (0) 1.40.07.00.20

Le Puits 73800 Coise-St-Jean
Tel.: 33 (0) 4.79.28.88.00 – Fax: 33 (0) 4.79.28.88.01
tourpuits@chateauxhotels.com
Raymond PREVOT
8 rooms: 150 € / 230 €
Breakfast: 18 €
Menu(s): 29 € / 84 € - **Carte:** 71 €

hotel annual closing
04/11 > 11/12
restaurant annual closing
04/11 > 11/12
equipments
telephone, internet, T.V.
Satellite, baby-sitting, valet
parking
environment
architecture 18e, park 7 ha,
garden, terrace 100 m², view,
vegetable garden, total calm
leisure, relaxation
heated pool, tennis 4 km, golf
course 30 km, horse-riding
10 km, solarium, fitness,
panoramic flights in helicopter

*Between Bauges nature park,
the Belledonne mountains
and winter resorts, on the ancient Lyon-Turin road, the
Château seems to belong to
another age. Rebuilt in the
18th century on 17 acres of
flowering woodland and orchards, this place is a tribute
to authenticity and the art of
gracious living.*

Visa ● Diners ● JCB ● MASTER CARD

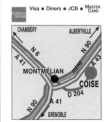

Road map p. 619

A43 dir. Albertville exit 23 Château-neuf

 Chambéry-Aix: 30 km

247, montée du Château
73190 Challes-Les-Eaux
Tel.: 33 (0) 4.79.72.86.71 – Fax: 33 (0) 4.79.72.83.83
challes@chateauxhotels.com
Antoine INFANTES

45 rooms: 57,17 € / 114,34 €
4 suites: 95,28 € / 114,34 €
Breakfast: 9,15 €
Menu(s): 19,06 € / 54,12 € -
1/2 board: 89,18 € / 189,04 €

6 km from Chambéry, this imposing house, built by the Challes family is composed of 3 wonderful buildings. The terrace affords splendid views overlooking the valley, ideal for relaxing, 1 restaurant opening into the park offers you delicious food. Lounge bar 5 mins on foot to the casino and centre.

hotel annual closing
17/12 > 26/12

equipments
telephone, T.V. Canal+

environment
architecture 13ᵉ, park 2 ha, garden, terrace, view, total calm

leisure, relaxation
tennis 1 km, golf course 22 km, horse-riding 10 km, thermal baths

Visa ● Diners ● MASTER CARD

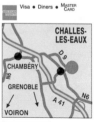

Road map p. 619

Ring road of Chambéry exit 18 - N6 dir. Challes

Chambéry-Voglans: 15 km

Le Jeu de Paume
Chamonix Mont-Blanc
www.chateauxhotels.com/jeupaume | reservation service: 33 (0) 1.40.07.00.20

705, route du Chapeau Le Lavancher
74400 Chamonix Mont-Blanc
Tel.: 33 (0) 4.50.54.03.76 – Fax: 33 (0) 4.50.54.10.75
jeupaume@chateauxhotels.com
Martine SCOMPARIN

19 rooms: 106 € / 177 €
1 flat: 382 € / 458 € - **3 suites:** 182 € / 229 €
Breakfast: 11 €
Menu(s): 30 € / 53 € - **Carte:** 47 €
1/2 board: 94 € / 130 €

hotel annual closing
05/05 > 05/06•07/09 > 14/12
restaurant annual closing
05/05 > 05/06•07/09 > 14/12
restaurant weekly closing
tue(lun), wen(lun)
equipments
lift, telephone, internet, T.V.
Satellite, minibar, safe
environment
garden, terrace, view, total calm

leisure, relaxation
heated pool/covered, tennis
2 km, golf course 3 km,
horse-riding 3 km, beauty
salon, thermal baths, sauna,
hammam, fitness, jacuzzi

On the edge of a pine forest, at the foot of Aigueilles of Chamonix and Mont-Blanc, is this marvellous chalet. The bedrooms and suites are in natural wood, each with balconies. Gourmets wil be seduced by the inventive cuisine at the Rosebud restaurant. Heated covered pool, sauna, snow sports.

Visa • Diners • JCB • MASTER CARD

Road map p. 619

A40 exit Le Fayet dir. Martigny (Switzerland)

 Genève: 100 km

Le Beau Rivage

Condrieu

www.chateauxhotels.com/beaurivage | reservation service: 33 (0) 1.40.07.00.20

2, rue du Beau Rivage 69420 Condrieu
Tel.: 33 (0) 4.74.56.82.82 – Fax: 33 (0) 4.74.59.59.36
beaurivage@chateauxhotels.com
Familles HUMANN & DONET
24 rooms: 84 € / 130 €
Breakfast: 13 €
Menu(s): 28 € / 95 € - **Carte:** 75 €

This former fisherman's house with its discreet charm will welcome you through the year. Its air conditioned gastronomic restaurant, overlooking the river, offers you the dishes of its chef together with regional specialities. Rooms are individually decorated and offer commodities.

Open all year

equipments
telephone, T.V. Satellite, minibar, valet parking

environment
terrace 100 m², view

leisure, relaxation
golf course 15 km

Visa ● Diners ● JCB ● Master Card

Road map p. 619

A7 exit Condrieu - RN86 dir. Valence

Lyon/St-Exupèry: 40 km

Rhône-Alpes

Les Roches Fleuries

Cordon I Megève

www.chateauxhotels.com/rochesfleuries | reservation service: 33 (0) 1.40.07.00.20

74700 Cordon/Megève
Tel.: 33 (0) 4.50.58.06.71 – Fax: 33 (0) 4.50.47.82.30
rochesfleuries@chateauxhotels.com
Jocelyne & Gérard PICOT
21 rooms: 85 € / 139 €
4 suites: 160 € / 259 €
Breakfast: 12,2 €
Menu(s): 26,70 € / 57,93 € - **Carte:** 38 €
1/2 board: 76 € / 122 €

hotel annual closing
15/04 > 10/05 • 15/09 > 15/12
restaurant annual closing
15/04 > 10/05 • 15/09 > 15/12
equipments
telephone, internet, T.V.
Satellite, safe, baby-sitting
environment
architecture contemporaine,
garden, terrace 80 m², view,
total calm

leisure, relaxation
heated pool, tennis 1 km, golf
course 8 km, horse-riding
1 km, beauty salon, hammam,
fitness, jacuzzi, mountain bikes
at the hotel

Close to Megève and facing Mont Blanc, all of the savoyard hospitality stimulates these two comfortable chalets where rooms with balcony or terrace are decorated with old-style savoyard furnishings. Cuisine of great reputation is in the two restaurants. A cosy nest for lovers of countryside.

Visa • Diners • JCB • MASTER CARD

SALLANCHES

D 113 · A40 · N 212 · N 205

CORDON

COMBLOUX

MEGÈVE · D909

Road map p. 619
A40 exit Sallanches

Genève-Cointrin: 60 km

Le Chabichou

Courchevel

www.chateauxhotels.com/chabichou | reservation service: 33 (0) 1.40.07.00.20

Rue des Chenus 1850 73120 Courchevel
Tel.: 33 (0) 4.79.08.00.55 – Fax: 33 (0) 4.79.08.33.58
chabichou@chateauxhotels.com
Michel ROCHEDY

38 rooms: 68,6 € / 207,33 €
2 suites: 167,69 € / 318,62 €
Breakfast: 15,24 €
Menu(s): 27,44 € / 114,34 € - **Carte:** 42 €

In the heart of the Courchevel ski station, this original light wood chalet offers inwinter and summer comfort, calm and culinary delights. The rooms are decorated in harmony with nature, mixing the nobility of mountains with the taste for well-being. Surrounding you a marvellous mountains landscape.

hotel annual closing
01/05 > 30/06 • 10/09 > 30/11
equipments
lift, T.V., minibar, safe
environment
terrace, view
leisure, relaxation
golf course 1 km, horse-riding 7 km, sauna, hammam, jacuzzi

Visa • Diners • MASTER CARD

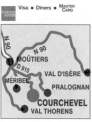

Road map p. 619

A6 then A43, exit Albertville. N90 Moutiers-Courchevel

Chambéry: 100 km

| Rhône-Alpes

Château des Avenières

Cruseilles

www.chateauxhotels.com/avenieres | reservation service: 33 (0) 1.40.07.00.20

Route du Salève 74350 Cruseilles
Tel.: 33 (0) 4.50.44.02.23 – Fax: 33 (0) 4.50.44.29.09
avenieres@chateauxhotels.com
Nicolas ODIN
12 rooms: 115 € / 245 €
Breakfast: 14,50 €
Menu(s): 26 € / 65 € - **Carte:** 55 €
1/2 board: 102 € / 167 €

hotel annual closing
03/11 > 04/12
restaurant annual closing
03/11 > 04/12
equipments
lift, telephone, internet, T.V., minibar
environment
architecture 19°, park 60 ha, garden, terrace 60 m², view, total calm
leisure, relaxation
tennis 6 km, golf course 10 km, horse-riding 8 km

Emotions and the extraordinary define this château built at the beginning of the XXth century by an eccentric American and fitted-out by a mystic Hindu. Today the hotel is devoted to tranquillity, harmony and the pleasures of life: luxurious rooms, princely lounges, and classical cuisine. Magnificent view!

Visa ● Diners ● MASTER CARD

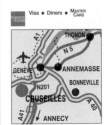

Road map p. 619

A40 exit St-Julien-en-Genevois. A41 exit Cruseilles

 Genève-Cointrin: 25 km

Royal Parc Evian Rive sud du Lac de Genève
74500 Evian-les-Bains
Tel.: 33 (0) 4.50.26.85.00 – Fax: 33 (0) 4.50.75.61.00
ermitage@chateauxhotels.com
87 rooms: 160 € / 600 €
1 flat: 380 € / 695 € - **3 suites:** 340 € / 600 €
Breakfast: 17 €
Menu(s): 42 € / 60 € - **Carte:** 58 € -
1/2 board: 115 € / 335 €

A charming hotel set in 42 acres of grounds on the shores of Lake Geneva. At the Hotel Ermitage, the cosy, easy-going atmosphere belies the luxury beneath. Rooms and suites open onto the lake or the gardens. Exclusive surroundings to relax and keep fit, to enjoy sports activities and fine food.

Visa ● Diners ● JCB ● Master Card

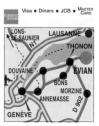

Road map p. 619

A40 exit Annemasse then 40 km

hotel annual closing
06/01 > 31/01 ● 11/11 > 06/02
restaurant annual closing
06/01 > 31/01 ● 11/11 > 06/02
equipments
lift, telephone, internet, T.V. Satellite/Canal+, minibar, safe, valet parking
environment
architecture 19e, park 17 ha, garden, terrace, view, total calm
leisure, relaxation
heated pool/covered, golf course 1 km, horse-riding, beauty salon, balneo, thermal baths, sauna, fitness, jacuzzi, steam room, adventure course, trekking

Genève-Cointrin: 45 km

Château de la Commanderie

Grenoble **I** Eybens

www.chateauxhotels.com/commanderie | reservation service: 33 (0) 1.40.07.00.20

17, avenue d'Echirolles 38320 Eybens
Tel.: 33 (0) 4.76.25.34.58 – Fax: 33 (0) 4.76.24.07.31
commanderie@chateauxhotels.com
Marc de BEAUMONT
25 rooms: 75 € / 130 €
Breakfast: 9,9 €
Menu(s): 27,29 € / 58,24 € - **Carte:** 26 €
1/2 board: 77 € / 100 €

hotel annual closing
23/12 > 25/12●31/12 > 03/01
restaurant annual closing
23/12 > 07/01
restaurant weekly closing
mon, sat(lun), sun(ev)
01/01 > 23/12
equipments
telephone, internet, T.V.
Satellite, minibar, safe
environment
architecture 18e, garden,
terrace 500 m², view
leisure, relaxation
tennis 0.5 km, golf course
3 km, horse-riding 2 km

*Former hospital/residence of
the knights of Malta. Warm
atmosphere, antique furniture,
18th-century wood-panelling,
Aubusson tapestries... Cuisine in tune with the place and
the seasons. Each room in a
different style, with all modern
comforts. Ten minutes from
the centre of Grenoble.*

Visa ● Diners ● MASTER CARD

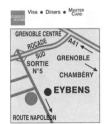

Road map p. 619

Grenoble Ring South exit 5 or 6

 St-Geoirs: 40 km

Rue Emile Chavant 38320 Bresson
Tel.: 33 (0) 4.76.25.25.38 – Fax: 33 (0) 4.76.62.06.55
chavant@chateauxhotels.com
Danièle & Jean-Pierre CHAVANT
5 rooms: 104 € / 125 €
2 flats: 160 €
Breakfast: 11 €
Menu(s): 32 € / 43,00 € - **Carte:** 46 €

Bresson, on the edge of the woods, is a pleasant and restful stopping-place. It is in this charming little village of Dauphiné, seven kilometres from Grenoble, that Chavant keeps on from father to son the traditions of French hospitality and cuisine. Meals served in the garden during fine weather.

hotel annual closing
24/12 > 30/12
restaurant annual closing
24/12 > 30/12
equipments
telephone, internet, T.V., minibar
environment
architecture, garden, terrace, total calm
leisure, relaxation
tennis 0.5 km, golf course 1 km, swimming pool, wine tasting

Visa ● Diners ● MASTER CARD

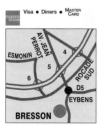

Road map p. 619

Grenoble south bypass exit n° 6 dir. Chambéry

Grenoble-St-Geoirs: 30 km

Le Clair de la Plume
Grignan
www.chateauxhotels.com/clairplume | reservation service: 33 (0) 1.40.07.00.20

Place du Mail 26230 Grignan
Tel.: 33 (0) 4.75.91.81.30 – Fax: 33 (0) 4.75.91.81.31
clairplume@chateauxhotels.com
Jean-Luc VALADEAU
10 rooms: 85 € / 150 €
Breakfast: included

hotel annual closing
03/02 > 02/03
equipments
telephone, internet, T.V.
Satellite, minibar, baby-sitting
environment
architecture 18^e, garden,
terrace 40 m^2, view
leisure, relaxation
tennis 0.5 km, golf course
12 km, horse-riding 0.5 km

In Provence, there is a little guesthouse: push open the gate, walk through the yard, and enter. Every room has a distinct personality, and boasts all modern amenities. Breakfast is prepared in the vaulted-ceiling kitchen, the legacy of the monk who founded this site.

Visa ● Diners ● JCB ● MASTER CARD

Road map p. 619

A7 exit Montélimar South (dir. Nyons)
or exit Bollène (by St-Paul 3 Chx)

 Valence: 70 km

www.chateauxhotels.com/roseraie | reservation service: 33 (0) 1.40.07.00.20

Route de Valreas 26230 Grignan
Tel.: 33 (0) 4.75.46.58.15 – Fax: 33 (0) 4.75.46.91.55
roseraie@chateauxhotels.com
Famille ALBERTS
15 rooms: 141 € / 184 €
2 suites: 267 € / 297,50 €
Breakfast: 15,25 €
Menu(s): 30,5 € / 58 € - **Carte:** 55 € -
1/2 board: 124 € / 145 €

The Manoir de la Roseraie is within striking distance of the Mont Ventoux and the Dentelles de Montmirail. Thousands of roses, superb lawns, swimming pool, tennis, etc. 17 deluxe guest rooms and suites. Delicious cuisine prepared from home-grown vegetable and fruit, accompanied by fine wines.

hotel annual closing
04/01 > 14/02 ● 02/12 > 12/12
restaurant annual closing
04/01 > 14/02 ● 02/12 > 12/12
hotel weekly closing
tue, wen
21/09 > 04/01 ● 15/02 > 20/04
restaurant weekly closing
tue, wen
21/09 > 04/01 ● 15/02 > 20/04
tue(lun), wen(lun)
21/04 > 20/09
equipments
telephone, internet, T.V.
Satellite, safe
environment
architecture 19ᵉ, furniture 18ᵉ,
park 3 ha, garden, terrace,
total calm
leisure, relaxation
heated pool, golf course
10 km, horse-riding 1.5 km,
tennis

Visa ● Diners ● MASTER CARD

Road map p. 619

A7 exit MontélimarSouth. D541 dir.
Nyons-Gap

Avignon: 90 km

Les Chalets de la Serraz

La Clusaz

www.chateauxhotels.com/serraz | reservation service: 33 (0) 1.40.07.00.20

route du col des aravis 74220 La Clusaz
Tel.: 33 (0) 4.50.02.48.29 – Fax: 33 (0) 4.50.02.64.12
serraz@chateauxhotels.com
Bernard & Marie Claude GALLAY
6 rooms: 90 € / 145 €
3 flats: 149 € / 190 € - **1 suite:** 137 € / 175 €
Breakfast: 11,50 €
Menu(s): 22 € / 33 € - **Carte:** 39 €
1/2 board: 75,5 € / 130 €

hotel annual closing
21/04 > 18/05 ● 29/09 > 08/11
restaurant annual closing
21/04 > 18/05 ● 29/09 > 08/11
equipments
telephone, internet, T.V.
Canal+, baby-sitting
environment
architecture 19e, park 1 ha,
garden, terrace, view, total
calm
leisure, relaxation
heated pool, golf course 8 km,
horse-riding 3 km, balneo

Once upon a time there was a real alpine chalet with a superb view of the mountains and a stream running by. Winter or summer, you will feel at home in the alpine-style guest rooms or split-level chalet apartments, and enjoy tasty and generous local specialities. 1/4 mile from the ski slopes.

Visa ● Diners ● MasterCard

Road map p. 619

A40 exit Bonneville - A41 exit Annecy/
Meythet - A43 exit Albertville

 Genève: 60 km

Hôtel Carlina

La Clusaz

Haut du village 74220 La Clusaz
Tel.: 33 (0) 4.50.02.43.48 – Fax: 33 (0) 4.50.02.63.02
carlina@chateauxhotels.com
Jean-Luc RUPHY
39 rooms: 60 € / 150 €
Breakfast: 12 €
Menu(s): 35 € - **Carte:** 35 € - **1/2 board:** 50 € / 130 €

Near the village centre and the ski slopes, this hotel at architecture savoyarde with wooden decor offers an unrivalled view of the Alps. Attractive rooms furnished in Savoyard style, nearly all with a large balcony looking out over the village. Sample great food and enjoy the cheery atmosphere in the bar from the comfort of the fireside.

Visa ● MASTER CARD

hotel annual closing
15/04 > 15/06 ● 15/09 > 01/12

equipments
lift, telephone, internet, T.V. Satellite, baby-sitting

environment
architecture, furniture 19^e, garden, terrace 100 m^2, view, total calm

leisure, relaxation
heated pool/covered, golf course 25 km, horse-riding 1 km, beauty salon, sauna, hammam, fitness, jacuzzi, hiking, tennis and mini-golf approximate

Road map p. 619

A41 exit Annecy South or A40 Bonneville

Genève: 60 km

| Rhône-Alpes

Au Gay Séjour

Faverges I Le Tertenoz

www.chateauxhotels.com/gaysejour | reservation service: 33 (0) 1.40.07.00.20

74210 Le Tertenoz
Tel.: 33 (0) 4.50.44.52.52 – Fax: 33 (0) 4.50.44.49.52
gaysejour@chateauxhotels.com
Bernard GAY
11 rooms: 60 € / 90 €
Breakfast: 10 €
Menu(s): 24 € / 68 € - **Carte:** 75 €
1/2 board: 66 € / 83 €

hotel annual closing 17/11 > 19/12	*A former Savoy farmhouse, in*
restaurant annual closing 17/11 > 19/12	*the heart of a hamlet close to the Tamié Abbey (11th cen-*
hotel weekly closing mon, sun(ev) 01/09 > 14/07	*tury). On the road to the major winter sports resorts (Megève, Méribel, Courchevel, Val*
restaurant weekly closing mon, sun(ev) 01/09 > 14/07	*d'Isère, ...). Cuisine famous for its fresh produce and lake fish.*
equipments telephone, internet, T.V.	*Walks, forests, Lake Annecy, hang-glidind, ski, etc.*
environment architecture 17e, garden, terrace 100 m², view, vegetable garden, total calm	
leisure, relaxation tennis 3 km, golf course 5 km, horse-riding 10 km	

Visa ● Diners ● JCB ● **MASTER CARD**

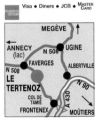

Road map p. 619

A41 exit Annecy South or A430 exit
Frontenex. dir. Faverges or col of
Tamie

 Annecy-Meythet: 30 km

74260 Les Gets
Tel.: 33 (0) 4.50.75.80.33 – Fax: 33 (0) 4.50.75.83.26
marmotte@chateauxhotels.com
Josette MIRIGAY
48 rooms: 130 € / 286 €
Breakfast: 9 €
Menu(s): 22 € / 28 € - **1/2 board:** 99 € / 175 €

At the foot of the ski trails of Gets lies this large mountain chalet from the 1930's. Ever since, the house and the family have expanded but the spirit remains the same: good-natured. One feels at home at La Marmotte. Spacious rooms with terraces, balanced menus and homemade jams.

hotel annual closing
07/04 > 29/06 ● 08/09 > 21/12

restaurant annual closing
07/04 > 29/06 ● 08/09 > 21/12

equipments
lift, telephone, T.V. Satellite, safe, baby-sitting

environment
terrace, view

leisure, relaxation
heated pool/covered, tennis 0.1 km, golf course 3 km, horse-riding 1 km, beauty salon, balneo, sauna, hammam, solarium, fitness, jacuzzi

Visa ● Diners ● JCB ● MASTER CARD

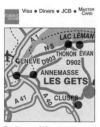

Road map p. 619

A40 dir. Chamonix, exit Cluze. D902 dir. Morzine

Genève-Cointrin: 55 km

Commanderie des Antonins

Lyon

www.chateauxhotels.com/antonins | reservation service: 33 (0) 1.40.07.00.20

30, quai Saint-Antoine 69002 Lyon
Tel.: 33 (0) 4.78.37.19.21 – Fax: 33 (0) 4.78.37.19.21
antonins@chateauxhotels.com
Famille SOUDAN
Menu(s): 19,82 € - **Carte:** 32,01 €

restaurant annual closing
22/07 > 21/08
environment
architecture 13e

Large 13th century chapter-house, with small vaulted chapels, evoking Rabelais. Traditional cuisine, baked in wood-fired ovens. Exquisite meats, fresh home-grown produce. Specialities: duck foie gras... Regular conference-meals on Cuisine of the Past (on request for groups).

Visa ● MASTER CARD

R. GRENETTE
Q. ST-ANTOINE
SAÔNE
RHÔNE
LYON
PL. BELLECOUR

Road map p. 619
Lyon centre, dir. "Vieux-Lyon"

Rhône-Alpes |

 Lyon/St-Exupéry: 35 km

www.chateauxhotels.com/alexandrin | reservation service: 33 (0) 1.40.07.00.20

83, rue Moncey 69003 Lyon
Tel.: 33 (0) 4.72.61.15.69 – Fax: 33 (0) 4.78.62.75.57
alexandrin@chateauxhotels.com
Alain ALEXANIAN
Menu(s): 26 € / 75 € - **Carte:** 64 €

If Lyon is the capital of French gastronomy, Alain Alexanian is one of the noblest representatives. In a stylish and contemporary decor, his dishes capture the flavours of the land... with added distinction that compels admiration. The charm of his wife Véronique is a bonus; she will advise you in english.

restaurant annual closing
28/07 > 19/08 ● 22/12 > 06/01

environment
architecture contemporaine,
furniture contemporain

Visa ● MASTER CARD

Road map p. 619

A7 exit Lyon-centre then dir. Part Dieu

La Tour Rose

Lyon
www.chateauxhotels.com/tourrose | reservation service: 33 (0) 1.40.07.00.20

22, rue du Boeuf 69005 Lyon
Tel.: 33 (0) 4.78.92.69.10 – Fax: 33 (0) 4.78.42.26.02
tourrose@chateauxhotels.com
Philippe CHAVENT

4 rooms: 215 € / 285 €
4 flats: 120 € / 150 € - **8 suites:** 315 € / 520 €
Breakfast: 18 €
Menu(s): 49 € / 107 € - **Carte:** 75 €

Open all year

equipments
lift, telephone, internet, T.V., minibar, safe, valet parking

environment
architecture 18e, garden, terrace, view, total calm

leisure, relaxation
tennis 3 km, golf course 8 km, horse-riding 8 km

More than just a hotel, a comfortable and convivial house. Second-half European Renaissance with terrace gardens, ponds and waterfalls. The chef, an aesthete, is inspired by the classics and combines his travel experiences with new products. P. Chavent welcomes you for a visit out of time.

Visa ● Diners ● JCB ● MASTER CARD

Road map p. 619

Follow "Vieux Lyon", Quartier St-Jean

 Lyon/St-Exupèry: 30 km

N79 01750 Replonges

Tel.: 33 (0) 3.85.31.03.55 – Fax: 33 (0) 3.85.31.10.24

huchette@chateaushotels.com

Fabrice ALRAN

11 rooms: 60,98 € / 106,71 €
1 flat: 152,45 € / 182,94 €
Breakfast: 10 €
Menu(s): 25,92 € / 41,16 € - **Carte:** 36 € -
1/2 board: 76,22 € / 91,47 €

A charming hotel with elegant decor, in a large park close to Mâcon, in the heart of the Bresse region. Very spacious rooms with view of the swimming-pool and the countryside. Fine cuisine and high-quality wines in the panoramic dining-room. Rich regional and artistic heritage.

hotel annual closing
05/11 > 27/11

restaurant annual closing
05/11 > 27/11

equipments
telephone, internet, T.V. Satellite, minibar, baby-sitting

environment
architecture, park 2 ha, garden, terrace

leisure, relaxation
heated pool, tennis 2 km, golf course 0.5 km, horse-riding 8 km

Visa ● Diners ● MASTER CARD

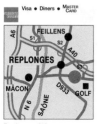

Road map p. 619

A40 exit n° 3 then N79 dir. Macon

Lyon-St-Exupéry: 80 km

Chalet Saint-Georges
Megève
www.chateauxhotels.com/saintgeorges | reservation service: 33 (0) 1.40.07.00.20

159, rue Mgr Conseil 74120 Megève
Tel.: 33 (0) 4.50.93.07.15 – Fax: 33 (0) 4.50.21.51.18
saintgeorges@chateauxhotels.com
Régine BENEDETTI-GOUDAL
M. & Mme. FOURNIER-CHBIB

19 rooms: 100 € / 265 €
3 suites: 315 € / 505 €
Breakfast: 15 €
Menu(s): 18,29 € / 33,50 € - **Carte:** 33,54 €
1/2 board: 95 € / 180 €

hotel annual closing
20/04 > 20/06 • 15/09 > 15/12
restaurant annual closing
20/04 > 20/06 • 22/09 > 26/10
restaurant weekly closing
mon, tue, wen
26/10 > 15/12
equipments
lift, telephone, internet, T.V.
Satellite/Canal+, minibar, safe,
baby-sitting
environment
terrace, view
leisure, relaxation
tennis 0.5 km, golf course
3 km, horse-riding 1.5 km,
beauty salon, sauna, fitness,
orse-drawn carriage rides

*nIn the heart of Megève, the
Chalet Saint-Georges offers
the finest in good taste and
hospitality. The warmth of the
wood interior is highlighted by
the refined decoration. After
an invigorating day skiing,
relax at the health and beauty
centre. Exquisite cuisine in regional dishes awaits you.*

Visa • Diners • MASTER CARD

Road map p. 619

A40 exit n° 20 Sallanches. N212 dir.
Albertville-Megève

 Genève: 65 km

Le Belvédère 73550 Méribel

Tel.: 33 (0) 4.79.00.56.00 – Fax: 33 (0) 4.79.00.59.28

allodis@chateauxhotels.com

Françoise & Yves FORNI

32 rooms: 138 € / 354 €
12 suites: 165 € / 430 €
Breakfast: 12,5 €
Menu(s): 27,5 € / 73,2 € - **Carte:** 33,5 € -
1/2 board: 89 € / 205 €

At the foot of the slopes, located in the Belvedere quarter, this spacious wooden chalet combines the charm of a Savoie decor and the comfort of wood-panelled rooms glowing with warm colours. High-quality cuisine. And all around, the fantastic Trois Vallées ski resort.

Visa ● MASTER CARD

hotel annual closing
21/04 > 30/06 ● 01/09 > 16/12

restaurant annual closing
21/04 > 30/06 ● 01/09 > 16/12

equipments
lift, internet, T.V. Canal+, safe, baby-sitting

environment
terrace, view

leisure, relaxation
heated pool/covered, golf course 2 km, horse-riding 4 km, sauna, hammam, skiing, cross country skiing, skating-rink

Road map p. 619

To Albertville, N90 dir. Moutiers-Meribel

Lyon: 200 km

Le Yéti

Méribel

www.chateauxhotels.com/yeti | reservation service: 33 (0) 1.40.07.00.20

Rond Point des pistes BP 52 73553 Méribel
Tel.: 33 (0) 4.79.00.51.15 – Fax: 33 (0) 4.79.00.51.73

yeti@chateauxhotels.com
Frédéric SAINT-GUILHEM

27 rooms: 140 € / 272 €
6 flats: 245 € / 511 €
Breakfast: 12,2 €
Menu(s): 25 € / 42 € - **Carte:** 30 €
1/2 board: 98 € / 173 €

hotel annual closing
22/04 > 06/07 • 26/08 > 15/12
restaurant annual closing
22/04 > 06/07 • 26/08 > 15/12
equipments
lift, telephone, T.V. Satellite,
safe
environment
architecture contemporaine,
garden, terrace 180 m², view
leisure, relaxation
heated pool, tennis 2 km, golf
course 1 km, horse-riding
2 km, thermal baths, sauna

*In Meribel, where every house
and hotel is a chalet, none can
compare with the Yeti. At the
edge of the forest, the Yeti
mirrors the character of its
owners, Sophie and Frédéric
Saint Guilhem, a mountain
guide. Cheerful and unassum-
ing, the atmosphere here is of
elegant simplicity rather than
overdone luxury.*

Visa • MASTER CARD

Road map p. 619

A43 exit Moutiers. D5 dir. Méribel

✈ Lyon: 150 km

Rue Victor-Hugo 69330 Meyzieu

Tel.: 33 (0) 4.78.04.21.32 – Fax: 33 (0) 4.72.02.85.72

montjoyeux@chateauxhotels.com

Jean-Bernard MOLLARD

20 rooms: 70 € / 87 €

Breakfast: 9,20 €

Menu(s): 20 € / 43 € - **Carte:** 25 €

Near Lyon, Satolas Airport and Eurexpo, a charming house in a contemporary and refined setting. The rooms open onto the park, the restaurant is perched over the lake. Simplicity and freshness on J.B. Mollard's new menu: fricassee of turbot with scallops, pan-fried veal sweetbreads with cider...

Open all year

equipments
telephone, internet, T.V., minibar, safe

environment
garden, terrace 600 m², view, total calm

leisure, relaxation
tennis 6 km, golf course 12 km, horse-riding 6 km

Visa • Diners • MASTER CARD

Road map p. 619

A46 exit Le Grand Large, dir. Le Grand Large

 Lyon-Satolas: 15 km

Rhône-Alpes

L'Auberge du Choucas
Monêtier-les-Bains
www.chateauxhotels.com/choucas | reservation service: 33 (0) 1.40.07.00.20

**Serre-Chevalier 1500 /
05220 Monêtier-les-Bains**
Tel.: 33 (0) 4.92.24.42.73 – Fax: 33 (0) 4.92.24.51.60
choucas@chateauxhotels.com
Nicole SANCHEZ-VENTURA
8 rooms: 100 € / 178 €
4 flats: 160 € / 230 €
Breakfast: 13 €
Menu(s): 16 € / 60 € - **1/2 board:** 85 € / 145 €

hotel annual closing
01/05 > 31/05●01/11 > 15/12
restaurant annual closing
15/04 > 31/05●15/10 > 15/12
restaurant weekly closing
mon(lun), tue(lun), wen(lun),
thi(lun)
15/12 > 15/04
mon(lun), tue(lun), wen(lun),
thi(lun)
15/09 > 15/10

equipments
telephone, internet, T.V.,
minibar, safe, valet parking

environment
architecture 17ᵉ, furniture
contemporain, garden, terrace
150 m², total calm

leisure, relaxation
tennis 0.4 km, golf course
25 km, horse-riding 4 km,
beauty salon, thalassotherapy,
balneo, thermal baths, sauna,
hammam, solarium, fitness,
jacuzzi, mountain bike,
snow-shoe trails

A 17th century mountain farm-house nestling in an old Alpine village on the edge of the Écrins National Park, in the Serre-Chevalier skiing area. Splendor of Alpine land-scapes, winter and summer sports, inventive and tasteful cooking. Just a few minutes' walk from the foot of the ski slopes.

Visa ● MasterCard

Road map p. 619

N91 between Col du Lautaret and
Briançon. Cross the village until the
Church

✈ Turin: 110 km

Château du Monard
Montboucher-sur-Jabron
www.chateauxhotels.com/monard | reservation service: 33 (0) 1.40.07.00.20

425

Domaine de la Valdaine
26740 Montboucher-sur-Jabron
Tel.: 33 (0) 4.75.00.71.30 – Fax: 33 (0) 4.75.00.71.31
monard@chateauxhotels.com
Delphine SARTRE

30 rooms: 114 € / 185 €
4 suites: 194 € / 276 €
Menu(s): 29 € / 40 € - **Carte:** 50 €

In the land of lavender and in the middle of a magnificent 18-hole golf course, this imposing 15th and 16th century château lives a second youth. The welcome is cordial, the rooms pleasant and the cuisine gastronomic. A place favourable for unwinding with sport and getting into shape.

Open all year

equipments
lift, telephone, T.V. Canal+, minibar, safe

environment
architecture 15e, furniture contemporain, park 77 ha, terrace, total calm

leisure, relaxation
horse-riding 5 km, sauna, hammam, solarium, fitness, jacuzzi

Visa ● Diners ● MASTERCARD

Road map p. 619

A7 exit South of Montélimar or N7 untill Montelimar (Drôme)

Avignon: 50 km

La Bastide des Monges

Nyons

www.chateauxhotels.com/monges | reservation service: 33 (0) 1.40.07.00.20

Quartier des Monges route d'Orange
26110 Nyons
Tel.: 33 (0) 4.75.26.99.69 – Fax: 33 (0) 4.75.26.99.70
monges@chateauxhotels.com
France & Richard SAUVAGE

8 rooms: 72 € / 120 €
1 suite: 153 € / 176 €
Breakfast: 10 €

hotel annual closing
01/01 > 27/03 • 14/10 > 12/04

equipments
telephone, T.V., minibar

environment
garden, terrace 50 m², view,
total calm

leisure, relaxation
tennis 1.5 km, golf course
25 km, horse-riding 4 km,
sauna, jacuzzi, mountain bike

Between the vineyards and the fields, under the sunlit skies of Provence, a beautifully restored old farmhouse looking across at Mont Ventoux. You will love the delightful rooms and the atmosphere of well-being, and the generous breakfasts are moments of pure pleasure.

Visa • MasterCard

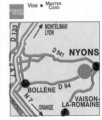

Road map p. 619

A7 exit Bollene dir.Nyons D94 - A7 exit South   Montelimar,D133,D941,to Nyons D94

 Avignon: 60 km

Rhône-Alpes

Michel Chabran 427
Pont-de-l'Isère
www.chateauxhotels.com/chabran | reservation service: 33 (0) 1.40.07.00.20

29, avenue du 45ème parallèle
26600 Pont de l'Isère
Tel.: 33 (0) 4.75.84.60.09 – Fax: 33 (0) 4.75.84.59.65
chabran@chateauxhotels.com
Michel CHABRAN
12 rooms: 77 € / 120 €
Breakfast: 16 €
Menu(s): 46 € / 125 € - **Carte:** 85 € -
1/2 board: 154 € / 260 €

Pont de l'Isere, set at the foot of the Hermitage vineyards and with Provence on the doorstep. Culinary magician Michel Chabran uses authentic local produce to turn his special brand of festive cuisine into an art form. Spend winter nights in front of the fireplace, and warm days in the garden or on the patio.

Visa ● Diners ● MASTERCARD

Road map p. 619

A7 exit Valence North, N7 dir. Lyon-Tain l'Hermitage (5km)

Lyon Saint Exupéry: 100 km

Open all year
hotel weekly closing
sun(ev)
01/11 > 31/03
restaurant weekly closing
wen(lun), thi(lun)
01/04 > 31/10
wen(lun), thi(lun), sun(ev)
01/11 > 31/03
equipments
telephone, T.V., valet parking
environment
garden, terrace 1000 m^2
leisure, relaxation
golf course 20 km, canoeing trip through the Ardèche gorges

670, route de Nîmes 07130 Soyons
Tel.: 33 (0) 4.75.60.83.55 – Fax: 33 (0) 4.75.60.85.21
chataigneraie@chateauxhotels.com
Philippe MICHELOT
14 rooms: 99 € / 139 €
Breakfast: 16 €
1/2 board: 85 € / 125 €
Menu(s) : 26 € / 61 €

hotel annual closing
01/11 > 31/03

equipments
telephone, internet, T.V.
Satellite, minibar, safe

environment
architecture 19^e, furniture 19^e,
garden, terrace 120 m^2

leisure, relaxation
golf course 15 km, horse-riding
10 km, sauna, solarium,
jacuzzi, own indoor and
outdoor tennis courts

This roomy renovated farm-house is an annex to the Musardiere Chateau. Sunny rooms decorated with fabrics from Provence and country-style furniture. Several rooms designed for large families. You can also enjoy all the services of La Musardiere including the tasty meals!

Visa ● Diners ● MASTER CARD

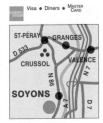

Road map p. 619

A7 exit Valence North, dir. City center,
bridge across Rhône - dir South - 9 km
N86 dir. Nîmes

 Valence: 14 km

670 route de Nîmes 07130 Soyons
Tel.: 33 (0) 4.75.60.83.55 – Fax: 33 (0) 4.75.60.85.21
musardiere@chateauxhotels.com
Philippe FERAULT – Philippe MICHELOT
12 rooms: 120 € / 200 €
Breakfast: 16 €
Menu(s): 26 € / 61 € - **1/2 board:** 99 € / 145 €

On the way to Nimes, visit this charmingly restored residence, which nestles in the shade of a three-hundred year-old cedar. Spacious rooms combine contemporary comfort with period furniture. True to the local gastronomic tradition, fresh market produce is the mainstay of exquisite menus.

hotel annual closing
Néant
restaurant annual closing
Néant
restaurant weekly closing
Néant
equipments
telephone, internet, T.V.
Satellite, minibar, safe
environment
architecture 19e, furniture 19e,
garden, terrace 120 m²
leisure, relaxation
golf course 15 km, horse-riding
10 km, sauna, solarium,
jacuzzi, own indoor and
outdoor tennis courts

Visa ● Diners ● MASTER CARD

Road map p. 619

A7 exit Valence North, dir. City center,
bridge across Rhône - dir South - 9 km
N86 dir. Nîmes

 Valence: 14 km

La Bouitte

Saint-Martin de Belleville

www.chateauxhotels.com/bouitte | reservation service: 33 (0) 1.40.07.00.20

Hameau de Saint-Marcel
73440 Saint-Martin de Belleville
Tel.: 33 (0) 4.79.08.96.77 – Fax: 33 (0) 4.79.08.96.03

bouitte@chateauxhotels.com
Marie-Louise & René MEILLEUR

5 rooms: 128 € / 145 €
Breakfast: 12,3 €
Menu(s): 28 € / 92 €

hotel annual closing
30/04 > 01/07 ● 01/09 > 15/12
restaurant annual closing
30/04 > 01/07 ● 01/09 > 15/12
equipments
telephone, T.V. Satellite,
minibar, safe
environment
terrace, view, total calm
leisure, relaxation
tennis 1 km, horse-riding 5 km

As soon as you walk into this delightful place, you will be captivated by its typically Savoyard charm and by the warm hospitality of Marie-Louise and René MEILLEUR. Elegant suites each have their own distinctive style. Creatively concocted culinary feasts. Authentic.

Visa ● Diners ● JCB ● MASTER CARD

Road map p. 619

Direction "Les Ménuires - Val Thorens"

Lyon Saint-Exupery: 100 km

Le Port au bord du lac 74290 Talloires
Tel.: 33 (0) 4.50.60.71.10 – Fax: 33 (0) 4.50.60.77.51
cottagebise@chateauxhotels.com
Christine & Jean-Claude BISE
35 rooms: 80 € / 215 €
Breakfast: 14 €
Menu(s): 22 € / 49 € - **Carte:** 30 € -
1/2 board: 76 € / 145 €

In the heart of the bay of Talloires, Jean-Claude Bise welcomes you in the refined scenery of rooms and garden, where you can savour delightful food. Traditional cuisine full of character. On the lakeside, shady terraces and gardens covered with flowers create an impressionist decor.

hotel annual closing
01/01 > 25/04
restaurant annual closing
01/01 > 25/04
equipments
lift, telephone, T.V. Satellite, safe
environment
garden, terrace, view
leisure, relaxation
heated pool, tennis 0.1 km, golf course 3 km, horse-riding 2 km

Visa ● Diners ● JCB ● MASTER CARD

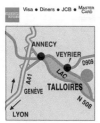

Road map p. 619
A41 exit south of Annecy

Annecy: 15 km

L'Abbaye de Talloires

Annecy | Talloires

www.chateauxhotels.com/talloires | reservation service: 33 (0) 1.40.07.00.20

chemin des moines 74290 Talloires
Tel.: 33 (0) 4.50.60.77.33 – Fax: 33 (0) 4.50.60.78.81
talloires@chateauxhotels.com
Paul-Maurice MOREL

29 rooms: 134 € / 300 €
4 suites: 243 € / 520 €
Breakfast: 15,24 €
Menu(s): 43 € / 90 € - **Carte:** 62 €
1/2 board: 121 € / 277 €

Open all year
equipments
telephone, internet, T.V., safe,
baby-sitting
environment
architecture 11ᵉ, park 4 ha,
garden, terrace, view, total
calm
leisure, relaxation
tennis 0.3 km, golf course
2 km, horse-riding 1 km,
beauty salon, sauna, jacuzzi,
(leisures free: golf, tennis,
mountain bikes)

The lovely façade of this former 11th century Benedictine abbey is mirrored in the shimmering waters of Annecy lake. An ancient cloister whose serenity is enhanced by birdsong. Splendid rooms overlooking the lake, chef Michel Renaud's inspired cuisine. Time stands still as you savour eternal moments.

Visa • MASTER CARD

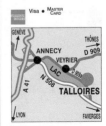

Road map p. 619

A41 exit North or South. D909 East bank of the lake dir. Thônes/ Veyrier. D909a

✈ Annecy-Meythet: 16 km

Rue André Theuriet 74290 Talloires

Tel.: 33 (0) 4.50.60.76.11 – Fax: 33 (0) 4.50.60.73.42

preslac@chateauxhotels.com
Marie-Paule CONAN
16 rooms: 151 € / 244 €
Breakfast: 15 €

A privileged site in a large park on the bank of the lake with a private beach. Breakfast served in the apartments or in the gardens. Rooms facing the lake, terrace or balcony, direct-dial telephone, fax/modem/Minitel connection, 4 rooms with jaccusi. Golf and riding club 2 km. Restaurants nearby.

hotel annual closing
08/10 > 01/04

equipments
telephone, internet, T.V. Satellite, minibar, safe, baby-sitting

environment
architecture contemporaine, park 1 ha, garden, terrace 3200 m², view, total calm

leisure, relaxation
golf course 2 km, horse-riding 2 km, private beach

Visa ● Diners ● MASTER CARD

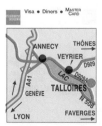

Road map p. 619

A41 exit North or South, D909 on the East bank, D909a from Veyrier

Genève: 45 km

Route du Port 74290 Talloires
Tel.: 33 (0) 4.50.60.71.14 – Fax: 33 (0) 4.50.60.74.06
fleurs@chateauxhotels.com
Famille JAEGLER
8 rooms: 79 € / 99 €
Breakfast: 11 €
Menu(s): 27 € / 46 € - **Carte:** 47 €
1/2 board: 85 € / 90 €

hotel annual closing
12/11 > 20/12

restaurant annual closing
12/11 > 20/12

equipments
telephone, internet, T.V.
Canal+, minibar

environment
park 0.4 ha, garden, terrace,
view

leisure, relaxation
tennis 0.2 km, golf course
3 km, horse-riding 2 km,
pedal-boats, boats for hire

Near La Clusaz and Le Grand Bornand (Alpine and Cross Country skiing) in a vast park, a 1900 restored villa. Elegance, comfort, superlative cuisine by chefs Charles et Sebastien Jaegler. Delectable dishes featuring fresh fish from Lake of Annecy. Breakfast, lunch and dinner served on the terrace.

Visa ● MASTER CARD

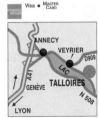

Road map p. 619

A41 exit Annecy North or South, D909a dir. Thones-Veyrier (on the lake river)

 Annecy/Meythet: 15 km

Bonnatrait 74140 Sciez-sur-Léman

Tel.: 33 (0) 4.50.72.62.33 – Fax: 33 (0) 4.50.72.57.28

coudree@chateauxhotels.com
Catherine REALE-LADEN

15 rooms: 120,43 € / 296,51 €
4 flats: 280,51 € / 344,53 €
Breakfast: 15,24 €
Menu(s): 51,83 € / 82,32 €

Such is the history that is bequeathed to us, the Château de Coudrée enrols into the category of residences of a very high class. Everything breathes of sophistication: delicate wall coverings, elegant panelling, and authentic rooms. The cuisine is familiar, as well, with the highest level.

hotel annual closing
27/01 > 22/02 • 27/10 > 29/11

restaurant annual closing
27/01 > 22/02 • 27/10 > 29/11

equipments
telephone, internet, T.V.
Satellite, minibar, safe,
baby-sitting, valet parking

environment
architecture 12°, furniture 18°,
park 4 ha, garden, terrace
800 m², view, total calm

leisure, relaxation
heated pool, golf course
15 km, horse-riding 2 km,
beauty salon, balneo, thermal
baths, sauna, hammam,
solarium, fitness, jacuzzi,
paragliding

Visa • Diners • MASTER CARD

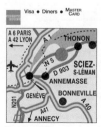

Road map p. 619

A40 exit Thonon/Evian. RN5 dir. Thonon

Genève-Cointrin: 28 km

Château de Chervinges

Villefranche-sur-Saône

www.chateauxhotels.com/chervinges | reservation service: 33 (0) 1.40.07.00.20

Gleize 69400 Villefranche-sur-Saône
Tel.: 33 (0) 4.74.65.29.76 – Fax: 33 (0) 4.74.62.92.42
chervinges@chateauxhotels.com
Famille LEGROS
10 rooms: 100 €
5 suites: 145 € / 150 €
Breakfast: 10 €
Menu(s): 28 € / 61 € - **1/2 board:** 95 €

hotel annual closing
02/01 > 25/01
restaurant annual closing
02/01 > 25/01
hotel weekly closing
mon, sun
01/11 > 15/04
restaurant weekly closing
mon, sun(ev)
01/11 > 15/04
equipments
lift, telephone, internet, T.V.,
minibar
environment
architecture 18e, terrace, view,
total calm
leisure, relaxation
golf course 10 km, horse-riding
5 km

Within view of the Beaujolais vineyards, this medieval farmhouse rebuilt in the XVIIIth century, is an ideal place to stay. Its 10 rooms and 5 apartments, its gastronomic restaurant, its park, its swimming-pool and tennis court, all invite you to enjoy a few hours away from it all.

Visa • JCB • MASTERCARD

Road map p. 619

A6 exit Villefranche. D38 dir. Roanne

Lyon/St-Exupèry: 45 km

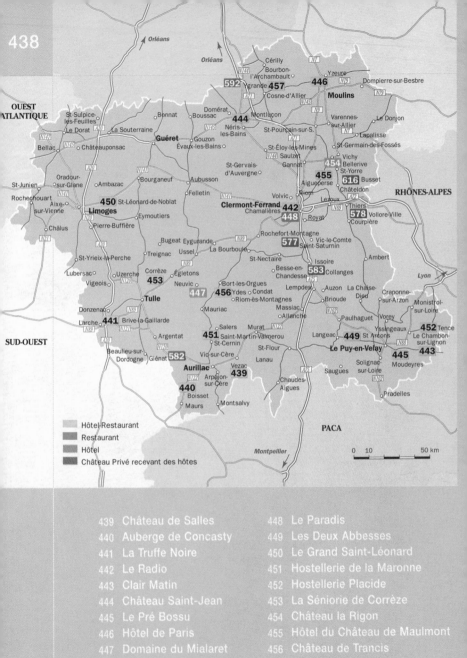

OUEST
ATLANTIQUE

RHÔNES-ALPES

SUD-OUEST

PACA

Orléans
Cérilly
Bourbon-l'Archambault
Yzeure
Dompierre-sur-Besbre
Ygrande
592 **457** **446**
Cosne-d'Allier
Moulins
Domérat
444
Varennes-sur-Allier
Le Donjon
Boussac
Montluçon
Bonnat
Néris-les-Bains
St-Pourçain-sur-S.
Lapalisse
Guéret
Gouzon
St-Germain-des-Fossés
La Souterraine
Évaux-les-Bains
St-Éloy-les-Mines
Vichy
Châteauponsac
Saulzet
Bellerive
454
Bellas
St-Gervais-d'Auvergne
Gannat
St-Yorre
Bourganeuf
455 Aigueperse
Busset **616**
Oradour-sur-Glane
Aubusson
Châteldon
Ambazac
Volvic
Riom
Felletin
St-Léonard-de-Noblat
450
Clermont-Ferrand **442**
Lezoux
Limoges
Chamalières
448 Royat
Thiers
Vollore-Ville **578**
Eymoutiers
Pierre-Buffière
Courpière
St-Junien
Rochefort-Montagne
St-Yrieix-la-Perche
Bugeat Eygurande
577
Vic-le-Comte
Châlus
Treignac
La Bourboule
Saint-Saturnin
Ambert
Ussel
St-Nectaire
Lubersac
Égletons
Issoire
Lyon
Corrèze
583 Collanges
Vigeois
453
Besse-en-Chandesse
Neuvic
Craponne-sur-Arzon
Uzerche
Bort-les-Orgues
Lempdes
Auzon
La Chaise-Dieu
Monistrol-sur-Loire
Tulle
447 **456** Ydes Condat
Riom-ès-Montagnes
Brioude
Vorey
Donzenac
Mauriac
Massiac
Yssingeaux
452 Tence
Larche
441 Brive-la-Gaillarde
Allanche
Paulhaguet
Le Chambon-sur-Lignon
Argentat
Salers Murat
Langeac
449 St Arcons
443
Beaulieu-sur-Dordogne
451 Saint-Martin-Valmerou
445
Glénat **582**
Vic-sur-Cère
St-Flour
Le Puy-en-Velay
Moudeyres
Aurillac
Vezac
St-Cernin
Lanau
Solignac-sur-Loire
Arpajon-sur-Cère
439
Saugues
Pradelles
440
Boisset
Chaudes-Aigues
Montsalvy
Maurs

Hôtel-Restaurant
Restaurant
Hôtel
Château Privé recevant des hôtes

Orléans
Orléans
Montpellier

0   10   50 km

15130 Vézac

Tel.: 33 (0) 4.71.62.41.41 – Fax: 33 (0) 4.71.62.44.14

salles@chateauxhotels.com
Roland PASQUIER

20 rooms: 79 € / 95 €
4 flats: 167 € / 300 € - **6 suites:** 125 €
Breakfast: 10 €
Menu(s): 22 € / 52 € - **Carte:** 14 € -
1/2 board: 71,5 € / 79,5 €

A traditional 15th century Auvergne-style watchtower, in a 20-acre park with centuries-old trees...Silence and style in the rooms, magnificent views of the Auvergne mountains, and a panoramic restaurant with carefully prepared cuisine.

hotel annual closing
04/11 > 31/03

restaurant annual closing
04/11 > 31/03

equipments
lift, telephone, T.V.
Satellite/Canal+

environment
architecture 15°, park 8 ha,
garden, terrace 70 m², view

leisure, relaxation
heated pool, golf course
0.8 km, horse-riding 3 km,
hammam, jacuzzi

Visa ● Diners ● MASTER CARD

Road map p. 619

A75 exit Massiac or N122 dir. Aurillac

Aurillac: 7 km

Auberge de Concasty

Boisset

www.chateauxhotels.com/concasty | reservation service: 33 (0) 1.40.07.00.20

Concasty 15600 Boisset
Tel.: 33 (0) 4.71.62.21.16 – Fax: 33 (0) 4.71.62.22.22
concasty@chateauxhotels.com
Martine & Omar CAUSSE-ADLLAL

12 rooms: 54 € / 91 €
1 suite: 103 € / 125 €
Breakfast: 9 €
Menu(s): 27 € / 38 € - **1/2 board:** 56 € / 97 €

hotel annual closing
01/01 > 15/03•20/11 > 15/03
restaurant annual closing
01/01 > 15/03•20/11 > 15/03
equipments
telephone, internet, T.V.
Canal+, minibar
environment
park 5 ha, garden, terrace
60 m², view, total calm
leisure, relaxation
heated pool, tennis 10 km, golf
course 14 km, horse-riding
10 km, hammam, jacuzzi,
signposted walking trails

In the heart of the Cantal a touch of the south is here, where tradition and freedom mean relaxation and respect, and this guest house nestling in greenery provides a refuge for epicureans. Martine and Omar thoughtfully select authentic dishes and fine wines. Reservation recommended.

Visa • Diners • MASTER CARD

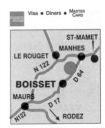

Road map p. 619

In south to Aurillac via N122 then D64

Aurillac: 25 km

22, boulevard Anatole France
19100 Brive-la-Gaillarde
Tel.: 33 (0) 5.55.92.45.00 – Fax: 33 (0) 5.55.92.45.13
truffenoire@chateauxhotels.com
Estelle BASTIEN-LACHAISE

23 rooms: 86 € / 105 €
Breakfast: 9,15 €
Menu(s): 23 € / 61 € - **Carte:** 40 € -
1/2 board: 67,5 € / 75 €

A warm welcome awaits the voyager to the heart of the Gaillard city. Located at the cross-roads of the Limousin, Quercy and Périgord regions, the hotel features. Estelle and her staff delight in serving you the chef's seasonal terroir specialities.

Open all year

equipments
lift, telephone, internet, T.V. Satellite/Canal+, minibar

environment
terrace 250 m²

leisure, relaxation
tennis 2 km, golf course 5 km, horse-riding 3 km, beauty salon, thalassotherapy, balneo, sauna, solarium, jacuzzi

Visa ● Diners ● JCB ● MASTER CARD

Road map p. 619

A20 exit Brive centre - N89 Brive centre

✈ Brive-Laroche: 2 km

Le Radio
Chamalières
www.chateauxhotels.com/radio | reservation service: 33 (0) 1.40.07.00.20

43, av. Pierre et Marie Curie
63400 Chamalières
Tel.: 33 (0) 4.73.30.87.83 – Fax: 33 (0) 4.73.36.42.44
radio@chateauxhotels.com
Caroline MIOCHE

25 rooms: 69 € / 120 €
1 flat: 142 € / 166 €
Breakfast: 10 €
Menu(s): 28 € / 81 € - **Carte:** 58 €
1/2 board: 79 € / 101 €

hotel annual closing
29/04 > 02/05 • 04/11 > 10/11
restaurant annual closing
29/04 > 02/05 • 04/11 > 10/11
equipments
lift, telephone, internet, T.V.
Satellite
environment
architecture Art Déco, garden,
view, total calm
leisure, relaxation
tennis 2 km, golf course 6 km,
horse-riding 10 km, thermal
baths, sauna, fitness

*Located in the heart of the
mysterious Auvergne, on the
heights of the Chamalières,
this 1930 hotel decorated in
pure Art deco style delicately
couples the quality of the welcome and room decorations
with a creative cuisine refined
by local produce. Panoramic
view.*

Visa ● Diners ● MASTER CARD

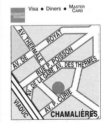

Road map p. 619
A71, A72,, A75 exit Clermont. dir.
Chamalières-royat

Clermont-Ferrand-Aulnat:
13 km

Les Barandons 43400 Le Chambon-sur-Lignon

Tel.: 33 (0) 4.71.59.73.03 – Fax: 33 (0) 4.71.65.87.66
clairmatin@chateauxhotels.com
Alain BARD

25 rooms: 45,73 € / 121,96 €
Breakfast: 7,62 €
Menu(s): 17,53 € / 45,73 € - **Carte:** 11,06 € -
1/2 board: 47,26 € / 80,80 €

Splendid exposed setting facing the Cévennes mountains. Ideal location for a revitalizing holiday. Ideal for visiting the southern Auvergne region. Organized children's games. Putting-green. Billiards, table-tennis, 18-hole golf course at Chambon-sur-Lignon. Walks in the forest, fishing, etc.

hotel annual closing
03/01 > 30/03 • 01/11 > 29/12
restaurant annual closing
03/01 > 30/03 • 01/11 > 29/12
equipments
internet, T.V. Canal+
environment
architecture 10º, park 1.5 ha, garden, terrace 80 m^2, view, total calm
leisure, relaxation
heated pool, horse-riding 0.5 km, thermal baths, sauna, hammam, solarium, fitness, jacuzzi, tennis, 4x4 cross-country trails, putting-green, golf 7 km

Visa • Diners • MASTER CARD

Road map p. 619

A47 exit Firminy-Fayol. D185 dir. Tence/St-Agrève

✈ Lyon-Satolas: 100 km

🚗 🅿 ≋ 🔍 ▶ ☀

Château Saint-Jean

Montluçon
www.chateauxhotels.com/saintjean | reservation service: 33 (0) 1.40.07.00.20

Parc Saint Jean 03100 Montluçon
Tel.: 33 (0) 4.70.02.71.71 – Fax: 33 (0) 4.70.02.71.70
saintjean@chateauxhotels.com
MM. TINDILIERE, DOUAULT & MAUGIS

14 rooms: 65 € / 93 €
1 flat: 222 € - **6 suites:** 115 €
Breakfast: 10 €
Menu(s): 30 € / 50 € - **Carte:** 39 €
1/2 board: 110 € / 155 €

Open all year

equipments
lift, telephone, internet, T.V.
Satellite/Canal+, minibar

environment
architecture 11^e, garden,
terrace 35 m^2

leisure, relaxation
heated pool/covered, tennis
5 km, golf course 5 km,
horse-riding 10 km, beauty
salon, thermal baths, solarium,
fitness (town center - 10 mn by
car)

This former residence of the Crusaders was converted into a hotel in 1925, continuing the hospitality that made it exceptional. Bordering on a magnificent park with hundred year old trees, this domain features 20 rooms, 5 suites, a heated indoor pool. An ideal stop-over for visits to Auvergne.

Visa ● Diners ● MASTER CARD

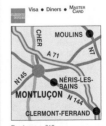

Road map p. 619

A71 exit 10 or N144 dir. Clermont-Ferrand/Néris-les-Bains

Montluçon-Guéret: 40 km

43150 Moudeyres
Tel.: 33 (0) 4.71.05.10.70 – Fax: 33 (0) 4.71.05.10.21
prebossu@chateauxhotels.com
Carlos GROOTAERT – Marleen MOREELS
10 rooms: 66 € / 83 €
Breakfast: 11,5 €
Menu(s): 40 € / 55 € - **1/2 board:** 88 € / 96 €

Old thatched cottage on the edge of the forest. Cosy and welcoming atmosphere. Beautiful dining-room in stone where you can savour simple, light, inventive cuisine, with regional produce and from their own kitchen-garden. Very comfortable rooms with rustic furniture. Picnic provided for your walks.

Visa ● M**ASTER** **C**ARD

hotel annual closing
01/11 > 30/03
restaurant annual closing
01/11 > 30/03
equipments
telephone
environment
architecture 18e, garden, terrace 100 m², view, vegetable garden, total calm
leisure, relaxation
tennis 5 km, golf course 30 km, horse-riding 6 km

Road map p. 619

A71 exit Brioude/Le Puy-En-Velay - D15 dir. Les Pendreaux

✈ Loudes-Le Puy: 40 km

Hôtel de Paris
Moulins
www.chateauxhotels.com/paris | reservation service: 33 (0) 1.40.07.00.20

21, rue de Paris 03000 Moulins
Tel.: 33 (0) 4.70.44.00.58 – Fax: 33 (0) 4.70.34.05.39
paris@chateauxhotels.com
Yveline GELY
23 rooms: 54 € / 100 €
4 suites: 122 €
Breakfast: 9 €
Menu(s): 24,50 € / 64 €

restaurant annual closing
03/01 > 23/01 • 04/08 > 24/08
restaurant weekly closing
mon, sat(lun), sun(ev)
equipments
lift, telephone, internet, T.V.
Canal+, minibar
environment
architecture 19e, garden,
terrace
leisure, relaxation
golf course 6 km

At the gates of the historic quarter near the museums, the Hotel, run by Yveline Gély, an expert cellar-master, has made a warm atmosphere and good food its hallmark. Yannick Guichaoua and his team invites you to partake of elegant dishes which change with the seasons, in perfect harmony with the wines.

Visa ● Diners ● MASTER CARD

Road map p. 619

A71 exit Montmarault - N7 dir.
Bourges/Roanne

 Vichy: 57 km

Route d'Egletons 19160 NEUVIC
Tel.: 33 (0) 5.55.46.02.61 – Fax: 33 (0) 5.55.46.02.65
mialaret@chateauxhotels.com
Marc VAN DER VEN
10 rooms: 106,50 € / 145 €
Menu(s): 19,80 € / 38,10 € - **1/2 board:** 116,50 €

Near the Dordogne Gorge, this magnificent property presides over a stunning 18 acre park. Here nature runs rife and you can frequently sight deer, will boar, foxes, otters and eagles! Calm and spacious rooms. For lovers of the open countryside.

Open all year
equipments
telephone, T.V., minibar, safe, baby-sitting
environment
architecture 19ᵉ, furniture 19ᵉ, park 45 ha, garden, terrace 100 m², view, total calm
leisure, relaxation
golf course 4 km, horse-riding 4 km

Visa ● MASTER CARD

Road map p. 619

A89 exit Ussel Est, RN 89 direction Brive

 Brive / Clermont-Ferrand: 100 km

Le Paradis
Royat
www.chateauxhotels.com/paradis | reservation service: 33 (0) 1.40.07.00.20

Avenue du Paradis 63130 Royat
Tel.: 33 (0) 4.73.35.85.46 – Fax: 33 (0) 4.73.35.64.41
paradis@chateauxhotels.com
M. & Mme. Alain BLANC
Menu(s): 14,94 € / 39,64 € - **Carte:** 22,87 €

restaurant annual closing
01/01 > 22/01 ● 29/07 > 06/08
environment
architecture 19ᵉ, terrace
300 m², view
leisure, relaxation
tennis 2 km, golf course 3 km

A chateau on a rocky spur overlooking Royat, panoramic terraces to enjoy delicious food. Walks in the natural Volcano Park. Nearby are Gallo-Roman spas, a 11th century fortified church, former craters which have become lakes and historic sites. Local accomodation available.

Visa ● MasterCard

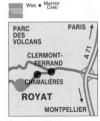

Road map p. 619

A71, A72, A75 exit Clermont. dir.
Chamalières-Royat

 Clermont-Aulnat: 10 km

Le Château 43300 Saint-Arcons-d'Allier
Tel.: 33 (0) 4.71.74.03.08 – Fax: 33 (0) 4.71.74.05.30
deuxabbesses@chateauxhotels.com
Laurence PERCEVAL-HERMET

5 rooms: 100 € / 170 €
3 flats: 160 € / 180 € - **2 suites:** 200 € / 240 €
Breakfast: 15 €
Table d'hôtes (sur rés.): 40 €

A "split hotel" full of surprises in a picturesque renovated village, where the château houses reception area, knights' hall, salons. The 10 bedrooms in the renovated houses are furnished in period style. Succulent food served by the masters of the house, candle-lit dinners.

hotel annual closing
12/11 > 30/04

restaurant annual closing
12/11 > 30/04

equipments
telephone, safe, baby-sitting

environment
architecture 12e, garden, terrace, view, vegetable garden, total calm

leisure, relaxation
tennis 5 km, golf course 30 km, horse-riding 5 km, helicopter and baloon: transfers and vulcano over flight

Visa ● JCB ● MASTER CARD

Road map p. 619

A71, A75 exit 20/22 Brioude, N102 dir. Le Puy, D56 dir. Langeac, D585 dir. Saugues, D30 dir. Prades

Loudes-Le Puy: 30 km

Le Grand Saint-Léonard

Saint-Léonard-de-Noblat

www.chateauxhotels.com/saintleonard | reservation service: 33 (0) 1.40.07.00.20

23, avenue du Champ de Mars
87400 Saint-Léonard-de-Noblat
Tel.: 33 (0) 5.55.56.18.18 – Fax: 33 (0) 5.55.56.98.32
saintleonard@chateauxhotels.com
Jean-Marc VALLET
13 rooms: 51 € / 55 €
Breakfast: 9 €
Menu(s): 23 € / 55 € - **Carte:** 61 € - **1/2 board:** 140 €

hotel annual closing 15/11 > 15/12	*Former post house in medieval city. Refined gourmet cuisine by Jean-Marc Vallet, featuring delicious fish dishes. Discover: Saint-Léonard and its 12th-13th century collegiate church, medieval town of Noblat, mills, 13th century bridge. 20 minutes away: Limoges, capital of arts and fireworks.*
restaurant annual closing 15/11 > 15/12	
hotel weekly closing mon 16/09 > 14/06	
restaurant weekly closing mon(lun) 15/06 > 15/09 mon, tue(lun) 16/09 > 14/06	
equipments telephone, T.V.	
environment architecture 19e, furniture 19e	
leisure, relaxation tennis 2 km, golf course 15 km	

Visa ● Diners ● MASTERCARD

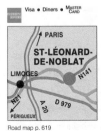

Road map p. 619

A20 Paris-Toulouse exit 34 - N141
dir.St-Léonard - Clermont-Ferrand

 Limoges Bellegarde: 25 km

Le Theil 15140 Saint-Martin-Valmeroux

Tel.: 33 (0) 4.71.69.20.33 – Fax: 33 (0) 4.71.69.28.22
maronne@chateauxhotels.com
Alain DECOCK

17 rooms: 81 € / 113 €
2 flats: 114 € / 138 € - **2 suites:** 114 € / 138 €
Breakfast: 11 €
Menu(s): 26 € / 38 € - **Carte:** 37 € -
1/2 board: 77 € / 106 €

The view over the Maronne Valley is unforgettable. This beautiful house located at the interior of the Park of volcanoes is a stopping place for lovers of architecture and culture. The cosy rooms and the renowned cuisine of Madame Decock receive all the votes. All around is the Cantal and its mysteries.

hotel annual closing
05/11 > 25/03

restaurant annual closing
05/11 > 25/03

equipments
lift, telephone, internet, T.V. Satellite, minibar, safe

environment
architecture 19e, park 1.5 ha, garden, view, total calm

leisure, relaxation
heated pool, golf course 35 km, horse-riding 1 km, tennis

Visa ● Diners ● JCB ● MASTER CARD

Road map p. 619

A75 exit Massiac , D680 dir. Salers

Aurillac: 33 km

Route d'Annonay 43190 Tence
Tel.: 33 (0) 4.71.59.82.76 – Fax: 33 (0) 4.71.65.44.46
placide@chateauxhotels.com
Véronique & Pierre-Marie PLACIDE
13 rooms: 69 € / 99 €
Breakfast: 10 €
Menu(s): 15 € / 49 € - **Carte:** 38 €
1/2 board: 61 € / 84 €

hotel annual closing
15/11 > 15/03
restaurant annual closing
15/11 > 15/03
hotel weekly closing
mon, tue, sun (ev)
01/09 > 30/06
restaurant weekly closing
mon(lun), tue(lun)
01/07 > 31/08
mon, tue, sun(ev)
01/09 > 30/06
equipments
telephone, internet, T.V.
environment
architecture 19ᵉ, garden
leisure, relaxation
tennis 0.5 km, golf course
10 km, horse-riding 2 km,
flowered garden with chaises
longues

*Nestling amid the lush green-
ery of the Velay region, the
Placide family knows how to
welcome you in his former
post house, tastefully renovated. Spacious and cosy
rooms, charms include breakfast in the garden. Refined
cuisine from master chef
served in a pretty room overlooking the garden.*

Visa ● MasterCard

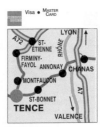

Road map p. 619

A7 exit Chanas or A72 exit Firminy-
Fayol

St-Étienne-Andrezieux:
60 km

Le Bourg 19800 Corrèze
Tel.: 33 (0) 5.55.21.22.88 – Fax: 33 (0) 5.55.21.24.00
correze@chateauxhotels.com
Gérard COSTES
29 rooms: 62,5 € / 122 €
Breakfast: 7,5 €
Menu(s): 16,5 € / 24,5 € - **Carte:** 36 € -
1/2 board: 54 € / 84 €

Overlooking a medieval village of Corrèze, this magnificent 19th century residence offers a warm welcome to an exceptional site. Delight in the calm of the original rooms before tasting the refined regional cooking served in the friendly atmosphere of the restaurant. Beautiful, natural sites nearby.

hotel annual closing
01/02 > 01/03
restaurant annual closing
01/02 > 01/03
hotel weekly closing
sat, sun
01/11 > 31/03
restaurant weekly closing
mon, sun
01/11 > 31/03
equipments
lift, telephone, internet, T.V.
Canal+, minibar, safe
environment
architecture 19^e, garden,
terrace 200 m^2, view, total
calm
leisure, relaxation
golf course 30 km, horse-riding
10 km, sauna

Visa ● Diners ● MASTER CARD

Road map p. 619

A20 exit Tulle, N89, N120 dir.Tulle/
Clermont-Ferrand

Brive: 45 km

Château la Rigon

Vichy | Bellerive-sur-Allier

www.chateauxhotels.com/rigon | reservation service: 33 (0) 1.40.07.00.20

Route de Serbannes 03700 Bellerive-sur-Allier
Tel.: 33 (0) 4.70.59.86.46 – Fax: 33 (0) 4.70.59.94.77
rigon@chateauxhotels.com
Lyliane VILLENEUVE
7 rooms: 48 € / 58 €
1 suite: 57 € / 84 €
Breakfast: 5,8 €

hotel annual closing
01/01 > 01/03 • 15/11 > 01/03

equipments
telephone, T.V.

environment
architecture 18e, park 3 ha,
garden, total calm

leisure, relaxation
heated pool/covered, tennis
1.5 km, golf course 2 km,
horse-riding 5 km,
thalassotherapy, thermal
baths, visit to "Vulcania"
site (35-min drive)

*Charming XIXth century resi-
dence. 2 km from Vichy, in a
8-acre park with 100-year-old-
trees. A haven of peace and
relaxation. Individually furnished rooms. Heated pool
under a 19th century glass
roof. Two golf courses, tennis
courts, horse riding, race
course, fishing and casinos
nearby.*

Visa • MASTER CARD

Road map p. 619

A71 or A72 exit Thiers. D984 dir.
Aigueperse

 Vichy-Charmeil: 5 km

St-Priest Bramefant 63310 Randan
Tel.: 33 (0) 4.70.59.03.45 – Fax: 33 (0) 4.70.59.11.88
maulmont@chateauxhotels.com
Mary BOSMAN-VAN DER ZALM
19 rooms: 65 € / 165 €
2 flats: 185 € / 260 € - **1 suite:** 180 € / 205 €
Breakfast: 10 €
Menu(s): 18 € / 45 € - **Carte:** déc-20 € -
1/2 board: 60 € / 110 €

The Château is a former royal residence standing on 54 acres of parkland. From the terrace and swimming pool there is a splendid view of the Allier valley. The oak-panelled dining-room proposes a fine menu. Apartment rooms, golf, horse-riding, heated pool, sauna, fitness center.

Visa ● **MASTER CARD**

Road map p. 619

A72 from Lyon, exit 2 Thiers/Vichy, N906 Puy Guillaume/Vichy, D43, D59 Maulmont

 Aulnat/Clermont Ferrand: 35 km

hotel annual closing
02/01 > 13/02
restaurant annual closing
02/01 > 13/02
equipments
telephone, internet, T.V. Satellite, minibar, safe, baby-sitting
environment
architecture 19°, park 22 ha, garden, terrace 400 m², view, total calm
leisure, relaxation
heated pool/covered, tennis 6 km, horse-riding, thermal baths, sauna, fitness, game shooting during autumn/winter season from October 1st

Château de Trancis
Ydes
www.chateauxhotels.com/trancis | reservation service: 33 (0) 1.40.07.00.20

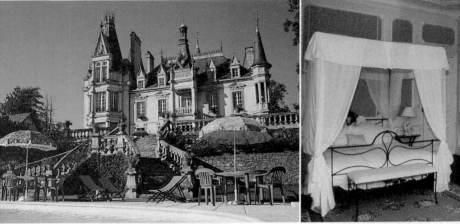

7, route de Saignes 15210 Ydes
Tel.: 33 (0) 4.71.40.60.40 – Fax: 33 (0) 4.71.40.62.13
trancis@chateauxhotels.com
Pierre & Roberta Van BEYMA

6 rooms: 70 € / 125 €
1 flat: 548 € / 799 €
Breakfast: 9 €
Menu(s): 29 € - **Carte:** 30 € - **1/2 board:** 75 € / 100 €

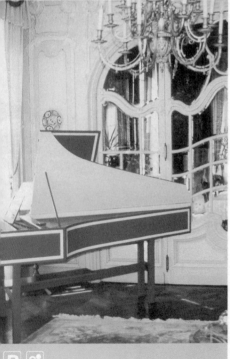

hotel annual closing
05/01 > 05/02
restaurant annual closing
05/01 > 05/02
equipments
telephone, internet, T.V.
environment
architecture 19e, park 3 ha,
garden, terrace 300 m^2, view,
total calm

leisure, relaxation
tennis 2 km, golf course
20 km, horse-riding 9 km

A magnificent château, situated at the gateway to the Auvergne National Volcanic Park and closeby the spectacular gorges of the Dordogne, where the cuisine is exquisite and the hospitality unparalled. The château has been tastefully restored and affords pleasant views over the valley of the Sumène. English and Dutch spoken.

Visa ● Diners ● JCB ● MASTER CARD

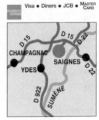

Road map p. 619

A71 exit 2 Clermont-Ferrand N89 dir. Bordeaux then D922 dir. Bort-Les-Orgues

 Clermont-Ferrand: 90 km

Le Mont 03160 Ygrande
Tel.: 33 (0) 4.70.66.33.11 – Fax: 33 (0) 4.70.66.33.63
ygrande@chateauxhotels.com
Pierre-Marie TISSIER
16 rooms: 85 € / 145 €
Breakfast: 10 €
Menu(s): 24 € / 35 € - **1/2 board:** 80 € / 110 €

Surrounded by 99 acres of gardens, woodland and meadows, this splendid hilltop castle commands an unrivalled view of the Bourbonnais countryside. A magnificent stud farm, lavishly renovated rooms and generous cuisine offer all the ingredients for relaxation. The service is particularly friendly.

Visa ● MASTER CARD

Road map p. 619

A71 exit St-Amand-Montrond. N144, D978a and D953

hotel annual closing
02/01 > 01/03
restaurant annual closing
02/01 > 01/03
restaurant weekly closing
sun(ev), mon
01/09 > 30/06
equipments
telephone, internet, T.V.
Satellite, safe
environment
architecture 19ᵉ, park 40 ha,
garden, terrace, view, total
calm
leisure, relaxation
heated pool, horse-riding,
thermal baths, sauna, fitness,
jacuzzi, table tennis, snooker
(set in tennis, golf &
horse-riding)

Clermont-Ferrand: 80 km

How to book ?

➜ At the Châteaux & Hôtels reservation centre:
- Tél : 00 33 (0) 1 40 07 00 20
- Fax : 00 33 (0) 1 40 07 00 30

➜ By Internet:
- www.chateauxhotels.com
- resa@chateauxhotels.com

➜ Directly with the establishement required

CHATEAUX & HOTELS
DE FRANCE®

Bourgogne Franche-Comté

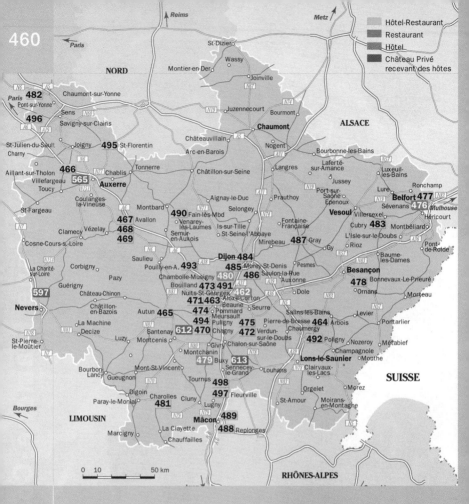

460

A book to devour!

117 recipes presented by their chefs,
to be followed or savoured,
Not in moderation !

Hôtel Villa Louise
Aloxe-corton
www.chateauxhotels.com/villalouise | reservation service: 33 (0) 1.40.07.00.20

21420 Aloxe-corton
Tel.: 33 (0) 3.80.26.46.70 – Fax: 33 (0) 3.80.26.47.16
villalouise@chateauxhotels.com
Véronique PERRIN
10 rooms: 92 € / 145 €
Breakfast: 12 €

Open all year
equipments
telephone, internet, T.V.
Satellite, minibar, safe,
baby-sitting
environment
architecture 17e, park 3 ha,
garden, view, total calm
leisure, relaxation
tennis 4 km, golf course 6 km,
horse-riding 4 km, bicycle hire

Owned by Veronique Perrin, a 3rd generation wine-grower, this hotel embodies the Burgundy dream, 17th c stone walls, grand cru wine-cellars, and breakfasts full of home-cooked surprises. Total peace reigns over a charming garden housing vines producing the only grand cru red of the Cote de Beaune.

Visa ● JCB ● MASTER CARD

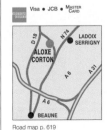

Road map p. 619

A6 exit N° 24 Savigny-Les-Beaune,
dir. Dijon by RN74, after 3 km Aloxe-
Corton

 Lyon: 170 km

Bourgogne Franche-Comté |

Aloxe-Corton I Ladoix Serrigny
www.chateaushotels.com/paulands I reservation service: 33 (0) 1.40.07.00.20

Aloxe-Corton 21550 Ladoix Serrigny
Tel.: 33 (0) 3.80.26.41.05 – Fax: 33 (0) 3.80.26.47.56
paulands@chateaushotels.com
Christophe FASQUEL
17 rooms: 65 € / 80 €
3 flats: 90 €
Breakfast: 9 €
Menu(s): 15 € / 76 € - **Carte:** 20 €

A must in Burgundy, between Côtes de Beaune and Côtes de Nuits. In this typical old residence, you will taste the famous regional specialities, an extraordinary wine list, and the comfort of the individually decorated rooms.

hotel annual closing
23/12 > 05/01
restaurant annual closing
23/12 > 05/01
hotel weekly closing
sun
restaurant weekly closing
sun
equipments
telephone, T.V.
environment
garden, terrace 50 m², view
leisure, relaxation
heated pool, tennis 5 km, golf course 8 km, horse-riding 4 km

Visa ● Diners ● JCB ● MASTER CARD

Road map p. 619

A6 exit 24 - Savigny-les-Beaune - North of Beaune

✈ Dijon-Longvic: 35 km

Moulin de la Mère Michelle
Arbois

Les Planches-en-Arbois 39600 Arbois
Tel.: 33 (0) 3.84.66.08.17 – Fax: 33 (0) 3.84.37.49.69
meremichelle@chateauxhotels.com
Jean-Claude DELAVENNE
20 rooms: 80 € / 130 €
2 suites: 168 €
Breakfast: 10 €
Menu(s): 36 € / 64 € - **Carte:** 60 €

Open all year
equipments
lift, telephone, internet, T.V.,
minibar
environment
architecture 18°, park 6 ha,
garden, terrace 40 m², view,
total calm
leisure, relaxation
heated pool/covered, golf
course 30 km, horse-riding
7 km, thalassotherapy, thermal
baths

*Near the Arbois vineyards, set
aside a small village, a restored old 18th century mill, at
the foot of a waterfall...Tran-
quillity and complete commu-
nication with nature, and
many touristic possibilities all
around.*

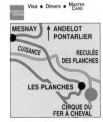

Visa ● Diners ● MASTER CARD

MESNAY ↑ ANDELOT
PONTARLIER
CUISANCE
RECULÉE
DES PLANCHES
LES PLANCHES
CIRQUE DU
FER A CHEVAL

Road map p. 619

A39 exit Dole Poligny. N83 dir. Lyon-
Besançon

 Tavaux Dole: 30 km

14, rue de Rivault 71400 Autun
Tel.: 33 (0) 3.85.86.58.58 – Fax: 33 (0) 3.85.86.23.07
ursulines@chateauxhotels.com
Michel GRELLET
36 rooms: 55 € / 93 €
7 suites: 111,5 € / 128 €
Breakfast: 9,2 €
Menu(s): 14,50 € / 64 € - **Carte:** 20 € -
1/2 board: 75,5 € / 141 €

An ancient convent (17th century), in the heart of the old quarters, with a view of the Morvan mountains. Quiet rooms, gastronomic restaurant, breakfast in the old chapel, French garden upon the historic town. Near the cathedral and the museums.

Open all year
equipments
lift, telephone, internet, T.V., minibar
environment
architecture 17e, furniture contemporain, garden, terrace 120 m², view, total calm
leisure, relaxation
tennis 0.5 km, golf course 1 km, horse-riding 1 km

Visa ● Diners ● JCB ● MASTER CARD

Road map p. 619

A6 exit Saulieu, Pouilly or Beaune

Dijon: 80 km

Domaine du Roncemay

Auxerre I Aillant-sur-Tholon

www.chateauxhotels.com/roncemay | reservation service: 33 (0) 1.40.07.00.20

89110 Aillant-sur-Tholon
Tel.: 33 (0) 3.86.73.50.50 – Fax: 33 (0) 3.86.73.69.46
roncemay@chateauxhotels.com
Christophe & Delphine DUFOSSE

15 rooms: 106 € / 191 €
3 suites: 214 € / 366 €
Breakfast: 17 €
Menu(s): 30 € / 92 € - **Carte:** 69 €
1/2 board: 126 € / 229 €

hotel annual closing
13/01 > 20/02
restaurant annual closing
13/01 > 20/02
equipments
telephone, internet, T.V.
Satellite/Canal+, minibar, safe
environment
architecture 19°, park 145 ha,
terrace, view, total calm
leisure, relaxation
heated pool, horse-riding
10 km, hammam, fitness,
guided tours of caves

In an outstanding setting of leafy tranquillity, the Domaine du Roncemay brings back the charm of the stately houses of olden times. All rooms overlook the 18-hole golf course designed by Jean Garaïalde. In the restaurant, Christophe Dufosse's culinary inventiveness offers a dazzling variety of subtle flavors.

Visa ● Diners ● JCB ● MASTER CARD

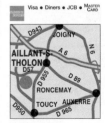

Road map p. 619

A6 exit Joigny, D955 dir. Aillant-Tholon, Les Ormes

 Orly: 150 km

11, rue du Château 89200 Avallon
Tel.: 33 (0)3.86.34.07.86 – Fax: 33 (0)3.86.34.16.36

vaultlugny@chateauxhotels.com
Elisabeth MATHERAT-AUDAN

4 rooms: 160 € / 230 €
1 flat: 430 € - **7 suites:** 285 € / 455 €
Menu(s): 45 € / 80 € - **Carte:** 50 € -
1/2 board: 120 € / 155 €
Table d'hôtes (sur rés.): 45 € / 80 €

An authentic 13th and 16th century chateau, built in the historic Burgungy, and transformed into a luxury hôtel in 1986. Some rooms, open onto the park, have a fireplace and are decorated with period furnitures. Superb cuisine combines with talent the freshness et richness of Burgundy terroir.

hotel annual closing
01/01 > 29/03 ● 11/11 > 28/03
restaurant annual closing
01/01 > 29/03 ● 11/11 > 28/03
restaurant weekly closing
mon(lun), tue(lun), wen, thi(lun), fri(lun)
29/03 > 11/11
equipments
telephone, internet, T.V. Satellite, minibar, safe, valet parking
environment
architecture 16ᵉ, park 15 ha, garden, terrace, view, vegetable garden, total calm
leisure, relaxation
horse-riding 2 km

Visa ● Diners ● JCB ● MASTER CARD

Road map p. 619

A6 exit Avallon. D957 dir. Vézelay.
First right at Pontaubert

Orly: 200 km

Hostellerie de la Poste
Avallon
www.chateauxhotels.com/poste | reservation service: 33 (0) 1.40.07.00.20

13, place Vauban 89200 Avallon
Tel.: 33 (0) 3.86.34.16.16 – Fax: 33 (0) 3.86.34.19.19
poste@chateauxhotels.com
Alain GAND

13 rooms: 93 € / 109 €
3 flats: 159 € - **14 suites:** 133 € / 159 €
Breakfast: 11 €
Menu(s): 20,5 € / 62,5 € - **Carte:** 44,35 €
1/2 board: 92 € / 127 €

hotel annual closing
01/01 > 15/03●15/11 > 15/03
restaurant annual closing
01/01 > 15/03●15/11 > 15/03
restaurant weekly closing
mon(lun), sun(ev)
21/06 > 29/09
mon, sun(ev)
15/03 > 21/06
equipments
lift, telephone, internet, T.V.
Satellite/Canal+
environment
architecture 18e, furniture 18e,
garden, terrace 40 m^2
leisure, relaxation
tennis 1 km, horse-riding 2 km

This former 18th century postal station continues the tradition of hospitality and conviviality that made it famous. All rooms are subtly and elegantly decorated and all meals are generous and typically terroir. Many cultural and touristic activities all aroud the splendid Burgundy.

Visa ● Diners ● JCB ● MASTER CARD

Road map p. 619
A6 exit 18 Avallon

Dijon: 100 km

Vallée du Cousin 89200 Avallon
Tel.: 33 (0) 3.86.34.97.00 – Fax: 33 (0) 3.86.31.65.47
ruats@chateauxhotels.com
Jean-Pierre & Jocelyne ROSSI
24 rooms: 61 € / 107 €
1 suite: 130 €
Breakfast: 10 €
Menu(s): 25 € / 37 € - **1/2 board:** 74,5 € / 97,5 €

Former mill set amidst a lovely green valley, the hotel is cradled by a gentle river. A restoring rest, rocked by the murmur of the water. And a gastronomic experience with the regional specialities.

hotel annual closing
11/11 > 15/02

restaurant annual closing
11/11 > 15/02

restaurant weekly closing
mon, tue(lun), wen(lun), thi(lun), fri(lun), sat(lun)

equipments
telephone, T.V., baby-sitting

environment
architecture 18^e, garden, terrace 100 m^2, view, total calm

leisure, relaxation
tennis 4 km, golf course 30 km, horse-riding 4 km

Visa ● Diners ● JCB ● MASTER CARD

AUXERRE
PARIS
A6
PONTAUBERT
AVALLON
D957
N6
D427
SAULIEU
COUSIN

Road map p. 619
A6 exit Avallon

Orly: 200 km

Château de Bellecroix

Beaune I Chagny
www.chateauxhotels.com/bellecroix | reservation service: 33 (0) 1.40.07.00.20

N6 71150 Chagny
Tel.: 33 (0) 3.85.87.13.86 – Fax: 33 (0) 3.85.91.28.62
bellecroix@chateauxhotels.com
Delphine GAUTIER
19 rooms: 85 € / 170 €
1 suite: 230 €
Breakfast: 13 €
Menu(s): 43 € / 57 €

hotel annual closing
20/12 > 13/02
restaurant annual closing
20/12 > 13/02
hotel weekly closing
wen
01/10 > 30/05
restaurant weekly closing
wen, thi(lun)
equipments
telephone, T.V., minibar
environment
architecture, park 1.5 ha,
garden, terrace, total calm
leisure, relaxation
heated pool, tennis 2 km, golf
course 12 km, horse-riding
8 km

Discover the heart of Burgundy and its heritage. This château from the 12th and 18th centuries is a gourmet's delight, where age-old traditions combine with illustrious wines in an elegant setting. Specialities include duck liver terrine, Bresse fowl in cream sauce and stewed snails.

Visa ● Diners ● MASTER CARD

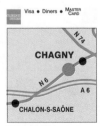

Road map p. 619

A6 exit Beaune south or Chalon-sur-Saône north

 Dijon-Longvic: 50 km

RN74 21200 Beaune
Tel.: 33 (0) 3.80.22.05.28 – Fax: 33 (0) 3.80.24.64.51
corton@chateauxhotels.com
André PARRA
1 room: 160 €
9 suites: 210 € / 300 €
Breakfast: 20 €
Menu(s): 38 € / 120 € - **Carte:** 80 €

In its shaded grounds opposite Corton Mountain this old Burgundian house offers an incomparable stay amidst the vintage wines of the region. The well-decorated rooms are equalled only by the inspiring cuisine of the chef André Parra who knows how to glorify the savours of a gastronomic region.

hotel annual closing
15/01 > 15/02
restaurant annual closing
15/01 > 15/02
restaurant weekly closing
sun(ev), mon, tue(lun)
equipments
telephone, internet, T.V.
Satellite/Canal+, minibar, safe
environment
garden, terrace, view
leisure, relaxation
tennis 3 km, golf course 3 km,
horse-riding 4 km, thermal
baths

Visa • Diners • JCB • MASTER CARD

Road map p. 619
A6 exit 24, N74 dir. Dijon

Longvic: 35 km

Hostellerie Bourguignonne

Beaune **I** Verdun-sur-le-Doubs
www.chateauxhotels.com/bourguigonne | reservation service: 33 (0) 1.40.07.00.20

**2, avenue Président Borgeot
71350 Verdun-sur-le-Doubs**
Tel.: 33 (0) 3.85.91.51.45 – Fax: 33 (0) 3.85.91.53.81
bourguigonne@chateauxhotels.com
Didier DENIS

8 rooms: 73,5 € / 88,5 €
1 suite: 94,5 €
Breakfast: 10 €
Menu(s): 27,44 € / 68,6 € - **Carte:** 22,87 €
1/2 board: 84,86 € / 92,36 €

hotel annual closing
28/01 > 02/03
restaurant annual closing
28/01 > 02/03
restaurant weekly closing
tue, wen(lun)
03/03 > 27/01
tue, wen(lun)
03/03 > 27/01
equipments
telephone, internet, T.V.,
minibar
environment
architecture, garden, terrace
leisure, relaxation
tennis 1 km, golf course
15 km, horse-riding 10 km

Travellers longing for relaxation will delight in this haven of wellbeing, fine cooking and greenery where the easy-going, country life offers instant peace of mind. The rooms are equalled only the charm of the flower-filled park. Expert cooking is a tasteful blend of tradition and innovation.

Visa ● MASTER CARD

Road map p. 619
A6 exit Beaune, dir. Lons-le-Saunier

 Dijon: 50 km

Hostellerie du vieux moulin 21420 Bouilland
Tel.: 33 (0) 3.80.21.51.16 – Fax: 33 (0) 3.80.21.59.90
vieuxmoulin@chateauxhotels.com
Jean-Pierre SILVA
20 rooms: 102 € / 140 €
2 flats: 198 € / 230 €
Breakfast: 13 €
Menu(s): 34 € / 61 €

The proverbial kindliness of the Burgundy people awaits you at this charming hotel, set among vineyards of renown. Pleasant rooms, beautiful garden and local dishes, prepared with feeling and talent by the master of the house. An ideal stopping place to explore a wonderful region for good food.

Visa ● MASTER CARD

Road map p. 619

A6 exit 24 Savigny-les-Beaune then dir. Bouilland

hotel annual closing
01/01 > 31/01
restaurant annual closing
01/01 > 31/01
hotel weekly closing
wen
01/11 > 30/04
restaurant weekly closing
mon(lun), wen(lun), thi(lun)
01/05 > 31/10
mon(lun), wen, thi(lun)
01/11 > 30/04
equipments
telephone, T.V.
environment
architecture contemporaine, furniture contemporain, garden, terrace 60 m^2, view, total calm
leisure, relaxation
heated pool/covered, tennis 0.5 km, golf course 20 km, horse-riding 10 km, sauna, fitness

Hôtel de la Poste

Beaune

www.chateauxhotels.com/hotelposte | reservation service: 33 (0) 1.40.07.00.20

5, bd Clemenceau 21200 Beaune
Tel.: 33 (0) 3.80.22.08.11 – Fax: 33 (0) 3.80.24.19.71
hotelposte@chateauxhotels.com
Françoise STRATIGOS-BABOZ
21 rooms: 106 € / 168 €
9 suites: 190 € / 230 €
Breakfast: 13 €
Menu(s): 20,50 € / 42 € - **Carte:** 34 €
1/2 board: 98 € / 129 €

hotel annual closing
24/12 > 25/12
restaurant annual closing
24/12 > 25/12
equipments
lift, telephone, internet, T.V.
Satellite, minibar, safe,
baby-sitting
environment
architecture 19ᵉ, furniture 19ᵉ,
garden, terrace, view
leisure, relaxation
tennis 5 km, golf course 5 km,
horse-riding 5 km, presentation
and tasting of Burgundy wines

Very beautiful house full of character and prestige, on the edge of the ramparts of the old town of Beaune. Rooms with old furniture. Safe, Bar, Restaurant, Lounge with Piano-bar and French Billiard are 1930' style. Cellar to taste famous burgundian wines.

Visa ● Diners ● JCB ● Master Card

Road map p. 619
A6 exit Beaune 24 or 24.1

✈ Dijon-Longvic: 35 km

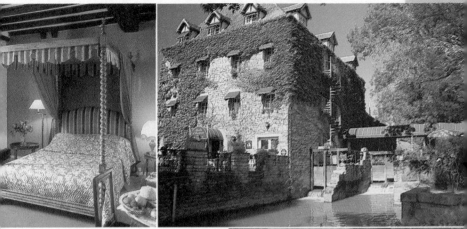

Hameau de Chaublanc
71350 St-Gervais-en-Vallière
Tel.: 33 (0) 3.85.91.55.56 – Fax: 33 (0) 3.85.91.89.65

hauterive@chateauxhotels.com
Michel MOILLE

6 rooms: 70 € / 100 €
14 suites: 145 € / 170 €
Breakfast: 11 €
Menu(s): 25 € / 62 € - **Carte:** 54 € -
1/2 board: 80 € / 100 €

This mill was built in the 12th century, on the banks of the Dheune, by the Cistercian monks. Today, it offers comfort and light cooking, rest and fitness: sauna, water jets, solarium, boby-building, health programme, Turkish baths, water-therapy. Ideal starting point for visiting Burgundy.

hotel annual closing
01/01 > 10/02●01/12 > 10/02
restaurant annual closing
01/01 > 10/02●01/12 > 10/02
hotel weekly closing
sun, mon
01/10 > 01/12
sun, mon
10/02 > 30/06
restaurant weekly closing
mon, tue(lun), wen(lun), thi(lun), fri(lun)
01/10 > 01/12
mon, tue(lun), wen(lun), thi(lun), fri(lun)
10/02 > 30/06
equipments
telephone, internet, T.V. Canal+, minibar, safe
environment
architecture 12e, park 3 ha, garden, terrace, view, total calm
leisure, relaxation
heated pool, golf course 10 km, horse-riding 8 km, sauna, hammam, solarium, jacuzzi

Visa ● Diners ● JCB ● Master Card

Road map p. 619

A6 exit Beaune Chagny, dir. Verdun-sur-le-Doubs

Dijon-Longvic: 50 km

Bourgogne Franche-Comté

Auberge de la Tour Penchée

Belfort I Sevenans

www.chateauxhotels.com/tourpenchee | reservation service: 33 (0) 1.40.07.00.20

2, rue de Delle 90400 Sevenans
Tel.: 33 (0) 3.84.56.06.52 - Fax: 33 (0) 3.84.56.16.04
tourpenchee@chateauxhotels.com
François DUTHEY
Menu(s): 26 € / 55 €

Open all year
restaurant weekly closing
sat(lun), sun(ev), mon
environment
architecture 20^e, terrace
40 m^2, vegetable garden

François Duthey is a master in the art of combining traditional cuisine and new delicacies: legendary foie gras, langoustine duo and famous recipes from grand-mother Alice! A baroque decor and unusual objects add the final touches of refinement to this Franche-Comté house. Exceptional cave.

Visa ● MASTER CARD

Road map p. 619

A6 exit 11 Héricourt Delle. Always turn on the right

 Bâle-Mulhouse: 50 km

9, rue Général-Négrier 90000 Belfort

Tel.: 33 (0) 3.84.21.41.85 – Fax: 33 (0) 3.84.57.05.57

servin@chateauxhotels.com
Lucie SERVIN

6 rooms: 67 €
1 flat: 77 €
Breakfast: 8 €
Menu(s): 20 € / 57 €

In its green park, this gastronomic stopover offers you both tranquillity and the warm intimacy of a manor house. Relaxation and calm in a Louis XV room, a Louis XIII suite. Refined cuisine. To be discovered: Belfort, the former fortified square transformed by Vauban, the Lion, the chateau.

Open all year
equipments
lift, telephone, T.V. Canal+
environment
park 25 ha, garden, terrace, total calm

Visa • Diners • MASTER CARD

Road map p. 619

A38 exit Belfort south

Bâle-Mulhouse: 65 km

Moulin du Prieuré

Bonnevaux-le-Prieuré

www.chateauxhotels.com/prieure | reservation service: 33 (0) 1.40.07.00.20

25620 Bonnevaux-le-Prieuré
Tel.: 33 (0) 3.81.59.21.47 – Fax: 33 (0) 3.81.59.28.79
moulinprieure@chateauxhotels.com
Philippe MIGOT
8 rooms: 56 € / 72 €
Breakfast: 10 €
Menu(s): 32 € / 74 € - **Carte:** 30 €

hotel annual closing
07/01 > 07/02
restaurant annual closing
07/01 > 07/02
restaurant weekly closing
tue, wen
01/10 > 31/05
equipments
telephone, internet, T.V.,
minibar
environment
architecture 13e, garden,
terrace, total calm
leisure, relaxation
golf course 16 km, horse-riding
5 km

This unique 13th century grain mill has been entirely restored for ultimate comfort and well-being. The four chalets set in the 5 acres park provide the absolute in intimacy. In the restaurant, experience the delights of the local fresh produce. Close by Ornans, the birthplace of Gustave Courbet.

Visa ● Diners ● MASTER CARD

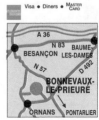

Road map p. 619

A36 exit Besançon north dir. Lausanne

Bourgogne Franche-Comté !

 La Veze: 8 km

4, rue Fontaine de Baranges 71390 Buxy
Tel.: 33 (0) 3.85.94.10.70 – Fax: 33 (0) 3.85.94.10.79
baranges@chateauxhotels.com
André LETOURNEAU
13 rooms: 55 € / 100 €
4 suites: 100 € / 115 €
Breakfast: 9 €

This XIXth century house of-fers charm and conviviality. Delicately decorated rooms feature balconies or private terraces overlooking the gar-den. An ideal starting point for a discovery tour of the historic and culinary heritage of this region. Bicycle track between Beaune and Cluny.

Open all year
equipments
telephone, internet, T.V., minibar
environment
architecture 19^e, garden, terrace 100 m^2, total calm
leisure, relaxation
tennis 0.3 km, golf course 20 km

Visa ● MASTER CARD

Road map p. 619

A6 exit Châlon-Saône south. D977 dir. Buxy Cluny

Lyon/St-Exupèry: 140 km

Château-Hôtel André Ziltener

Chambolle-Musigny

www.chateauxhotels.com/ziltener | reservation service: 33 (0) 1.40.07.00.20

rue de la Fontaine 21220 Chambolle-Musigny
Tel.: 33 (0) 3.80.62.41.62 – Fax: 33 (0) 3.80.62.83.75

ziltener @chateauxhotels.com
Doris SCHWARZ

3 rooms: 200 € / 200 €
2 flats: 350 € - **5 suites:** 200 € / 260 €
Breakfast: 15 €

hotel annual closing
01/12 > 14/03

equipments
telephone, internet, T.V.,
minibar, safe, baby-sitting

environment
architecture 18°, garden,
terrace, view, total calm

leisure, relaxation
tennis 5 km, golf course 20 km

Only a short distance from the famous Clos de Vougeot, this history-filled XVIIIth century residence ranks among the most beautiful of Burgundy. The rooms are decorated with special care and the memorable breakfast's augur well with days filled with tasting the best wines from the region in the cellar.

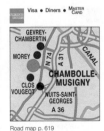

Visa ● Diners ● MASTER CARD

Road map p. 619

A6, A36, A31 exit Dijon/Nuits St-Georges. N74 dir. Dijon

Dijon: 20 km

Hôtel Moderne
Charolles
www.chateauxhotels.com/moderne | reservation service: 33 (0) 1.40.07.00.20

481

Avenue Joanny Furtin 71120 Charolles
Tel.: 33 (0) 3.85.24.07.02 – Fax: 33 (0) 3.85.24.05.21
moderne@chateauxhotels.com
Jean BONIN
17 rooms: 54 € / 95 €
Breakfast: 7,5 €
Menu(s): 17 € / 46 € - **1/2 board:** 58 € / 80 €

Along Burgundy's Romanesque church road, pleasant stop-over for sampling famous Charolais beef in unique setting. Dining rooms overlooks garden and pool, bordering the green meadows crossed by a river. Winter dining-room decorated with woodwork. To be visited: the abbey of Cluny, Paray-le-Monial.

hotel annual closing
26/12 > 01/02
restaurant annual closing
26/12 > 01/02
hotel weekly closing
mon
14/07 > 18/08
mon, sun
19/08 > 13/07
restaurant weekly closing
mon, tue(lun), sun(ev)

equipments
telephone, internet, T.V.
environment
architecture 19e, garden, terrace 60 m²
leisure, relaxation
tennis 1 km, golf course 25 km, horse-riding 10 km

Visa • MASTER CARD

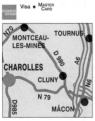

Road map p. 619
A6 exit Mâcon South, dir. Moulin N79

Lyon-Satolas: 130 km

Bourgogne Franche-Comté

Le Château de Chaumont

Chaumont

www.chateauxhotels.com/chaumont | reservation service: 33 (0) 1.40.07.00.20

5, rue de la Montagne 89340 Chaumont
Tel.: 33 (0) 3.86.96.61.69 – Fax: 33 (0) 3.86.96.61.28
chaumont@chateauxhotels.com
David HASSOUNI
30 rooms: 61 € / 113 €
Breakfast: 10 €
Menu(s): 22 € / 37 € - **Carte:** 37 € -
1/2 board: 72 € / 106 €

Open all year
hotel weekly closing
mon, sun
01/10 > 31/03
restaurant weekly closing
mon, sun(ev)
01/10 > 31/03
equipments
lift, telephone, internet, T.V.
Canal+, minibar
environment
architecture 18e, park 20 ha,
terrace 465 m², view, total
calm
leisure, relaxation
tennis 20 km, golf course
15 km, horse-riding 20 km

One hour from Paris, at the gateway of Burgundy, this magnificent château welcomes you in the heart of a 37-acre park. The high-confort bedrooms are designed for relaxation and calm. The restaurant offers a creative cooking and reputed regional wines. Fontainebleau and Sens are near.

Visa ● MASTER CARD

Road map p. 619

A6 exit Fontainebleau. A5 exit Sens or
Marolles-sur-Seine

Orly: 70 km

25680 Cubry

Tel.: 33 (0) 3.81.86.00.10 – Fax: 33 (0) 3.81.86.01.06
bournel@chateauxhotels.com
Marquis Léonel de MOUSTIER
Reinier WESTPALM van HOORN
12 rooms: 130 € / 175 €
2 flats: 195 € / 240 € - **1 suite:** 195 € / 240 €
Breakfast: 10 €
Menu(s): 25 € / 50 € - **Carte:** 40 €
1/2 board: 108 € / 130,5 €

The Hotel in the 18th c. Vieux Château welcomes golfers and holiday visitors to a property which has belonged to the same family for five centuries. 15 luxuriously fitted guestrooms, delicious gourmet food. The 200-acre park, laid out in the English style, features an excellent 18-hole golf course.

hotel annual closing
01/01 > 28/03●03/11 > 27/03

restaurant annual closing
01/01 > 28/03●03/11 > 27/03

equipments
lift, telephone, T.V. Satellite, minibar

environment
architecture 19ᵉ, furniture contemporain, park 80 ha, terrace 200 m², view, total calm

leisure, relaxation
golf, tennis

Visa ● MASTER CARD

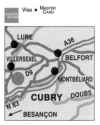

Road map p. 619

A36 exit N° 5 Baume-les-Dames, D50
dir. Lure - Villersexel

Bâle-Mulhouse: 120 km

Stéphane Derbord & l'Hôtel Wilson
Dijon
www.chateauxhotels.com/derbord | reservation service: 33 (0) 1.40.07.00.20

Place Wilson 21000 Dijon
Tel.: 33 (0) 3.80.66.82.50 – Fax: 33 (0) 3.80.36.41.54
derbord@chateauxhotels.com
Mmes. ETIEVANT-DESCAILLOT & DERBORD
27 rooms: 58 € / 81 €
Breakfast: 9 €
Menu(s): 21,34 € / 68,6 € - **Carte:** 64,79 €

restaurant annual closing
02/01 > 10/01 ● 01/08 > 26/08
equipments
lift, telephone, internet, T.V.,
safe, baby-sitting
environment
architecture 17ª, total calm
leisure, relaxation
tennis 1 km, golf course
10 km, horse-riding 1 km

Authentic first-rate produce, seasonally inspired, is combined with a dash of creativity and feeling, to provide here the quintessence of good food. An extensive selection of the best Burgundy wines. A former 17th c. staging post adjacent to the restaurant, the Hotel Wilson holds 27 pleasant guestrooms.

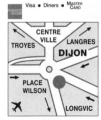

Visa ● Diners ● MasterCard

Road map p. 619

A38 exit Dijon - N5 dir. city centre

7, rue Très Girard 21220 Morey-Saint-Denis
Tel.: 33 (0) 3.80.34.33.09 – Fax: 33 (0) 3.80.51.81.92
tresgirard@chateauxhotels.com
Sébastien PILAT – Didier PETITCOLAS
6 rooms: 115 € / 115 €
2 flats: 150 €
Breakfast: 11 €
Menu(s): 19 € / 60 € - **Carte:** 45 €

Along the celebrated "Wine Road", a lovely Bourgogne-style inn, entirely restored in 2000, mingles modern comforts with old beams and original stonework. The chef, who trained with the greatest, prepares creative gourmet dishes. Sublime wine list with over 1000 references.

Open all year
equipments
telephone, internet, T.V. Satellite, minibar, safe, baby-sitting
environment
architecture 18ᵉ, garden, terrace
leisure, relaxation
tennis 2 km, golf course 10 km, horse-riding 10 km

Visa ● Diners ● JCB ● Master Card

DIJON
A 38
GEVREY-CHAMBERTIN
MOREY-SAINT-DENIS
A 6
NUITS-SAINT-GEORGES
BEAUNE

Road map p. 619
A31 exit Nuits St Georges

Dijon-Longvic: 10 km

Château de Saulon

Gevrey-Chambertin I Saulon-la-Rue

www.chateauxhotels.com/saulon I reservation service: 33 (0) 1.40.07.00.20

Route de Seurre 21910 Saulon-la-Rue
Tel.: 33 (0) 3.80.79.25.25 – Fax: 33 (0) 3.80.79.25.26
saulon@chateauxhotels.com
Alain ROSENZWEY – Didier & Lionel PETITCOLAS

30 rooms: 60 € / 95 €
Breakfast: 9 €
Menu(s): 28 € / 35 € - **Carte:** 33 €
1/2 board: 60 € / 76 €

hotel annual closing
27/01 > 04/03
restaurant annual closing
27/01 > 04/03
equipments
telephone, internet, T.V.,
minibar
environment
architecture 17e, park 27 ha,
garden, terrace, view
leisure, relaxation
heated pool, golf course
15 km, horse-riding 10 km

Sixteen miles from Dijon in the heart of a 68-acre wooded park, the château of Saulon-la-Rue is a superb 17th century residence offering peace and tranquillity. The 30 personalised bedrooms feature every contemporary convenience and look onto the magical park. Traditional burgundy cuisine.

Visa ● Diners ● **MASTER CARD**

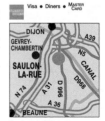

Road map p. 619

A31 exit Dijon South, dir. Londvic then
Seurre D996

Dijon-Longvic: 6 km

Rigny 70100 Gray

Tel.: 33 (0) 3.84.65.25.01 – Fax: 33 (0) 3.84.65.44.45

rigny@chateauxhotels.com

Jacques MAUPIN

29 rooms: 61 € / 185 €
Breakfast: 9,5 €
Menu(s): 29 € / 55 € - **Carte:** 40 €
1/2 board: 71 € / 131 €

In Franche-Comté, at the gates of Burgundy, the serenity of a park bordering the Saône. Lounges, winter garden, rooms combining charm, authenticity and comfort. Personalised welcome, refined cuisine. Swimming pool, tennis, bicycles. Everything to make your stay an unforgettable one.

Open all year

equipments
telephone, T.V. Canal+, minibar, safe

environment
architecture 18e, furniture 18e, park 5 ha, garden, terrace 175 m², view

leisure, relaxation
heated pool

Visa • Diners • MASTER CARD

Road map p. 619

From the north A31 exit N° 6 Gray, from west A36 exit N° 3 of Besançon, from the south exit N° 4 Dijon

✈ Dijon-Longvic: 45 km

Bourgogne Franche-Comté

Hostellerie Sarrasine

Macon I Replonges

www.chateauxhotels.com/sarrasine I reservation service: 33 (0) 1.40.07.00.20

N79 01750 Replonges
Tel.: 33 (0) 3.85.31.02.41 – Fax: 33 (0) 3.85.31.11.74
sarrasine@chateauxhotels.com
A. BEVY

6 rooms: 61 € / 145 €
1 suite: 210 € / 250 €
Breakfast: 11 €
Menu(s): 16 € / 53 €
restaurant open evenings only for hotel residents only

hotel annual closing
08/01 > 13/02●05/11 > 18/12

restaurant annual closing
08/01 > 13/02●05/11 > 18/12

hotel weekly closing
tue, wen
15/10 > 15/04

restaurant weekly closing
mon(lun), tue(lun), wen, thi(lun),
fri(lun), sat(lun), sun(lun)
15/04 > 15/10
mon(lun), tue, wen, thi(lun),
fri(lun), sat(lun), sun(lun)
15/10 > 15/04

equipments
telephone, T.V. Satellite,
minibar, safe

environment
architecture 17e, park, garden,
terrace

leisure, relaxation
heated pool, tennis 3 km, golf
course 1 km, horse-riding 3 km

*Amidst fountains and flowers,
Bressane farm, delightful base
to visit Burgundy. Fine traditional cuisine using the best
local produce, served with excellent region wines. Comfortable and spacious rooms with
air-conditioning. Private parking closed at night. 6 golf
courses.*

Visa ● Diners ● MASTER CARD

Road map p. 619

A40 exit 2. A6 exit Mâcon-sud

Lyon-Satolas: 80 km

Les Maritonnes 489
Mâcon I Romaneche-Thorins
www.chateauxhotels.com/maritonnes | reservation service: 33 (0)1.40.07.00.20

Route de Fleurie 71570 Romaneche-Thorins
Tel.: 33 (0)3.85.35.51.70 – Fax: 33 (0)3.85.35.58.14
maritonnes@chateauxhotels.com
Willemina MEIJBOOM

20 rooms: 70 € / 95 €
Breakfast: 10 €
Menu(s): 25 € / 70 € - **Carte:** 35 € -
1/2 board: 90 € / 102,5 €

Set in a flower-filled, tree-lined park, with period furniture and authentic country cuisine, Les Maritonnes provides the perfect surroundings for relaxing. A sought-after spot from which to discover Beaujolais from Macon, picturesque villages and the start of the Wine Trail.

Visa ● Diners ● JCB ● Master Card

LA CHAPELLE DE GUINCHAY
ROMANECHE THORINS
N6
A6
FLEURIE
CD 32
LES MARITONNES
LA MAISON BLANCHE

Road map p. 619

A6 from Paris/Nancy/Strasbourg, exit Mâcon south, from Lyon exit Belleville

Saint-Exupéry: 70 km

hotel annual closing
01/01 > 24/01 ● 19/12 > 23/01
restaurant annual closing
01/01 > 24/01 ● 19/12 > 23/01
equipments
telephone, internet, T.V. satellite at lounge, minibar
environment
park 1.5 ha, terrace 120 m², view
leisure, relaxation
heated pool, golf course 25 km, horse-riding 10 km, beauty salon 6 km, balneotherapy 6 km, solarium 6 km

Château de Malaisy
Montbard
www.chateauxhotels.com/malaisy | reservation service: 33 (0) 1.40.07.00.20

Fain-les-Montbard 21500 Montbard
Tel.: 33 (0) 3.80.89.46.54 – Fax: 33 (0) 3.80.92.30.16
malaisy@chateauxhotels.com
Famille GILINSKY
22 rooms: 52 € / 105 €
1 flat: 120 € - **1 suite:** 130 €
Breakfast: 8 €
Menu(s): 24 € / 54 € - **Carte:** 46 €
1/2 board: 56 € / 81 €

Open all year
equipments
telephone, internet, T.V.
environment
architecture 17e, furniture
contemporain, park 15 ha,
garden, terrace 180 m², view,
total calm
leisure, relaxation
tennis 1 km, golf course
10 km, horse-riding 6 km,
sauna, solarium, fitness,
cycling trails

In the heart of Fontenay valley, this splendid 17th century residence is surrounded by a 37-acre animal park. Rest, relaxation, keep-fit, unspoilt nature - that's the program. Sunny rooms, warm welcome, succulent food with regional Burgundy flavors. A haven of peace in an idyllic setting.

Visa ● MASTER CARD

Road map p. 619

A6 exit Bièrre-les-Semur, dir. Montbard, D905 - A31/A5 exit Troyes, D905

✈ Dijon-Longvic: 75 km

La Gentilhommière

Nuits-Saint-Georges

www.chateauxhotels.com/gentilhommiere | reservation service: 33 (0) 1.40.07.00.20

13, vallée de la Serrée
21700 Nuits-Saint-Georges
Tel.: 33 (0) 3.80.61.12.06 – Fax: 33 (0) 3.80.61.30.33
gentilhommiere@chateauxhotels.com
René PIANETTI
20 rooms: 75 € / 75 €
Breakfast: 8 €
Menu(s): 22,5 € / 53,5 € - **Carte:** 46 €

At the gates of Nuits-Saint-Georges, between Beaune and Dijon, a former 16th century hunting lodge in a vast park crossed by a trout-filled stream. The rooms look out over the countryside, tennis courts and swimming pool beckon, not to forget the fine food, the pride of the locality.

hotel annual closing
15/12 > 15/01
restaurant annual closing
15/12 > 15/01
equipments
telephone, internet, T.V., baby-sitting
environment
architecture 16e, park 13 ha, garden, terrace 500 m², view, total calm
leisure, relaxation
heated pool, golf course 20 km, horse-riding 5 km, jet-skiing (5 km, Quincey)

Visa ● Diners ● MASTER CARD

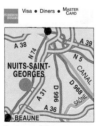

Road map p. 619

A31 exit Nuits-Saint-Georges, N74

✈ Longvic: 20 km

| Bourgogne Franche-Comté

Hostellerie des Monts de Vaux

Poligny
www.chateauxhotels.com/montvaux | reservation service: 33 (0) 1.40.07.00.20

Aux Monts de Vaux 39800 Poligny
Tel.: 33 (0) 3.84.37.12.50 – Fax: 33 (0) 3.84.37.09.07
montsvaux@chateauxhotels.com
Famille CARRION
8 rooms: 110 € / 154 €
2 flats: 183 €
Breakfast: 13 €
Menu(s): 28 € / 62 € - **Carte:** 62 €
1/2 board: 130 € / 145 €

hotel annual closing
30/10 > 27/12
restaurant annual closing
30/10 > 27/12
hotel weekly closing
tue(ev)
01/09 > 30/06
restaurant weekly closing
tue(lun), wen(lun)
equipments
telephone, T.V. Satellite, minibar
environment
architecture 18°, park 3 ha, garden, terrace, view
leisure, relaxation
golf course 25 km, thermal baths

The view over the plain is magnificent. This XVIIIth century coaching inn has welcomed travellers for two centuries. Traditional hospitality, old-style regional decoration and rooms opening upon the gardens give this place a certain peaceful elegance for an ideal stopover.

Visa ● Diners ● MASTER CARD

Road map p. 619
A39 exit 7 Poligny, N5 dir. Genève

Genève: 110 km

Sainte-Sabine 21320 Pouilly-en-Auxoix
Tel.: 33 (0) 3.80.49.22.01 – Fax: 33 (0) 3.80.49.20.01
saintesabine@chateauxhotels.com
Famille GILINSKY

21 rooms: 51 € / 180 €
2 suites: 196 €
Breakfast: 8 €
Menu(s): 23 € / 54 € - **Carte:** 23 € -
1/2 board: 59 € / 118 €

In the heart of a famous wine-growing region, this 17th century residence was built on a former 11th century monastery. Standing majestically in the centre of a 20-acre park, the château combines elegance of the past with comfort of the present. In the restaurant, gourmet or traditional cooking.

Visa ● MASTER CARD

hotel annual closing
03/01 > 22/02
restaurant annual closing
03/01 > 22/02
equipments
lift, telephone, T.V., safe
environment
architecture 17e, park 8 ha, terrace 200 m², view, total calm
leisure, relaxation
tennis 3 km, golf course 15 km, horse-riding 1 km, mountain bikes for hire

Road map p. 619

A6 A38, exit Pouilly-en-Auxois, D970 dir. Bligny-sur-Ouche

Dijon: 40 km

Le Montrachet
Puligny-Montrachet
www.chateauxhotels.com/montrachet | reservation service: 33 (0) 1.40.07.00.20

Place des Marronniers
21190 Puligny-Montrachet
Tel.: 33 (0) 3.80.21.30.06 – Fax: 33 (0) 3.80.21.39.06
montrachet@chateauxhotels.com
M. & Mme. GAZAGNES
35 rooms: 90 €
2 suites: 145 € / 168 €
Breakfast: 11,50 €
Menu(s): 35 € / 71 € - **Carte:** 30,49 €

hotel annual closing
01/12 > 10/01
restaurant annual closing
01/12 > 10/01
equipments
telephone, T.V. Satellite
environment
terrace, view, total calm
leisure, relaxation
tennis 0.2 km, golf course
15 km

In the region where the best white wines in the world are produced lies a village manor house with an elegantly rustic interior. Modernised regional cuisine uses fresh local produce. The wine waiter is an expert on Burgundian wine. Comfortable rooms. To be visited: Beaune, local wine cellars...

Visa ● Diners ● JCB ● MASTER CARD

Road map p. 619

A6 exit Beaune South or Châlon North. N74 dir. Chagny

Lyon: 150 km

3, rue des Capucins 89600 Saint-Florentin
Tel.: 33 (0) 3.86.35.15.12 – Fax: 33 (0) 3.86.35.33.14
lachaumiere@chateauxhotels.com
Jean-Pierre BONVALOT
10 rooms: 53,36 € / 129,58 €
Breakfast: 9,76 €
Menu(s): 24,39 € / 79,27 €
1/2 board: 77,75 € / 85,37 €

25 km from Auxerre, between Champagne and Burgundy, in a charming village, a delightful gourmet stop-over in pleasant hostelry. Terraced garden. Comfortable and elegant rooms, tastefully furnished. Boat trips on the canal, chateaux, museums, the famous Chablis vineyard, the forest of Othe.

Visa ● Diners ● JCB ● Master Card

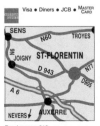

Road map p. 619

A6 exit Joigny/Auxerre North or A5 exit Sens/Vulaine. N77 dir. Troyes

hotel annual closing
01/09 > 09/09
restaurant annual closing
01/09 > 09/09
hotel weekly closing
wen
09/09 > 31/05
restaurant weekly closing
wen, thi(lun)
09/09 > 31/05
equipments
telephone, T.V.
environment
architecture contemporaine, furniture contemporain, garden, terrace
leisure, relaxation
tennis 1 km, golf course 30 km, horse-riding 2 km

Orly/Charles-de-Gaulle

Bourgogne Franche-Comté

Le Château de Clairis

Savigny-sur-Clairis

www.chateauxhotels.com/clairis | reservation service: 33 (0) 1.40.07.00.20

Domaine de Clairis 89150 Savigny-sur-Clairis
Tel.: 33 (0) 3.86.86.30.01 – Fax: 33 (0) 3.86.86.39.40
clairis@chateauxhotels.com
David HASSOUNI
20 rooms: 61 € / 92 €
Breakfast: 10 €
Menu(s): 22 € / 37 € - **Carte:** 37 €
1/2 board: 69 € / 92 €

hotel annual closing
07/01 > 27/01
restaurant annual closing
07/01 > 27/01
equipments
telephone, T.V. Canal+
environment
architecture 18e, park 250 ha,
garden, terrace 300 m², total
calm
leisure, relaxation
heated pool/covered,
horse-riding, sauna, hammam

A charming stopover on the doorstep of Paris in the gâtinais region, this beautiful residence nestled in an estate of 250 ha is made for the lovers of sports of all kinds. Attentive service, welcoming rooms and quality cuisine. A good destination for keeping fit.

Visa

Road map p. 619

A6 exit Courtenay. D103 dir. Savigny-sur-Clairis

Orly/Charles-de-Gaulle:
85 km

71260 Fleurville

Tel.: 33 (0) 3.85.33.12.17 – Fax: 33 (0) 3.85.33.95.34

fleurville@chateauxhotels.com

Pascal LEHMANN

14 rooms: 74 € / 135 €
1 suite: 168 €
Breakfast: 9 €
Menu(s): 25 € / 43 € - **Carte:** 38 €

A 16th-17th century residence between Tournus and Mâcon built by Counts of Fleurville, a name that conjures up the works of the Countess of Ségur. Calm flowered and wooded park, heated swimming pool. A perfect location for visiting the Roman churches and abbeys, vineyards.

Visa ● **MASTER CARD**

DIJON ↑

FLEURVILLE
CLUNY

TOURNUS
D 2

AZÉ

PONT
DE-VAUX

A 40

LYON ↓   MÂCON

Road map p. 619

A6 exit Mâcon North or Tournus. A40 exit Mâcon-centre

hotel annual closing
02/01 > 28/02

restaurant annual closing
02/01 > 28/02

equipments
telephone, internet, T.V., minibar

environment
architecture 17e, park 1.5 ha, garden, terrace 100 m^2

leisure, relaxation
heated pool, golf course 5 km, horse-riding 5 km, sauna

✈ Lyon/Satolas: 100 km

Le Domaine de Trémont

Tournus

www.chateauxhotels.com/tremont | reservation service: 33 (0) 1.40.07.00.20

Route de Plottes 71700 Tournus
Tel.: 33 (0) 3.85.51.00.10 – Fax: 33 (0) 3.85.32.12.28
tremont @chateauxhotels.com
Michèle WILSON

6 rooms: 67 € / 112 €
1 suite: 128 € / 208 €
Breakfast: 8 €
Menu(s): 18 € / 26 € - **Carte:** 31 €
1/2 board: 55,5 € / 77,5 €

Open all year
equipments
telephone, T.V.
environment
architecture 19ᵉ, garden,
terrace 100 m², total calm
leisure, relaxation
tennis 5 km, golf course 20 km

A house of pink stone covered
with wisteria and Virginia
creeper, a park with squirrels.
A dining-room in which to
enjoy a warm atmosphere,
simple and traditional cuisine
with set menus, a lounge with
old books, brightly-coloured
rooms with old furniture...
Roman art, fine cuisine and
wines.

Visa • MASTER CARD

Road map p. 619

A6 exit Tournus. D56 dir. Lugny-Plottes

Lyon-Satolas/Lyon-St-Exupéry: 100 km

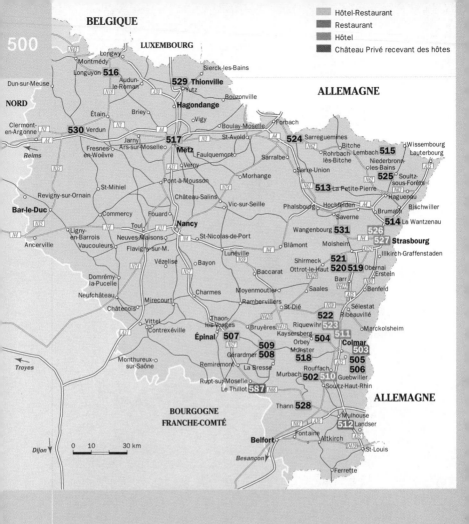

BELGIQUE

LUXEMBOURG

ALLEMAGNE

NORD

Bar-le-Duc

Troyes

Dijon

BOURGOGNE FRANCHE-COMTÉ

ALLEMAGNE

Besançon

Hôtel-Restaurant
Restaurant
Hôtel
Château Privé recevant des hôtes

500

0   10   30 km

Alsace Lorraine

WATTWILLER

L'Eau Rare

Les grandes sources de Wattwiller

2 rue de Guebwiller - Wattwiller - BP 89 - 68703 Cernay Cedex - France
Tél. 03 89 75 76 77 - Fax 03 89 75 76 76 - http//www.wattwiller.com

Hostellerie Saint-Barnabé

Buhl I Murbach

www.chateauxhotels.com/saintbarnabe I reservation service: 33 (0) 1.40.07.00.20

53, rue de Murbach 68530 Buhl
Tel.: 33 (0) 3.89.62.14.14 – Fax: 33 (0) 3.89.62.14.15
saintbarnabe@chateauxhotels.com
Clémence & Eric ORBAN
24 rooms: 76 € / 183 €
Breakfast: 14 €
Menu(s): 26 € / 75 € - **Carte:** 54 €
1/2 board: 96 € / 150 €

hotel annual closing
24/12 > 27/12●06/01 > 09/03
restaurant annual closing
06/01 > 09/03
hotel weekly closing
sun
05/11 > 01/04
restaurant weekly closing
mon(lun), tue(lun), wen(lun),
thi(lun), fri(lun)
28/03 > 04/11
mon(lun), tue(lun), wen(lun),
thi(lun), fri(lun), sun(ev)
05/11 > 01/04
equipments
telephone, T.V. Satellite,
minibar, safe
environment
park 4 ha, garden, terrace
50 m², view, vegetable garden,
total calm
leisure, relaxation
golf course 15 km, horse-riding
2 km, mini-golf at the hotel

Amidst the stunning Vosges mountains along the famous wine route. Only 10 mn from the Alsace Ecology Museum, hal-way between Colmar and Mulhouse. Attentive service from Clémence Orban and imaginative cuisine from Eric Orban.

Visa ● Diners ● JCB ● MASTER CARD

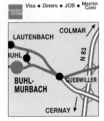

Road map p. 619

A35 exit center of Colmar - N83 dir.
Belfort-Guebwiller

Mulhouse: 56 km

52, Grand'rue 68000 Colmar
Tel.: 33 (0) 3.89.41.37.24 – Fax: 33 (0) 3.89.23.82.24
ferrouge@chateauxhotels.com
Patrick FULGRAFF
Breakfast: 45 €
Menu(s): 63 € / 91 €

More than the authentic decorations of Alsace and in addition as well to the perfect service from all accounts it is the talent of Patrick Fulgraff that makes the difference here. With this natural cook, the land revives, tradition becomes creative and flavours exactly right.

restaurant annual closing
06/01 > 16/01 ● 27/07 > 07/08
restaurant weekly closing
mon, sun
environment
architecture 16e, furniture contemporain, terrace 80 m^2, view
leisure, relaxation
heated pool/covered, tennis 2 km, golf course 10 km, horse-riding 3 km

Visa ● Diners ● MASTER CARD

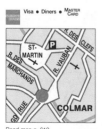

Road map p. 619

Dir. City cente / place of "Ancienne Douane"

Mulhouse: 50 km

Hôtel Restaurant Chambard

Colmar I Kaysersberg

www.chateauxhotels.com/chambard | reservation service: 33 (0) 1.40.07.00.20

9-13 rue du Général de Gaulle
68240 Kaysersberg
Tel.: 33 (0) 3.89.47.10.17 – Fax: 33 (0) 3.89.47.35.03
chambard@chateauxhotels.com
Famille NASTI
20 rooms: 100 € / 115 €
Breakfast: 10 €
Menu(s): 40 € / 65 € - **Carte:** 22 €
1/2 board: 78,50 € / 125 €

Open all year

equipments
lift, telephone, T.V.

environment
park 1 ha, terrace 60 m², view,
total calm

leisure, relaxation
heated pool/covered, tennis
1 km, golf course 3 km, sauna,
hammam, solarium, jacuzzi

In the very heart of the village, opposite the vineyard, the Chambard welcomes you to a unique environment, where chef Olivier Nasti masterfully uses his creative culinary talent to enhance traditional menus from Alsace. The hosts cultivate the art of well-being for their guests in a warm and friendly atmosphere.

Visa ● Diners ● MASTER CARD

Road map p. 619

A35 exit Houssen direction Kaysersberg

Bâle Mulhouse: 70 km

4-6 pl. des 6 Montagnes noires
La petite Venise 68000 Colmar
Tel.: 33 (0) 3.89.41.60.32 – Fax: 33 (0) 3.89.24.59.40
marechal@chateauxhotels.com
Roland BOMO

28 rooms: 70 € / 215 €
2 suites: 245 €
Breakfast: 12,5 €
Menu(s): 22 € / 70 € - **Carte:** 34 €
1/2 board: 125 € / 270 €

In the heart of the "little Venice", this beautiful 15th century residence amorously lets time flow past like the waters that border it. The rooms are welcoming and the cuisine speaks in praise of the gourmand delights of the region. A good address for visiting a unique place.

Open all year

equipments
lift, internet, T.V. Satellite, minibar, safe

environment
architecture 15e, terrace 20 m², view, total calm

leisure, relaxation
tennis 5 km, golf course 10 km, jacuzzi

Visa ● Diners ● Master Card

Road map p. 619

A35 exit Colmar south - Semm

Bâle/Mulhouse: 60 km

Maison des Têtes

Colmar

www.chateauxhotels.com/tetes | reservation service: 33 (0) 1.40.07.00.20

19, rue des Têtes 68000 Colmar
Tel.: 33 (0) 3.89.24.43.43 – Fax: 33 (0) 3.89.24.58.34

tetes@chateauxhotels.com
Carmen & Marc ROHFRITSCH
20 rooms: 91 € / 230 €
1 flat: 208 € / 247 €
Breakfast: 12 €
Menu(s): 27 € / 56 €

hotel annual closing
28/01 > 28/02
restaurant annual closing
28/01 > 28/02
equipments
lift, telephone, internet, T.V.
Satellite, minibar, safe,
baby-sitting
environment
architecture 17e, terrace
leisure, relaxation
golf course 10 km, horse-riding
2 km, jacuzzi

On the facade of this beautiful XVIIth century residence glistens a constellation of grotesque masks and figurines. This unusual house was once the wine trading building and still features many of its original architecture oddities. Converted in 1898 to a restaurant, it is today a luxury hotel.

Visa • Diners • MASTER CARD

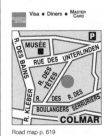

Road map p. 619

A35 exit Colmar city centre

 Bâle-Mulhouse: 55 km

5, avenue de Provence 88000 Epinal

Tel.: 33 (0) 3.29.29.55.55 – Fax: 33 (0) 3.29.29.55.56

lemanoir@chateauxhotels.com

Frédéric CLAUDEL

10 rooms: 74 € / 84 €
2 suites: 115 €
Breakfast: 7 €
Menu(s): 29,50 € / 76 €

This fabulous Tudor mansion was entirely renovated in 2001. All the rooms and suites, have been decorated in a luxurious style, and are equipped with the latest technology (Wide screen, DVD, fax, game console, ADSL etc). One of the best places to eat in the area.

Visa ● Diners ● MASTER CARD

Road map p. 619

RN57 exit Epinal, dir. Prefecture centre

Open all year

equipments
lift, telephone, internet, T.V. Satellite/Canal+, minibar, safe, baby-sitting

environment
architecture 19°, furniture 18/19°, garden, terrace 60 m^2, view, total calm

leisure, relaxation
tennis 1 km, golf course 2 km, horse-riding, beauty salon, balneo, thermal baths, solarium, fitness

Mirecourt: 30 km

Alsace Lorraine

Le Grand Hôtel

Gérardmer

www.chateauxhotels.com/grandhotel | reservation service: 33 (0) 1.40.07.00.20

Place du Tilleul 88400 Gérardmer
Tel.: 33 (0) 3.29.63.06.31 – Fax: 33 (0) 3.29.63.46.81
grandhotel@chateauxhotels.com
Claude & Fabienne REMY
48 rooms: 77 € / 145 €
6 flats: 168 € - **4 suites:** 168 € / 250 €
Breakfast: 11 €
Menu(s): 21 € / 60 € - **Carte:** 14,50 € / 28,50 €
1/2 board: 62,55 € / 122 €

Open all year
equipments
lift, telephone, internet, T.V., safe, valet parking
environment
architecture 18e, garden, terrace
leisure, relaxation
heated pool/covered, tennis 0.3 km, horse-riding 1.5 km, sauna, jacuzzi, fantasticâble

An invigorating landscape of lakes and forests in the Vosges, a hotel of tradition where hospitality is the key. Spacious rooms and suites, good food and local fare at the two restaurants. Fitness center with swimming pool, swimming against the current, jacuzzi, sauna, body-building.

Visa ● Diners ● MASTER CARD

Road map p. 619

A36 exit Colmar. A5/A31 exit Vittel dir. Epinal

Alsace Lorraine |

 Mulhouse-Bâle: 85 km

59, Ch. Droite du Lac 88400 Gérardmer
Tel.: 33 (0) 3.29.27.10.20 – Fax: 33 (0) 3.29.27.10.27
lac@chateauxhotels.com
Marie-Luce VALENTIN
9 rooms: 122 € / 214 €
2 flats: 305 € / 488 € - **2 suites:** 260 € / 305 €
Breakfast: 15,5 €
Menu(s): 40 € / 40 €
open to hotel residents only

This historic lakeside residence, in the heart of a restful and natural environment, offers guests tastefully decorated bedrooms, each with its own special touch, harking back to the famous guests of yesteryear. You will feel completely at home in these simple yet luxurious surrounding.

Open all year
equipments
lift, telephone, internet, T.V. Satellite, minibar, safe, baby-sitting, valet parking
environment
architecture 19^e, furniture 19^e, garden, terrace 100 m^2, view
leisure, relaxation
heated pool/covered, tennis 1 km, golf course 30 km, horse-riding 3 km, sauna, hammam, fantasticâble

Visa ● Diners ● MASTER CARD

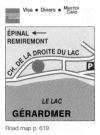

ÉPINAL ←
REMIREMONT
CH. DE LA DROITE DU LAC
P
LE LAC
GÉRARDMER

Road map p. 619
A5-A31 exit Vittel dir. Epinal

Mulhouse/Strasbourg:
100 km

Alsace Lorraine

Château de la Prairie

Guebwiller

www.chateauxhotels.com/prairie | reservation service: 33 (0) 1.40.07.00.20

Allée des Marronniers 68500 Guebwiller
Tel.: 33 (0) 3.89.74.28.57 – Fax: 33 (0) 3.89.74.71.88
prairie@chateauxhotels.com
Caroline ZIMMERMANN
13 rooms: 55 € / 89 €
2 suites: 105 € / 169 €
Breakfast: 8 €

Open all year
equipments
telephone, internet, T.V., valet parking

environment
architecture 19e, park 3 ha, garden, terrace 400 m², view, total calm

leisure, relaxation
tennis 1 km, golf course 7 km, horse-riding 3 km, 4x4 trail in the Vosges mountains

19th century château at the foot of the vineyards, in the Florival valley, in a magnificent 5-acres park. Very comfortable rooms, lounges, bar, terraces, a warm welcome to entice you from the start. Ideal for discovering the Vosges. 30 min. from Germany and switzerland. Closed parking.

Visa • Diners • MASTER CARD

Road map p. 619

A5 exit Neuenburg. A36 exit Bourtzwiller

Bâle-Mulhouse: 40 km

2-4 rue Foch 68240 Kientzheim
Tel.: 33 (0) 3.89.47.16.00 – Fax: 33 (0) 3.89.78.29.73
alspach@chateauxhotels.com
Annick SCHWARTZ
29 rooms: 58 € / 122 €
4 suites: 183 €
Breakfast: 8,4 €

History is the rendezvous in this 11th century abbey, a former Clarisses convent, converted to stylish hotel. The architecture of the past has retained all of its charm in combination with modern comforts. The rooms are decorated and the breakfast copious. Ideal stopping place for visiting Alsace.

hotel annual closing
06/01 > 15/03

equipments
telephone, internet, T.V., minibar

environment
architecture 11e, garden, total calm

leisure, relaxation
golf course 3 km, sauna, fitness

Visa ● Diners ● MASTER CARD

KIENTZHEIM
D28
STRASBOURG
SÉLESTAT
AMMERSCHWIHR
N 415
HOUSSEN
N 83
A 35
TURCKHEIM COLMAR
MULHOUSE

Road map p. 619
A35 exit Colmar, N415, D28, exit n° 23

Colmar: 10 km

Hostellerie Paulus
Landser
www.chateauxhotels.com/paulus | reservation service: 33 (0) 1.40.07.00.20

4, Place de la Paix 68440 Landser
Tel.: 33 (0) 3.89.81.33.30 – Fax: 33 (0) 3.89.26.81.85
paulus@chateauxhotels.com
Hervé PAULUS
Menu(s): 20 € / 65 €

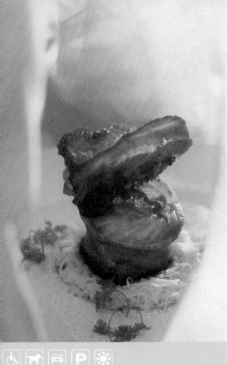

restaurant annual closing
05/08 > 19/08 • 23/12 > 10/01
environment
architecture 17°, furniture
contemporain, garden, terrace
240 m²

Hervé Paulus is an honoured chef as his restaurant joins the best tables of the region, and the people of Alsace are gourmets difficult to please! His cuisine that combines tradition and the search for savours is exceptional. A great address brightened by the smile and grace of his wife.

Visa • MASTER CARD

Road map p. 619

A36 exit Rixheim/Habsheim. D432 dir. Altkirch

Bâle/Mulhouse: 15 km

La Petite-Pierre
www.chateauxhotels.com/clairiere | reservation service: 33 (0) 1.40.07.00.20

63, route d'Ingwiller 67290 La Petite-Pierre
Tel.: 33 (0) 3.88.71.75.00 – Fax: 33 (0) 3.88.70.41.05
clairiere@chateauxhotels.com
Famille STROHMENGER
50 rooms: 84 € / 119 €
Menu(s): 22 € / 51 € - **Carte:** 21 €
1/2 board: 70 € / 88 €

La Petite-Pierre, an interesting old walled town with a castle, museums and craftshops, makes a wonderful setting. La Clairière offers a magnificent view on the surrounding forest and a variety of French and Alsatian culinary delights. Invigorating leisure activities and cultural visits are also on offer.

Visa ● Diners ● MASTER CARD

Road map p. 619

A4 exit Sarre-Union. dir. Drulingen

Open all year
equipments
lift, telephone, internet, T.V. Satellite, minibar
environment
architecture contemporary, garden, terrace 80 m², view, total calm
leisure, relaxation
heated indoor pool/covered, golf course 20 km, horse-riding 6 km, sauna, solarium, fitness, ropes, challenge course, english bar and billard

✈ Strasbourg/Entzheim: 50 km

Alsace Lorraine

Relais de la Poste

La Wantzenau

www.chateauxhotels.com/relaisposte | reservation service: 33 (0) 1.40.07.00.20

21, rue du Général de Gaulle
67610 La Wantzenau
Tel.: 33 (0) 3.88.59.24.80 – Fax: 33 (0) 3.88.59.24.89
relaisposte@chateauxhotels.com
Jérôme DAULL

17 rooms: 61 € / 122 €
2 suites: 130 €
Breakfast: 10 €
Menu(s): 28 € / 73 € - **Carte:** 61 €
1/2 board: 122 €

hotel annual closing
02/01 > 22/01 ● 22/07 > 02/08
restaurant annual closing
02/01 > 22/01 ● 22/07 > 02/08
equipments
lift, telephone, internet, T.V.
Satellite, safe
environment
architecture 18e, terrace 40 m²
leisure, relaxation
tennis 1 km, golf course 1 km,
horse-riding 2 km

Former post house with half timbering dating back to 1789. Delightful inn in charming Alsace village, 10 min. north of Strasbourg. Features exquisite gourmet cuisine in picturesque setting. Walks in the Rhine forest and bird sanctuary. Charming decor for the Alsacian-style rooms.

Visa ● Diners ● MASTER CARD

Road map p. 619
A4 exit Reichstett (N° 49)

Strasbourg-Entzheim: 25 km

4, rue de Wissenbourg 67510 Lembach
Tel.: 33 (0) 3.88.94.41.86 – Fax: 33 (0) 3.88.94.20.74
chevalblanc@chateauxhotels.com
Fernand MISCHLER
1 room: 106,71 €
5 suites: 137,20 € / 198,18 €
Breakfast: 9,15 €
Menu(s): 32,01 € / 81,56 € - **Carte:** 64 €

The Mischler family has built their gastronomic fame in this former Post house since 1740. Conviviality is not just a word here and the renowned cuisine of Fernand Mischler is bolstered by fresh regional products that he subtly blends with original savours. Great wines from Alsace.

hotel annual closing
03/02 > 01/03●01/07 > 19/07
equipments
telephone, internet, T.V., minibar
environment
architecture 18ᵉ, garden

Visa ● Diners ● MASTER CARD

Road map p. 619
A4 exit Haguenau

Starsbourg : 90 km

Le Mas & la Lorraine
Longuyon
www.chateauxhotels.com/lorraine | reservation service: 33 (0) 1.40.07.00.20

Place de la Gare 54260 Longuyon
Tel.: 33 (0) 3.82.26.50.07 – Fax: 33 (0) 3.82.39.26.09
lorraine@chateauxhotels.com
Gérard TISSERANT
14 rooms: 43 € / 53 €
Breakfast: 7 €
Menu(s): 18,50 € / 59 € - **Carte:** 33 €
1/2 board: 52 € / 60 €

hotel annual closing
04/01 > 31/01
restaurant annual closing
04/01 > 31/01
equipments
telephone, T.V.
environment
architecture, furniture
contemporain, garden, terrace
50 m², vegetable garden
leisure, relaxation
tennis 2 km, horse-riding
10 km

At the meeting-point of three
borders, the Tisserants welcome you in the calm and
warmth of their old, family-
owned hostelry, entirely renovated in 1995. In the restaurant, modern and high-quality
cuisine according to the seasons. Famous wine cellar.
Fantastic menu for sampling
specialities.

Visa • Diners • MASTER CARD

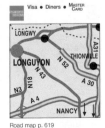

Road map p. 619

A30 or A4 exit Longwy

Luxembourg: 45 km

www.chateauxhotels.com/theatre | reservation service: 33 (0) 1.40.07.00.20

1-3 rue du Pont St-Marcel - Port St-Marcel
57000 Metz
Tel.: 33 (0) 3.87.31.10.10 – Fax: 33 (0) 3.87.30.04.66
theatre@chateauxhotels.com
Laure CAZENAVE

33 rooms: 75 € / 115 €
1 flat: 165 € - **4 suites:** 130 € / 145 €
Breakfast: 9,5 €
Menu(s): 16 € / 28 € - **Carte:** 25 € -
1/2 board: 68 € / 85 €

In the heart of historical Metz, along the Moselle river, facing the Cathedrale, the Lorraine tradition is here waitered in the regional costume since 1649. The hotel offers an ideal location for discovering Metz, garden city, with 3000 years history. Overflow swimming pool, whirlpool.

Open all year

equipments
lift, telephone, internet, T.V. Satellite, minibar

environment
architecture 17e, furniture contemporain, terrace 300 m^2, view

leisure, relaxation
tennis 1 km, golf course 3 km, horse-riding 5 km, sauna, hammam, jacuzzi, swimming pool

Visa ● Diners ● JCB ● MASTER CARD

Road map p. 619

A4/A31 exit Metz-centre/Theatre-Prefecture. Dir.parking of "Port St-Marcel"

Metz-Nancy-Lorraine: 23 km

Hôtel Restaurant Verte Vallée

Munster

www.chateauxhotels.com/vertevallee | reservation service: 33 (0) 1.40.07.00.20

10, rue Alfred Hartmann 68140 Munster
Tel.: 33 (0) 3.89.77.15.15 – Fax: 33 (0) 3.89.77.17.40
vertevallee@chateauxhotels.com
Yvon & Patricia GAUTIER
99 rooms: 70 € / 80 €
5 flats: 125 € / 135 € - **3 suites:** 100 € / 110 €
Breakfast: 11 €
Menu(s): 16 € / 47 € - **Carte:** 35 €
1/2 board: 64 € / 69 €

hotel annual closing
06/01 > 31/01

restaurant annual closing
06/01 > 31/01

equipments
lift, telephone, internet, T.V.
Canal+, minibar, safe

environment
garden, terrace 70 m²

leisure, relaxation
heated pool/covered, golf
course 20 km, horse-riding
8 km, beauty salon, balneo,
sauna, hammam, solarium,
jacuzzi

In a leafy riverside garden, near the wine route at the foot of the Vosges mountains, this hotel is aptly named the "Green Valley". Tranquillity, relaxation and good food await nature lovers, sports enthusiasts and families. Two pools, balneotherapy complex, sauna, hammam, games rooms.

Visa ● Diners ● MASTER CARD

Road map p. 619

A35 exit Colmar, dir. Gerardmer by
D10 or D417

Mulhouse: 60 km

169, route d'Ottrott 67210 Obernai
Tel.: 33 (0) 3.88.95.50.08 – Fax: 33 (0) 3.88.95.37.29
hotelparc@chateauxhotels.com
Monique & Marc WUCHER
44 rooms: 110 € / 180 €
6 suites: 225 € / 260 €
Breakfast: 13 €
Menu(s): 38 € / 64 € - **Carte:** 53 €
1/2 board: 100 € / 142,5 €

25 km from Strasbourg, and 16 km from Entzheim airport, Obernai is at the foot of Mont Sainte-Odile, on the wine route. Charming hotel, sauna, Turkish baths, jacuzzi, solarium... Two swimming pools, one in the garden, the other indoors. Bowling, billiards, equestrian centre, 10 tennis courts.

Visa ● MASTER CARD

Road map p. 619

A35 exit Obernai

hotel annual closing
05/12 > 10/01 ● 01/07 > 12/07
restaurant annual closing
05/12 > 10/01 ● 01/07 > 12/07
equipments
lift, telephone, T.V. Satellite, safe
environment
garden, terrace, total calm
leisure, relaxation
heated pool/covered, tennis 0.2 km, golf course 18 km, horse-riding 0.1 km, sauna, hammam, solarium, jacuzzi, snooker, pinball, bowling, table football

Strasbourg: 20 km

Hostellerie des Châteaux

Ottrott-le-Haut

www.chateauxhotels.com/deschateaux | reservation service: 33 (0) 1.40.07.00.20

11, rue des Châteaux 67530 Ottrott-le-Haut
Tel.: 33 (0) 3.88.48.14.14 – Fax: 33 (0) 3.88.48.14.18

deschateaux@chateauxhotels.com
Sabine & Ernest SCHAETZEL
59 rooms: 107 € / 198 €
1 flat: 397 € - **5 suites:** 259 €
Breakfast: 13 €
Menu(s): 34 € / 80 € - **Carte:** 69 €
1/2 board: 112 € / 156 €

hotel annual closing
01/02 > 28/02
restaurant annual closing
01/02 > 28/02
equipments
lift, telephone, internet, T.V.
Satellite, safe
environment
architecture 17°, furniture 18°,
garden, terrace 30 m², view,
total calm
leisure, relaxation
heated pool/covered, tennis
0.8 km, golf course 30 km,
horse-riding 4 km

On the edge of the forest, a large house with the fragrance of the traditions of Alsace. Calm and delicious flavours in the restaurant. Comfort, intimacy, refinement. Fitness centre: indoor swimming pool, massage, jacuzzi, sauna, solarium... All-inclusive rate for charming week-ends.

Visa ● Diners ● MASTER CARD

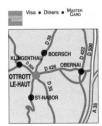

Road map p. 619

A35 exit Obernai, dir. Ottrott

Strasbourg-Entzheim: 25 km

Place de l'Église 67530 Ottrott-le-Haut
Tel.: 33 (0) 3.88.95.80.61 – Fax: 33 (0) 3.88.48.14.18
beausite@chateauxhotels.com
Sabine & Ernest SCHAETZEL
18 rooms: 71,65 € / 144,83 €
Breakfast: 9,91 €
Menu(s): 13,72 € / 44,21 € - **Carte:** 53,36 €

Friendly, authentic and gourmet... the charms of Alsace are well known, but they must be experienced to be believed! The Beau site is the ideal establishment for discovering Alsace. Nestling in the heart of a village on the Wine Route, the Beau Site offers you a landscape of hills and vineyards.

hotel annual closing
01/02 > 01/03•23/07 > 05/08
restaurant annual closing
01/02 > 01/03•23/07 > 05/08
equipments
lift, telephone, T.V., safe
environment
garden, terrace 40 m²
leisure, relaxation
tennis 0.5 km, golf course 30 km, horse-riding 4 km

Visa • MASTER CARD

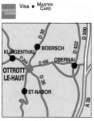

Road map p. 619

A35 exit Obernai, dir. Ottrott

Strasbourg-Entzheim: 25 km

Le Clos Saint-Vincent

Ribeauvillé

www.chateauxhotels.com/saintvincent | reservation service: 33 (0) 1.40.07.00.20

Route de Bergheim 68150 Ribeauvillé
Tel.: 33 (0) 3.89.73.67.65 – Fax: 33 (0) 3.89.73.32.20

saintvincent@chateauxhotels.com
Arthur et Emmanuel CHAPOTIN

12 rooms: 120 € / 160 €
3 flats: 175 € / 190 €
Menu(s): 30 € / 40 € - **Carte:** 40 €
1/2 board: 100 € / 120 €

hotel annual closing
15/11 > 15/03
restaurant annual closing
15/03 > 15/03
equipments
telephone, internet, T.V.
Satellite, minibar, safe
environment
park 1.2 ha (garden), terrace,
view, total calm
leisure, relaxation
heated pool/covered, tennis
2 km, golf course 10 km,
horse-riding 10 km

Le Clos Saint-Vincent is a tranquil stopover with 15 rooms. in the heart of Alsace, along the famous wine route bordering Germany and Switzerland. A quiet haven with only the birds and the rustle of leaves to serenade you. Generous and sunbathed cuisine reflecting the richness of the region.

Visa • MASTER CARD

Road map p. 619

A35 exit Ribeauvillé, N83, D106, dir.
Ribeauvillé

Strasbourg/Bâle: 50 km

5, rue de la Couronne 68340 Riquewihr
Tel.: 33 (0) 3.89.49.03.03 – Fax: 33 (0) 3.89.49.01.01
lacouronne@chateauxhotels.com
Arnaud CLAUDEL
36 rooms: 55 € / 62 €
4 suites: 100 € / 136 €
Breakfast: 7 €

In the heart of Riquewihr and the Alsace vineyards, on the edge of the Vosges forest. Modern comforts combined with the charms of yesteryear in a 15th-16th century patrician residence. Bar, meeting-room. In one of France's most beautiful villages. Trips to the forest and to medieval castles.

Open all year
equipments
telephone, internet, T.V., safe, baby-sitting
environment
architecture 15^e, furniture 19^e, terrace 20 m^2
leisure, relaxation
tennis 2 km, golf course 10 km

Visa ● Diners ● JCB ● MasterCard

Road map p. 619

A35 exit Colmar. N83 dir. Ribeauvillé

Mulhouse-Bâle-Strasbourg: 60 km

Alsace Lorraine

Auberge Saint-Walfrid

Sarreguemines

www.chateauxhotels.com/saintwalfrid | reservation service: 33 (0) 1.40.07.00.20

58, rue de Grosbliederstroff
57200 Sarreguemines
Tel.: 33 (0) 3.87.98.43.75 – Fax: 33 (0) 3.87.95.76.75
saintwalfrid@chateauxhotels.com
Jean-Claude & Stéphan SCHNEIDER
11 rooms: 92 € / 109 €
Breakfast: 12 €
Menu(s): 20 € / 65 € - **1/2 board:** 115 € / 300 €

restaurant annual closing
01/01 > 22/01 ● 01/08 > 22/08

equipments
lift, telephone, internet, T.V.,
minibar

environment
architecture 18^e, garden,
terrace 70 m^2, vegetable
garden, total calm

leisure, relaxation
tennis 3 km, golf course 1 km,
horse-riding 6 km

Here, in the heart of the Sarroise Valley, is a residence that blends a taste of most certain elegance and sobriety with comfortable rooms, meticulous decoration and a cuisine with gentle rural fragrances. Faïence Museums and the archaeological sites of Bliesbrück are near-by.

Visa ● MASTER CARD

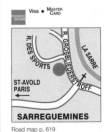

Road map p. 619

A4 exit Sarreguemines dir.Sarrebrück,exit to golf -Le Hohberg

Alsace Lorraine

Saarbrücken: 15 km

25, rue de la Marne 68360 Soultz
Tel.: 33 (0) 3.89.62.23.68 – Fax: 33 (0) 3.89.62.23.70
anthes@chateauxhotels.com
Philippe & Christophe SCHMERBER
20 rooms: 64 € / 90 €
Breakfast: 10,7 €
Menu(s): 12 € / 38 € - **1/2 board:** 83 € / 98 €

Close to the Ballon d'Alsace and the great wine trail, this historically rich Renaissance chateau provides you with a warm welcome. Elegant rooms, traditional food served in the winstub or gastronomic delights in the Poushkine, a summer terrace in the magnificent park woods: in a nutshell, the art of living.

Visa • MASTER CARD

Road map p. 619

A35 & A36 exit Boutzwiller, express way CD430

Open all year
restaurant weekly closing
mon, sun(ev)
01/01 > 31/12

equipments
telephone, internet, T.V.
Satellite/Canal+, minibar

environment
architecture 17e, furniture contemporain, park 1 ha, garden, terrace 40 m², view, total calm

leisure, relaxation
tennis 1 km, golf course 30 km, horse-riding 2 km, beauty salon, sauna, hammam, solarium, fitness, jacuzzi, bicycles, mountain bikes, hiking

Bâle Mulhouse: 40 km

Cardinal de Rohan
Strasbourg
www.chateauxhotels.com/cardinal | reservation service: 33 (0) 1.40.07.00.20

17-19, rue du Maroquin 67000 Strasbourg
Tel.: 33 (0) 3.88.32.85.11 – Fax: 33 (0) 3.88.75.65.37
cardinal@chateauxhotels.com
Nicole & Rolf VAN MAENEN
28 rooms: 82,50 € / 122 €
Breakfast: 10 €

Open all year
equipments
lift, telephone, T.V. Satellite,
minibar, safe

leisure, relaxation
shopping, museums, historical
center town

environment
cathedral

Just at the cathedral, in the historical part of Strasbourg, this classic building combines superbly elegant interior design with charm. Rooms are in a classic or rustic style. Warm hospitality: the perfect place to discover a town steeped in history.

Visa ● Diners ● JCB ● MASTER CARD

Road map p. 619

Exit "place de l'Etoile", dir.cathedral, underground car park "place Gutemberg"

Alsace Lorraine |

Strasbourg: 15 km

4, rue des Francs-Bourgeois 67000 Strasbourg
Tel.: 33 (0) 3.88.32.08.60 – Fax: 33 (0) 3.88.22.43.73
maisonrouge@chateauxhotels.com
Patrick ASTRUGUE – Carine CHRISTMANN
140 rooms: 93 € / 109 €
2 suites: 220 € / 250 €
Breakfast: 12 €

Magnificently situated in the heart of Strasbourg, between the cathedral and the Petite France district, just at the edge of the pedestrian zone, the hotel shelters behind its stunning façade a real haven of peace and rest. Everything in this place is different to anything you have ever seen.

Open all year

equipments
lift, telephone, T.V.
Satellite/Canal+, minibar, safe

leisure, relaxation
tennis 3 km, golf course
15 km, horse-riding 10 km

Visa ● Diners ● MASTER CARD

Road map p. 619

A4 exit Strasbourg-Place des Halles,
N4 dir. Strasbourg

Strasbourg-Entzheim: 15 km

Le Parc

Thann

www.chateauxhotels.com/hotelduparc | reservation service: 33 (0) 1.40.07.00.20

23, rue Kleber 68800 Thann
Tel.: 33 (0) 3.89.37.37.47 – Fax: 33 (0) 3.89.37.56.23
hotelduparc@chateauxhotels.com
Didier MARTIN
20 rooms: 58 € / 176 €
Breakfast: 15 €
Menu(s): 26,68 € / 38 € - **Carte:** 25 €
1/2 board: 75 € / 126 €

Open all year
equipments
telephone, internet, T.V.
Satellite, minibar, safe
environment
architecture 19ᵉ, furniture 19ᵉ,
garden, terrace 80 m²
leisure, relaxation
heated pool, tennis 0.5 km,
golf course 16 km, horse-riding
5 km, sauna, hammam,
fitness, jacuzzi

This beautiful residence invites you to lap up its art de vivre, Italian masterpieces on the salon walls, a warm feeling around the Louis XVI fireplace, calm from the tree-filled park, relaxation around the pool... Terroir cuisine served with the Alsace region's best wines.

Visa ● Diners ● MASTER CARD

Road map p. 619
A36 exit Thann or N66 dir. Thann

Bâle-Mulhouse: 35 km

www.chateauxhotels.com/horizon | reservation service: 33 (0) 1.40.07.00.20

50, route du Crève-Coeur 57100 Thionville
Tel.: 33 (0) 3.82.88.53.65 – Fax: 33 (0) 3.82.34.55.84
horizon@chateauxhotels.com
Jean-Pascal SPECK
12 rooms: 96 € / 145 €
Breakfast: 11 €
Menu(s): 30 € / 53 € - **Carte:** 46 €
1/2 board: 106 € / 126 €

In Lorraine, towards Trèves la Romaine and Luxembourg, welcome this beautiful residence with its flowering gardens, its panoramic terrace on the edge of the forest. Warm atmosphere. Restaurant with a view over the Moselle Valley. Nearby: The Maginot Line, Longwy faience, Moselle vineyards.

Visa • Diners • MASTER CARD

Road map p. 619

A31 exit n° 40. Exit Thionville Ring road dir. Bel-Air Hospital and Crève-Cœur

Luxembourg: 30 km

hotel annual closing
01/01 > 10/02
restaurant annual closing
01/01 > 10/02
hotel weekly closing
sun
01/11 > 27/02
restaurant weekly closing
mon(lun), sat(lun)
01/03 > 31/10
mon(lun), sat(lun), sun(ev)
01/11 > 27/02
equipments
telephone, internet, T.V. Satellite
environment
contemporary architecture, garden, terrace 120 m², view
leisure, relaxation
golf course 15 km, sauna, Maginot line tours

Hostellerie du Coq-Hardi

Verdun

www.chateauxhotels.com/coqhardi | reservation service: 33 (0) 1.40.07.00.20

8, avenue de la Victoire 55100 Verdun
Tel.: 33 (0) 3.29.86.36.36 – Fax: 33 (0) 3.29.86.09.21

coqhardi@chateauxhotels.com
Patrick LELOUP

35 rooms: 60,30 € / 125 €
2 flats: 129,58 € / 228,67 € - **1 suite:** 228,67 € /
365,88 €
Breakfast: 12,20 €
Menu(s): 35,10 € / 73,94 € - **Carte:** 61 €

hotel annual closing
24/12 > 25/12

equipments
lift, telephone, internet, T.V.,
minibar, safe

environment
architecture 10ª, terrace
80 m², view, total calm

leisure, relaxation
tennis 2 km, golf course
35 km, horse-riding 3 km

A hotel since 1827! In the heart of Verdun, a place as bold as they get! The charm of its brazenly polished half-timbering and brashly mellow provincial-style rooms. A place where the coq crows nothing but the finest ingredients and the miracles of invention performed by a chef hardly 30 years old.

Visa ● Diners ● MASTER CARD

VERDUN
R. de la BELLE VIERGE   RUE L. MAURY
Rue St-PIERRE
RUE MAZEL   RUE St-PAUL
Av. de la VICTOIRE
QUAI DE LONDRES
MEUSE   Pont Chaussée
QUAI DE LA REPUBLIQUE   Place de la Nation
Av. DE DOUAUMONT

Road map p. 619

A4 exit "Voie Sacrée"

Metz: 70 km

39, rue du Général de Gaulle
67710 Wangenbourg
Tel.: 33 (0) 3.88.87.31.72 – Fax: 33 (0) 3.88.87.38.00
parchotel@chateauxhotels.com
Daniel GIHR

21 rooms: 33,5 € / 90,5 €
1 suite: 85,5 € / 90 €
Breakfast: 8,5 €
Menu(s): 18 € / 42 € - **Carte:** 11 €
1/2 board: 56,5 € / 68,5 €

Set in a bird-filled park, this beautiful ancestral residence offers the ultimate in rest and relaxation. The rooms, some with a balcony offer all comforts. Covered and heated pool, Jet stream, sauna, tennis, gym, billiards, garden terrace, library, panoramic views, walking paths...

hotel annual closing
01/01 > 28/03 • 06/11 > 24/12
restaurant annual closing
01/01 > 28/03 • 06/11 > 24/12
equipments
lift, telephone, internet, T.V. Satellite, safe
environment
garden, terrace 1500 m^2, view, total calm
leisure, relaxation
heated pool/covered, golf course 30 km, horse-riding 10 km, sauna

Visa ● MASTER CARD

Road map p. 619

A4 exit Saverne. N4 dir. Wasselonne

Strasbourg-Entzheim: 38 km

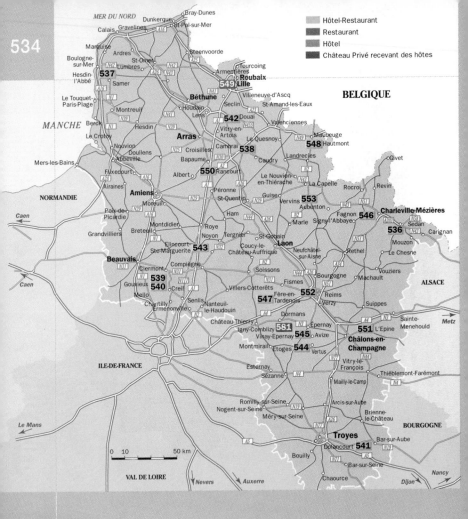

Hôtel-Restaurant
Restaurant
Hôtel
Château Privé recevant des hôtes

L'abus d'alcool est dangereux pour la santé, à consommer avec modération.

Château de Bazeilles

Bazeilles

www.chateauxhotels.com/bazeilles | reservation service: 33 (0) 1.40.07.00.20

08140 Bazeilles

Tel.: 33 (0) 3.24.27.09.68 – Fax: 33 (0) 3.24.27.64.20

bazeilles@chateauxhotels.com

Patrick GUILHAS

20 rooms: 66 € / 76 €

Breakfast: 8,1 €

Menu(s): 19 € / 54 € - **Carte:** 38 €

1/2 board: 70 € / 98 €

Open all year

equipments
telephone, internet, T.V.
Satellite, minibar, safe

environment
park 7 ha, garden, terrace
300 m², vegetable garden

leisure, relaxation
tennis 4 km, golf course
29 km, horse-riding 8 km

An 18th century residence, with its summer-château and its park setting with follies ans dovecotes, in the beautiful region, the Ardennes... Complete relaxation, comfort and freestanding rooms overlooking gardens. Country cuisine, light and innovative.

Visa • Master Card

Road map p. 619

A203 exit Bazeilles. N43 Metz-Verdun

 Bruxelles: 170 km

Avenue du Château 62360 Hesdin-l'Abbé
Tel.: 33 (0) 3.21.83.19.83 – Fax: 33 (0) 3.21.87.52.59
clery@chateauxhotels.com
Emmanuel LARD
22 rooms: 55 € / 145 €
Breakfast: 10 €
Menu(s): 24 € / 45 €

In the green hills of Boulonnais, on the Opal Coast, an elegant 18th century château, nestling in a 12 acre park. Walking along the paths ornamented with 100-year old trees is a delight. An attentive team watch over the intimate and warm atmosphere. Lounge with fireplace to chat, read, dream.

hotel annual closing
01/01 > 25/01
restaurant annual closing
01/01 > 25/01
equipments
telephone, T.V. Satellite
environment
architecture 18e, park 5 ha, garden, view, total calm
leisure, relaxation
golf course 7 km, horse-riding 7 km

Visa ● Diners ● MASTER CARD

Road map p. 619

A16 exit 28 Isques then N1 dir.Samer

Le Touquet: 25 km

Château de la Motte Fénelon
Cambrai
www.chateauxhotels.com/fenelon | reservation service: 33 (0) 1.40.07.00.20

Square du Château 59403 Cambrai
Tel.: 33 (0) 3.27.83.61.38 – Fax: 33 (0) 3.27.83.71.61
fenelon@chateauxhotels.com
Marie-Anne DELEVALLEE
40 rooms: 55 € / 230 €
Breakfast: 10 €
Menu(s): 20 € / 37 € - **Carte:** 30 €
1/2 board: 80 € / 277 €

Open all year
equipments
lift, telephone, T.V.
Satellite/Canal+, minibar,
baby-sitting
environment
architecture 19ᵉ, park 8 ha,
garden
leisure, relaxation
horse-riding 2 km

*In the historic city of Cambrai,
this 19th century Château is
situated within a 20-acre park.
With its restaurant Les
Douves, the hotel offers a
high-class cuisine in a refined
setting under century-old-
arches. The sumptuous re-
ception rooms, the bedrooms,
the park offer you an elegant
stay.*

Visa ● Diners ● MASTER CARD

Road map p. 619

A1 or A2 exit 14 Cambrai, dir. Valen-
cienne Le Cateau

 Lille-Lesquin: 70 km

Chemin de la Chaussée 60270 Gouvieux
Tel.: 33 (0) 3.44.62.38.38 – Fax: 33 (0) 3.44.57.31.97
chateautour@chateauxhotels.com
Olivier LANTHOINNETTE
41 rooms: 110 € / 195 €
Breakfast: 13 €
Menu(s): 35 € / 50 € - **Carte:** 40 €
1/2 board: 90 € / 129 €

Located in a unique setting only 18 miles from Paris, this elegant turn-of-century residence blends past beauty with modern comfort. Rooms and terrace overlook the vast, magnificent park. Outdoor pool, spa, tennis and other sports facilities complement the unforgettable cooking and hospitality.

restaurant annual closing
21/12 > 28/12

equipments
telephone, internet, T.V.
Satellite, minibar

environment
architecture 19^e, furniture 19^e, park 5 ha, terrace 300 m^2

leisure, relaxation
heated pool, golf course 3 km, horse-riding 3 km, jacuzzi, mountain bikes available

Visa ● Diners ● JCB ● Master Card

Road map p. 619

A1 exit Survilliers

Roissy/Charles-de-Gaulle:
20 km

Château de Montvillargenne

Chantilly I Gouvieux
www.chateauxhotels.com/montvillargenne I reservation service: 33 (0) 1.40.07.00.20

Avenue François Mathet 60270 Gouvieux
Tel.: 33 (0) 3.44.62.37.37 – Fax: 33 (0) 3.44.57.28.97
montvillargenne@chateauxhotels.com
Patrick SALAS

94 rooms: 158 € / 300 €
6 suites: 300 €
Breakfast: 15 €
Menu(s): 34 € / 66 € - **Carte:** 53,5 €
1/2 board: 116 € / 192 €

Open all year
equipments
lift, telephone, internet, T.V.,
minibar, safe
environment
architecture 19^e, park 6 ha,
garden, terrace 700 m^2
leisure, relaxation
heated pool/covered, tennis
2 km, golf course 2 km,
horse-riding 2 km, sauna,
hammam

The Château de Montvillargenne located in Chantilly, in the heart of a 15-acre park, is approximately 21 miles north of Paris, and 15 min from Charles de Gaulle airport. Le Vilargene is a gourmet restaurant with a wide selection. Facilities include an indoor pool, a sauna, tennis, steam room.

Visa • Diners • MASTER CARD

Road map p. 619

A1 exit 7 Survilliers - By N16 dir. Chantilly

Roissy/Charles-de-Gaulle: 25 km

Dolancourt

www.chateauxhotels.com/landion | reservation service: 33 (0) 1.40.07.00.20

5, rue St-Léger 10200 Dolancourt
Tel.: 33 (0) 3.25.27.92.17 – Fax: 33 (0) 3.25.27.94.44
landion@chateauxhotels.com
Paul BAJOLLE
16 rooms: 61 € / 74 €
Breakfast: 7,6 €
Menu(s): 17,50 € / 52 € - **Carte:** 54 € -
1/2 board: 59 € / 74 €

Elegant 16th century watermill restored with care to ally the character of the past (timber facade, sluice gates, working mill-wheel) with modern comforts. Rooms, English garden and inventive meals served on the waterside terrace, all add their touch to a taste of serenity.

hotel annual closing
20/11 > 15/02
restaurant annual closing
20/11 > 15/02
equipments
telephone, internet, T.V., minibar
environment
architecture 16°, furniture contemporain, garden, terrace 35 m^2
leisure, relaxation
tennis 2 km, golf course 25 km

Visa ● Diners ● MASTER CARD

Road map p. 619

A5/A26. N19 dir. Bar/Aube / Chaumont: 0,5 km

 Orly/Charles-de-Gaulle:
200 km

La Terrasse

Douai

www.chateauxhotels.com/terrasse | reservation service: 33 (0) 1.40.07.00.20

36, terrasse St Pierre 59500 Douai
Tel.: 33 (0) 3.27.88.70.04 – Fax: 33 (0) 3.27.88.36.05
terrasse@chateauxhotels.com
Emile HANIQUE
24 rooms: 45 € / 105 €
Breakfast: 7,5 €
Menu(s): 20,50 € / 66 €

Open all year
equipments
telephone, internet, T.V.
Canal+, minibar
leisure, relaxation
golf course 12 km

At La Terrasse, you will enjoy refinement, culinary delights and warm hospitality. The charm of yesterday mingles with the comfort of today in this superb residence. Gourmets will be thrilled by the finesse of the inventive cuisine accompanied by execeptional Burgundy wines which can be purchased.

Visa ● MASTER CARD

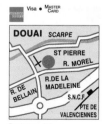

Road map p. 619

A1-A26 exit Fresnes-lès-Montauban,
dir. Douai centre-ville

 Lille-Lesquin: 20 km

Elincourt-Sainte-Marguerite

www.chateauxhotels.com/bellinglise | reservation service: 33 (0) 1.40.07.00.20

Route de Lassigny
60157 Elincourt-Sainte-Marguerite
Tel.: 33 (0) 3.44.96.00.33 – Fax: 33 (0) 3.44.96.03.00
bellinglise@chateauxhotels.com
Raffaello SAISI

33 rooms: 190 € / 305 €
2 suites: 300 € / 335 €
Menu(s): 30 € / 75 € - **Carte:** 60 €

This elegant 16 century castle is situated in 400 acres of woods and gardens. The 35 rooms with delicate fabrics reflect splendour and Art de Vivre. You will dine in a wood-panelled decorated with candelabras and warmed by open log fires. The chef invite you to discover the finest French cuisine.

Open all year

equipments
lift, telephone, internet, T.V. Satellite, minibar, safe

environment
architecture 16^e, park 140 ha, garden, terrace, total calm

leisure, relaxation
golf course 15 km, horse-riding 10 km, hot-air ballooning, excursions

Visa ● Diners ● JCB ● MASTER CARD

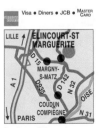

Road map p. 619

A1 exit 11 Ressons-Montdidier or D142 dir. Lassigny

 Orly/Charles-de-Gaulle: 60 km

| Nord Picardie

Château d'Etoges
Epernay I Etoges
www.chateauxhotels.com/etoges I reservation service: 33 (0) 1.40.07.00.20

4 Rue Richebourg 51270 Etoges
Tel.: 33 (0) 3.26.59.30.08 – Fax: 33 (0) 3.26.59.35.57

etoges@chateauxhotels.com
Anne FILLIETTE-NEUVILLE
19 rooms: 110 € / 190 €
1 suite: 190 €
Breakfast: 12 €
Menu(s): 30 € / 60 € - **Carte:** 45 €
1/2 board: 90 € / 140 €

hotel annual closing
27/01 > 20/02
restaurant annual closing
27/01 > 20/02
restaurant weekly closing
mon(lun), tue(lun), wen(lun),
thi(lun), fri(lun)
01/01 > 31/03
mon(lun), tue(lun), wen(lun),
thi(lun), fri(lun)
31/10 > 31/03
equipments
telephone, internet, T.V., safe
environment
architecture 17e, furniture 18e,
park 20 ha, garden, terrace
150 m², view, vegetable
garden, total calm
leisure, relaxation
tennis 5 km, golf course
20 km, horse-riding 10 km,
solarium, guided tour of cellars
and champagne-tasting

Listed as a historical monument, this chateau resembles a ship sailing on the waters of Champagne. Wide moats, a horizon of gardens, ponds and orchards, enlivened by natural springs which astonished Louis XIV. Champagne and countryside, fireplaces and canopied beds. Bicycles, croquet, boating.

Visa ● Diners ● JCB ● MASTER CARD

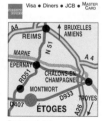

Road map p. 619

A4 exit La Ferté-sous-Jouarre. D407
dir. Châlons-en-Champagne then
D933

Reims: 48 km

4, route de Sézanne 51530 Vinay

Tel.: 33 (0) 3.26.59.99.99 – Fax: 33 (0) 3.26.59.92.10

briqueterie@chateauxhotels.com
Christel VINOGRAD-TROUILLARD

40 rooms: 127 € / 176 €
2 suites: 225 € / 235 €
Breakfast: 14 €
Menu(s): 22 € / 68 € - **Carte:** 54 €

A gastronomic stopover in the heart of the Champagne vineyards. An elegant setting to savour the cuisine wich follows the rythm of the seasons, created by a chef from Lyon. Park. Two saunas and a heath centre. Visits to prestigious wine cellars. Rheims cathedral, helicopter and balloon trips.

Visa ● MASTER CARD

hotel annual closing
22/12 > 29/12
restaurant annual closing
22/12 > 29/12
equipments
telephone, internet, T.V. Satellite/Canal+, minibar, safe, baby-sitting
environment
architecture, park 4 ha, garden, terrace 100 m^2
leisure, relaxation
heated pool/covered, tennis 2 km, golf course 30 km, horse-riding 1 km, sauna, solarium, fitness, visit of wine cellars and tour of vineyards

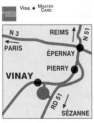

Road map p. 619

A4 exit Epernay or D 51 dir. Sézanne

✈ Orly/Charles-de-Gaulle: 120 km

Abbaye de Sept Fontaines

Fagnon

www.chateauxhotels.com/septfontaines | reservation service: 33 (0) 1.40.07.00.20

08090 Fagnon
Tel.: 33 (0) 3.24.37.38.24 – Fax: 33 (0) 3.24.37.58.75
septfontaines@chateauxhotels.com
Michel NICOLLE
23 rooms: 72 € / 197 €
Breakfast: 10 €
Menu(s): 23 € / 60 € - **Carte:** 45 €
1/2 board: 71 € / 98 €

Open all year
equipments
telephone, internet, T.V.
Satellite/Canal+, minibar
environment
architecture 17e, park 30 ha,
garden, terrace, view,
vegetable garden, total calm

*On the ruins of an old XIIth
century abbey this magnificent history-filled residence
presently finds new spirit
thanks to its restoration. Spacious rooms, gastronomic cuisine and the 9-hole golf course
are a true invitation for discovering Picardy.*

Visa ● Diners ● MASTER CARD

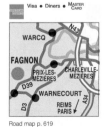

Road map p. 619

A203 exit Prix Les Mézières. D39

Nord Picardie |

Orly/Charles-de-Gaulle:
230 km

Château de Fère

Fère-en-Tardenois

Route de Fismes 02130 Fère-en-Tardenois
Tel.: 33 (0) 3.23.82.21.13 – Fax: 33 (0) 3.23.82.37.81
fere@chateauxhotels.com
Jo-Andréa FINCK
19 rooms: 130 € / 290 €
6 suites: 200 € / 350 €
Breakfast: 16 €
Menu(s): 45 € / 80 € - **Carte:** 70 €

One hour from east Paris, in a 175-acre wooded park. A pleasant and gastronomic stopover in Champagne, on the sacred royal route, in an exceptional setting. Each room is unique, which enhances the authenticity of the place to which the old feudal château gave a royal peace.

hotel annual closing
02/01 > 12/02
restaurant annual closing
02/01 > 12/02
equipments
telephone, T.V. Canal+, minibar, valet parking
environment
architecture 16e, park 10 ha, garden, terrace, view, total calm
leisure, relaxation
golf course 15 km, horse-riding 3 km, heated swimming-pool

Visa ● Diners ● JCB ● MASTER CARD

Road map p. 619
A4 exit Château-Thierry

Orly/Charles-de-Gaulle:
80 km

Nord Picardie

Hôtel de l'Abbaye

Hautmont

www.chateauxhotels.com/hautmont | reservation service: 33 (0) 1.40.07.00.20

7, place du Général de Gaulle 59330 Hautmont
Tel.: 33 (0) 3.27.64.01.05 – Fax: 33 (0) 3.27.64.10.03

hautmont@chateauxhotels.com
Alfred DEMOERSMAN
76 rooms: 60,98 € / 121,96 €
Breakfast: 11,43 €
Menu(s): 45,73 € / 91,47 € - **Carte:** 68,80 €

opening during the year
equipments
lift, telephone, internet, T.V.
Canal+, minibar, safe
environment
architecture 18º, garden,
terrace, view
leisure, relaxation
heated pool/covered, beauty
salon, balneo, sauna,
hammam, jacuzzi

On the banks of the Sambre in the Hautmont area, this hotel is located in a former Benedictine abbey - an unexpectedly impressive ensemble, and a perfect place for a contemplative and relaxing holiday. Fitness center, balneotherapy complex, sightseeing and fine food.

Visa ● Diners ● Master Card

Road map p. 619

A1 Valenciennes, A2 Maubeuge, N49
Maubeuge-Bavay, D405 Hautmont

Nord Picardie |

Bruxelles/Lille-Lesquin:
80 km

www.chateauxhotels.com/compostelle | reservation service: 33 (0) 1.40.07.00.20

4, rue Saint Etienne 59800 Lille
Tel.: 33 (0) 3.28.38.08.30 – Fax: 33 (0) 3.28.38.08.39
compostelle@chateauxhotels.com
Alain ROUSSIEZ
Menu(s): 21,19 € / 33,54 € - **Carte:** 26,68 €

Only 50 meters from the Grand Place of Lille, this former coaching inn on the trail of Santiago de Compostela brings together the sober charm of the past and gastronomy of today. A place where the gourmets of the city gather, the proposed fare is fine regional French cuisine.

Open all year

environment
architecture 16ª, furniture contemporain, terrace

leisure, relaxation
tennis 2 km, golf course 2 km, horse-riding 3 km

Visa ● Master Card

Road map p. 619

Lille-centre and Grand-Place

Lille-Lesquin: 4 km

| Nord Picardie

Le Prieuré
Rancourt
www.chateauxhotels.com/leprieure | reservation service: 33 (0) 1.40.07.00.20

RN17 80360 Rancourt
Tel.: 33 (0) 3.22.85.04.43 – Fax: 33 (0) 3.22.85.06.69
leprieure@chateauxhotels.com
Francine BOIDIN
27 rooms: 58 € / 63,30 €
Breakfast: 7 €
Menu(s): 13,50 € / 40,50 €

Open all year
equipments
telephone, T.V. Canal+
environment
architecture, garden, total calm
leisure, relaxation
, scottish bar, billiards,
horse-riding 8 km, golf course
25 km, parachute jump, "Great
War" museum and souvenir
tour 6 km

Ideal place for your seminars, week-end, holidays... with an elegant frame, pretty rooms, a regional and creative kitchen. Since our hotel restaurant, you will discover the cultural wealth of Somme, Aisne and Pas de Calais... (battlefield of the great war).

Visa ● MASTER CARD

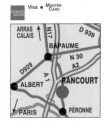

Road map p. 619

A1 exit 14 Bapaume/Albert dir. N17
Péronne/Bapaume (30 mn from
Arras, St Quentin or Cambrai)

Lesquin: 65 km

www.chateauxhotels.com/armeschampagne | reservation service: 33 (0) 1.40.07.00.20

31, Avenue du Luxembourg 51460 L'Epine
Tel.: 33 (0) 3.26.69.30.30 – Fax: 33 (0) 3.26.69.30.26
armeschampagne@chateauxhotels.com
Jean-Paul PERARDEL
35 rooms: 76 € / 150 €
2 suites: 230 € / 267 €
Breakfast: 13 €
Menu(s): 37 € / 83 € - **Carte:** 76 €

In the heart of the Champagne-Ardenne, this charming hotel with comfortable rooms boasts the know-how of Gilles Blandin. This former pupil of Alain Ducasse puts his passion and his talent in a cuisine made in the respect of authenticity and good taste. Here, the art of living has breathing space.

Visa ● Diners ● MASTER CARD

Road map p. 619

A4 or A26 exit 28. N3 dir. Metz/Verdun

hotel annual closing
02/01 > 07/02
restaurant annual closing
02/01 > 07/02
hotel weekly closing
mon, sun(ev)
01/11 > 31/03
restaurant weekly closing
mon, sun(ev)
01/11 > 31/03
equipments
telephone, T.V. Satellite, minibar
environment
garden, terrace, vegetable garden
leisure, relaxation
golf course 5 km

Reims: 45 km

L'Assiette Champenoise

Reims I Tinqueux

www.chateauxhotels.com/champenoise I reservation service: 33 (0) 1.40.07.00.20

40, av Paul Vaillant Couturier 51430 Tinqueux
Tel.: 33 (0) 3.26.84.64.64 – Fax: 33 (0) 3.26.04.15.69
champenoise@chateauxhotels.com
Jean-Pierre LALLEMENT
33 rooms: 95 € / 118 €
22 flats: 148 € / 237 €
Breakfast: 13 €
Menu(s): 45 € / 76 € - **Carte:** 50 €

Open all year
equipments
lift, telephone, internet, T.V.
Satellite, minibar, safe,
baby-sitting, valet parking
environment
architecture 19e, park 3 ha,
garden, terrace
leisure, relaxation
heated pool/covered, tennis
0.5 km, golf course 10 km,
sauna

This delightful residence, amidst the calm of a 4-acre park, just a few miles from the Champagne vineyards and within minutes of Reims, is a haven for gourmets. Guests are welcomed into refined luxury, and invited to sample truly outstanding, customised cuisine by chefs Jean-Pierre & Arnaud Lallement.

Visa ● Diners ● JCB ● MASTER CARD

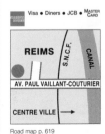

Road map p. 619
A4 exit 22 Reims/Tinqueux

Reims-Betheny: 10 km

La Tour du Roy 02140 Vervins

Tel.: 33 (0) 3.23.98.00.11 – Fax: 33 (0) 3.23.98.00.72

tourroy@chateauxhotels.com

Annie & Claude DESVIGNES

17 rooms: 53,36 € / 121,96 €
5 suites: 121,96 € / 228,67 €
Breakfast: 12,2 €
Menu(s): 30,5 € / 60,98 € - **Carte:** 26,68 €

A Manor house where Henry IV's ascension to the throne was announced. Two duplex rooms, twin bath-tubs, Sire de Coucy room. Fully renovated: stained-glass windows, hand-painted bathrooms, rooms overlooking terraces, park or landscaped square. Elegant cuisine by Annie. A perfect stop-over.

Open all year

equipments
telephone, T.V. Satellite/Canal+, minibar, safe, baby-sitting, valet parking

environment
architecture 12ᵉ, garden, terrace, view

leisure, relaxation
tennis 0.2 km, golf course 6 km, horse-riding 10 km, beauty salon, jacuzzi, 18-hole golf course (40 km, Golf de l'Ailette)

Visa ● JCB ● MASTER CARD

Road map p. 619

A26 exit Laon N°13, N2 between Paris and Bruxelles

Reims: 70 km

JUSQU'À 3 VOLS PAR JOUR AU DÉPART DE PARIS VERS LA RÉUNION

Renseignez-vous auprès de votre agence de voyages ou contactez le **0 825 805 805** (0,15 € TTC/mn), en France Métropolitaine ou le **0262 94 77 77** à la Réunion. Vous pouvez également consulter le **36 15 AIR LIB** (0,34 € TTC/mn) **ou** **www.airlib.fr**

ON NE PEUT PAS SE PASSER D'AIR LIB.

Hôtel-Restaurant

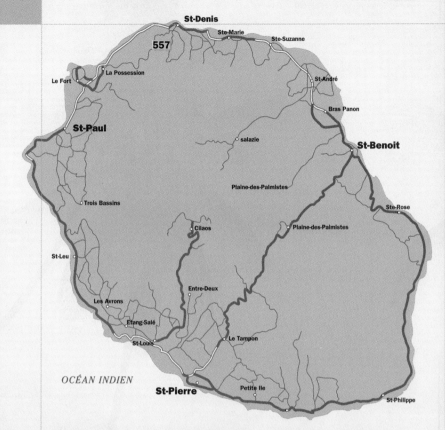

St-Denis

557

Ste-Marie

Ste-Suzanne

La Possession

Le Fort

St-André

Bras Panon

St-Paul

salazie

St-Benoit

Plaine-des-Palmistes

Trois Bassins

Ste-Rose

Cilaos

Plaine-des-Palmistes

St-Leu

Entre-Deux

Les Avirons

Etang-Salé

Le Tampon

St-Louis

OCÉAN INDIEN

Petite Ile

St-Pierre

St-Philippe

557 Domaine des Jamroses

6, chemin du Colorado 97417 La Montagne
Tel.: 33 (0) 2.62.23.59.00 – Fax: 33 (0) 2.62.23.93.37
jamroses@chateauxhotels.com
Joëlle LAMARQUE-CLAIN
12 rooms: 93 € / 130 €
8 suites: 162 € / 176 €
Menu(s): 29 € - **Carte:** 57 € -
1/2 board: 88 € / 151 €

Five miles from St Denis, this charmingly authentic hotel welcomes you warmly with its acre of tropical park. Let yourself be carried away by the old-fashioned appeal of traditional creole houses complete with period furniture and a veranda with colonnades, as well as sumptuous local cuisine.

Open all year

equipments
telephone, T.V., minibar, safe

environment
architecture 19e, furniture 19e, park 2 ha, terrace, view, total calm

leisure, relaxation
heated pool, sauna, squash, american billiard, VTT, fitness

proximity
horse-riding, golf course, tennis, helicopter tour

Visa ● MASTER CARD

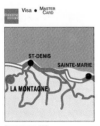

ST-DENIS
SAINTE-MARIE
LA MONTAGNE

Road map p. 619

Exit of "St-Denis", dir. Port, dir. "Golf du Colorado"

Roland Garros: 14 km

ı île de la Réunion

How to book ?

→ At the Châteaux & Hôtels reservation centre:
- Tél : 00 33 (0) 1 40 07 00 20
- Fax : 00 33 (0) 1 40 07 00 30

→ By Internet:
- www.chateauxhotels.com
- resa@chateauxhotels.com

→ Directly with the establishement required

CHATEAUX & HOTELS
DE FRANCE®

Châteaux et Demeures privés

Châteaux privés-Private Castles

Agréable demeure de famille
Pleasant family residence

Confortable demeure de caractère
Confortable manor house of character

Belle demeure offrant des prestations luxueuses
Period residence offering luxurious standards

Châteaux ou demeures privés recevant des hôtes :

Prestigieuses et authentiques, ces demeures se distinguent de l'hôtellerie traditionnelle : le propriétaire d'un château privé accueille ses hôtes comme des amis et ne leur propose que le bonheur de vivre quelques heures ou quelques jours dans une atmosphère familiale et un cadre privilégié.

Private castles or manors receving guests:

These prestigious establishments offer a different kind of hotel services: the owners of private castles receive their guests as they where friends and offer them the privilege of spending a few hours, or a few days, in a memorable atmosphere and distinguished surroundings.

La Pauline

Aix-en-Provence

www.chateauxhotels.com/pauline | reservation service: 33 (0) 1.40.07.00.20

Ch. de la Fontaine des Tuiles Les Pinchinats
13100 Aix-en-Provence
Tel.: 33 (0) 4.42.17.02.60 – Fax: 33 (0) 4.42.17.02.61
pauline@chateauxhotels.com
Régis MACQUET
4 rooms: 150 € / 165 €
1 suite: 300 €
Breakfast: 10 €

hotel annual closing
01/01 > 31/01 • 01/12 > 31/12

equipments
telephone, T.V. Canal+

environment
architecture 18°, park 8 ha,
garden, view, total calm

leisure, relaxation
heated pool, tennis 0.5 km,
horse-riding 1 km, thermal
baths, spa bath center of town

Only 2 miles from Aix-en-Provence, at the heart of a 25-acre park, stands a ravishing Directoire-style residence, originally built for Pauline Borghèse, Napoléon's sister. Calm, serenity and emotion characterise this richly historical spot, where the 4 bedrooms and suite, each with private terrace reside.

Road map p. 619

Motorway-south exit Aix town centre
then "route des Alpes" dir. Les Pinchinats

✈ Marignane Marseille: 30 km

72610 Saint-Paterne

Tel.: 33 (0) 2.33.27.54.71 – Fax: 33 (0) 2.33.29.16.71

saintpaterne@chateauxhotels.com

Charles-Henry & Ségolène de VALBRAY

4 rooms: 85 € / 150 €
4 suites: 130 € / 200 €
Breakfast: 9 €
Menu(s): 38 €

This Renaissance château was the scene of Henry IV's love affairs. A family property for generations, where hospitality is venerable duty. Elegant rooms, diners in small table, theme holidays. Château available for rental. The hallmarks of a gracious home with the amenities of a hotel of character.

hotel annual closing
01/01 > 15/04

equipments
telephone, baby-sitting

environment
architecture 15e, furniture 18e, park 10 ha, garden, terrace 200 m², vegetable garden, total calm

leisure, relaxation
heated pool, tennis 0.15 km, golf course 3 km, horse-riding 3 km

Visa ● MasterCard

Road map p. 619

A28 exit19 Alençon/Mamers, dir. St-Paterne center, or A11 exit Nogent le Rotrou, dir. Alençon

Orly/Charles-de-Gaulle: 180 km

Château de Vergières

Arles | Saint-Martin-de-Crau
www.chateauxhotels.com/vergieres | reservation service: 33 (0) 1.40.07.00.20

13310 Saint-Martin-de-Crau
Tel.: 33 (0) 4.90.47.17.16 – Fax: 33 (0) 4.90.47.38.30
vergieres@chateauxhotels.com
Jean & Marie-Andrée PINCEDE
5 rooms: 129,58 € / 144,83 €
1 suite: 182,94 € / 243,92 €
Breakfast: 10,67 €
Table d'hôtes (sur rés.): 47.26 €

hotel annual closing
15/11 > 30/03
restaurant annual closing
15/11 > 30/03
environment
architecture 18ᵉ, furniture 18ᵉ,
park 10 ha, garden, terrace
100 m², view, total calm
leisure, relaxation
tennis 10 km, golf course
15 km, horse-riding 8 km, 4x4
trails around the Crau and the
Camargue

A striking scene of pebble-stones as far as the eye can seen, an oasis of meadows and trees for a peaceful and comfortable stay. Antique furniture, lively and refined atmosphere. Near the Camargue, the Alpilles, the Baux de Provence and Saint-Rémy. The château is located on an ornithological site.

Visa • MASTER CARD

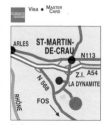

Road map p. 619

A54 exit St-Martin-de-Crau. D24 dir.
Fos-sur-Mer, Port St-Louis

Provence-Alpes-Côte-d'Azur |

 Marseille Provence: 70 km

Auxerre **ı** Villefargeau
www.chateauxhotels.com/manoirbruyeres | reservation service: 33 (0) 1.40.07.00.20

5, allée de Charbuy aux Bruyères
89240 Villefargeau
Tel.: 33 (0) 3.86.41.32.82 – Fax: 33 (0) 3.86.41.28.57
manoirbruyeres@chateauxhotels.com
Monique & Pierre JOULLIE
2 rooms: 91,47 € / 121,96 €
2 suites: 152,45 € / 182,94 €
Menu(s): 38,11 €
Table d'hôtes (sur rés.): 19.06 €

1h30 from Paris, this charming 18th century residence, oozing with the perfume of Tuscany, is in the middle of a 247-acre forest. Rooms are in period style with vast canopy beds. Breakfast is served fireside in the spacious Louis XIII dining room. Regional cuisine, famous vintage wines.

Open all year
equipments
internet, T.V. Satellite/Canal+, safe, baby-sitting
environment
architecture 18e, furniture 18e, park 1 ha, garden, terrace 300 m², view, vegetable garden, total calm
leisure, relaxation
tennis 3 km, golf course 15 km, horse-riding 1.5 km, ice-skating (10 km)

Road map p. 619

A6 exit N.of Auxerre, N6 dir.Auxerre, D158, D89, D22

 Branches: 9 km

Bourgogne Franche-Comté

Château Meyre
Avensan
www.chateauxhotels.com/meyre | reservation service: 33 (0) 1.40.07.00.20

16, route de Castelnau 33480 Avensan
Tel.: 33 (0) 5.56.58.10.77 – Fax: 33 (0) 5.56.58.13.20
meyre@chateauxhotels.com
Bruno & Corinne BONNE
8 rooms: 70 € / 100 €
1 suite: 180 €
Breakfast: 10 €

hotel annual closing
15/12 > 01/03

equipments
telephone, internet

environment
architecture 18e, park 0.5 ha,
garden, terrace 50 m², view

leisure, relaxation
golf course 15 km, horse-riding
20 km, sauna

30 km from Bordeaux in the Médoc, this 18th c. stately house stands proudly amidst its vineyards. With their sense of hospitality, Bruno and Corinne Bonne will be delighted to share their passion for winegrowing and let you taste the château's excellent vintages. Golf course nearby.

Visa ● MASTER CARD

Road map p. 619

A10 exit 7 Eysines/Le Verdon, D1 dir. Lesparre/Le Verdon

 Merignac: 28 km

Manoir de la Rémonière
Azay-le-Rideau
www.chateauxhotels.com/remoniere | reservation service: 33 (0) 1.40.07.00.20

567

« La Rémonière » La Chapelle-St-Blaise
37190 Azay-le-Rideau
Tel.: 33 (0) 2.47.45.24.88 – Fax: 33 (0) 2.47.45.45.69
remoniere@chateauxhotels.com
Carole & Chantale PECAS
7 rooms: 90 € / 176 €

This manor, in an unique setting facing the château of Azay le Rideau, offers magnificent views by day and night. Nothing except birdsong disturbs the serenity of the 80 acres of grounds bordered by the Indre river, in a place steeped in two thousand years of mystery and imagination.

Open all year
from November to March: on request

equipments
T.V., safe

environment
architecture 15e, park 33 ha, garden, terrace 300 m², view, vegetable garden, total calm

leisure, relaxation
tennis 0.6 km, golf course 17 km, horse-riding 10 km, sauna, hot-air balloon trips

Road map p. 619

A10 exit Joué-Les-Tours then D751 dir. Chinon

 Tours/St-Symphorien: 30 km

Château d'Arbieu

Bazas

www.chateauxhotels.com/arbieu | reservation service: 33 (0) 1.40.07.00.20

Route de Casteljaloux 33430 Bazas
Tel.: 33 (0) 5.56.25.11.18 – Fax: 33 (0) 5.56.25.90.52
arbieu@chateauxhotels.com
Famille de CHENERILLES
4 rooms: 68 € / 80 €
1 suite: 95 € / 131 €

hotel annual closing
15/02 > 04/03•31/10 > 07/11
environment
architecture 18°, park 30 ha,
garden, view, vegetable
garden, total calm
leisure, relaxation
tennis 1 km, golf course
15 km, horse-riding 1 km

*1 km from Bazas, an artistic
and historic town, this hotel
offers a simple, warm welcome. Tastefully decorated
rooms. Enjoy a dinner in the
company of friends. Lounge
with billiards, miniature football, swimming pool. Visits to
nearby chateaux and vine-
yards.*

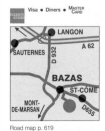

Visa ● Diners ● MASTER CARD

Road map p. 619

A62 exit Langon. D655 dir. Casteljaloux

Bordeaux: 70 km

Route d'Arbonne 64210 Bidart
Tel.: 33 (0) 5.59.41.90.85 – Fax: 33 (0) 5.59.41.87.62
bassilour@chateauxhotels.com
Charlotte VACHET
5 rooms: 50 € / 100 €
1 flat: 111 € / 134 € - **2 suites:** 100 € / 117 €
Breakfast: 10 €

This beautiful Second Empire mansion, surrounded by a large garden, awaits you only 2 miles from Biarritz. The enthusiasm and charm of the owners will enchant you as will the intimate warmth of the sumptuous rooms. Breakfast fit for a king with home-made bread and jam. Booking strongly advised: from November to March

Open all year
equipments
T.V., baby-sitting

environment
architecture 19e, park 15 ha, garden, view, vegetable garden

leisure, relaxation
golf course 2 km, horse-riding 3 km, thalassotherapy

Road map p. 619

A63 exit Biarritz dir. Technopole Izarbel

Biarritz-Parme: 3 km

Château du Pian

Bordeaux **I** Bouliac

www.chateauxhotels.com/pian | reservation service: 33 (0) 1.40.07.00.20

73, avenue de la Belle Etoile 33270 Bouliac
Tel.: 33 (0) 5.56.20.99.18 – Fax: 33 (0) 5.56.20.52.91

pian@chateauxhotels.com

3 rooms: 140 €
3 suites: 185 € / 215 €
Breakfast: 13 €

hotel annual closing
01/01 > 01/03 ● 01/12 > 31/01

equipments
lift, telephone, internet, T.V.
Satellite, minibar

environment
architecture 19ᵉ, furniture 19ᵉ,
park 5 ha, view, total calm

leisure, relaxation
tennis 2 km, golf course
13 km, sauna

Tucked away in the rural wilds near Bordeaux, this beautiful chateau dating from the 14th c and restored in the 19th c, offers rest and relaxation. Wander about the 3 acre park, sample breakfast fit for a king, enjoy the friendly hospitality. A top spot for nature-lovers as well as wine-lovers!

Road map p. 619

A10 from Paris / A63 from Toulouse /
A89 dir. Périgueux, ring road. exit 24
ou 23

 Bordeaux Mérignac: 25 km

Avenue de la Dame Blanche
33320 Le Taillan-Médoc
Tel.: 33 (0) 5.56.35.46.47 – Fax: 33 (0) 5.56.35.48.75
lelout@chateauxhotels.com
Colette & Olivier SALMON

5 rooms: 105 € / 125 €
2 suites: 155 € / 180 €
Breakfast: 11 €
Table d'hôtes (on rés.): 40 €

The recently restored Château Le Lout is an Italian-inspired residence marrying past charm with modern comfort. Set in a beautiful park, only 15 min. from downtown Bordeaux, the Château boasts period-furnished rooms, overlooking the park and the pool, each one rich in history and dreams.

Open all year

equipments
telephone, internet, T.V.

environment
architecture 19e, park 9 ha, terrace 60 m², view, total calm

leisure, relaxation
, vineyard, guided tour of castels, golf 36-hole 5 km, tennis 3 km, horse-riding 2 km

Visa ● Diners ● MASTER CARD

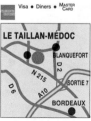

Road map p. 619

A10 - Dir. Mérignac (Airport) - Rocade exit 7 dir. Lesparre-Le Verdon, 1,5 km D2 dir. Pauillac

 Bordeaux-Mérignac: 6 km

Château de Thaumiers

Bourges | Thaumiers

www.chateauxhotels.com/thaumiers | reservation service: 33 (0) 1.40.07.00.20

18210 Thaumiers

Tel.: 33 (0) 2.48.61.81.62 – Fax: 33 (0) 2.48.61.81.82

thaumiers@chateauxhotels.com

Philippe & Chantal de BONNEVAL

8 rooms: 110 € / 140 €

2 suites: 170 € / 190 €

Table d'hôtes (sur rés.): 36 €

hotel annual closing
15/11 > 01/04

equipments
telephone, baby-sitting

environment
architecture 15e, park 100 ha,
garden, total calm

leisure, relaxation
heated pool, tennis court,
horse-riding 12 km

At the heart of Berry, set in a magnificent 247-acre park, is this superb 15th-18th century château. Hospitality, calm and refinement describe your stay perfectly. Group bookings are welcome with the possibility of reserving part of the chateau. Vineyards close by.

Visa • MASTER CARD

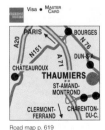

Road map p. 619

A71 exit Bourges or St-Amand-Montrond

 Orly: 230 km

14310 Saint Louet sur Seulles

Tel.: 33 (0) 2.31.77.96.30 – Fax: 33 (0) 2.31.77.96.30

riviere@chateauxhotels.com

Famille HOUDRET

3 rooms: 69 € / 100 €
1 suite: 91 € / 131 €
1/2 board: 99 € / 130 €
Table d'hôtes (sur rés.): 28 €

Just two hours from Paris, this Manor and 16th c farmhouse is a welcoming family home nestling in the hills amongst 30 acres of Normandy woodland. Here the rooms, with terrace or loggia, are decorated with family memorabilia. A unique place from which to discover an area steeped in history.

Open all year

equipments
baby-sitting

environment
architecture 16e, park 15 ha, garden, terrace 100 m², view, vegetable garden, total calm

leisure, relaxation
tennis 4 km, golf course 20 km, horse-riding 2 km, outing to the market

Visa ● MASTER CARD

Road map p. 619

Dir. Rennes/le Mont-St-Michel (A84), exit Villers-Bocage

Caen/Carpiquet: 20 km

| Normandie

Château des Briottières

Champigné
www.chateauxhotels.com/briottieres | reservation service: 33 (0) 1.40.07.00.20

route de Marigné 49330 Champigné
Tel.: 33 (0) 2.41.42.00.02 – Fax: 33 (0) 2.41.42.01.55
briottieres@chateauxhotels.com
François & Hedwige de VALBRAY
6 rooms: 115 € / 229 €
3 suites: 275 € / 320 €
Breakfast: 10 €
Table d'hôtes (sur rés.): 46 €

hotel annual closing
01/01 > 25/12 ● 08/02 > 25/02
restaurant annual closing
01/01 > 25/12 ● 08/02 > 25/02
equipments
telephone, internet, T.V.
Satellite/Canal+, safe,
baby-sitting
environment
architecture 18ᵉ, park 50 ha,
garden, terrace, view, total
calm
leisure, relaxation
heated pool, tennis 3 km, golf
course 4 km, horse-riding
15 km

The long path takes you to the great staircase, leads to the canopied beds you have dreamed of. Candles are on the table, you are awaited in this romantic, 18th century domain. A 100-acre park, outdoor, heated swimming-pool. Bicycles available, fishing, billiards. English spoken.

Visa ● MASTER CARD

Road map p. 619

A11 exit11 Durtal / A81 exit Joué-en-Charnie / from Angers exit Montreuil-Juigne

 Angers / Marcé: 25 km

St-Mars des Prés 85110 Chantonnay

Tel.: 33 (0) 2.51.46.96.71 – Fax: 33 (0) 2.51.46.80.07

ponsay@chateauxhotels.com

Mme. de PONSAY

5 rooms: 57 € / 100 €

1 suite: 107 €

Breakfast: 8 €

Table d'hôtes (sur rés.): 30 €

Historic monument back to the XVth century. Belonging to the same family since 1644. In 1472, Louis XI came here to hunt, his room is waiting for you. Warm welcome, candle-light dinners, vast and comfortable rooms, tranquillity. Nearby, the fabulous Puy du Fou show and charming Venise Verte.

hotel annual closing
30/11 > 01/04

environment
architecture 15e, furniture 18e, park 10 ha, garden, view, total calm

leisure, relaxation
tennis 5 km, golf course 35 km

Road map p. 619

N137 - between Nantes and La Rochelle

Nantes: 70 km

Château de la Tour
Rivarennes
www.chateauxhotels.com/rivarennes | reservation service: 33 (0) 1.40.07.00.20

36800 Rivarennes
Tel.: 33 (0) 2.54.47.06.12 – Fax: 33 (0) 2.54.47.06.08
rivarennes@chateauxhotels.com
Duchesse Dre de CLERMONT-TONNERRE
5 rooms: 110 € / 215 €
1 flat: 336 €
Breakfast: 10 €
Table d'hôtes (sur rés.): 55 €

Open all year
equipments
T.V., minibar
environment
architecture 14ᵉ, park 12 ha,
view, total calm
leisure, relaxation
golf course 15 km, horse-riding
12 km

14th century château on the banks of the river Creuse in a charming country setting. Comfortable rooms, big open fires for atmosphere. Many strongholds in the region. Romanesque churches and remarkable prehistoric sites nearby. Other visits: the Futuroscope at Poitiers, the Arguzon dam.

Road map p. 619

Paris A10 exit Orléans, A71 dir. Clermont-Ferrand, exit Vierzon

 Châteauroux: 32 km

Place de l'Ormeau 63450 Saint-Saturnin
Tel.: 33 (0) 4.73.39.39.64 – Fax: 33 (0) 4.73.39.09.73
saintsaturnin@chateauxhotels.com
MM. CHAFFENET & GUEDES
2 rooms: 100 € / 115 €
2 suites: 130 € / 153 €
Breakfast: 8 €
Table d'hôtes (on request)

This vast royal chateau stands at the heart of one France's 100 most beautiful villages. Revel in its prestigious past as you discover the rich natural wonders of this well-preserved region. The rooms, drenched in history, are decorated with period furniture and provide inimitable comfort.

hotel annual closing
15/12 > 15/01

environment
architecture 13ᵉ, park 6 ha, garden, terrace 300 m², view

leisure, relaxation
golf course 15 km, horse-riding 2 km, thermal baths

Road map p. 619

A75 dir. Montpellier exit 5 St-Amant-Tallende-Aydat

Aulnat: 15 km

Château de Vollore

Clermont-Ferrand I Courpière

www.chateauxhotels.com/vollore I reservation service: 33 (0) 1.40.07.00.20

Vollore-ville 63120 Courpière

Tel.: 33 (0) 4.73.53.71.06 – Fax: 33 (0) 4.73.53.72.44

vollore@chateauxhotels.com

M. & Mme. Michel AUBERT LA FAYETTE

2 rooms: 100 € / 150 €

3 suites: 200 € / 260 €

Breakfast included

Open all year

equipments
T.V., safe

environment
architecture 12/17e, park
10 ha, garden, terrace 800 m²,
view, total calm

leisure, relaxation
golf course 50 km, horse-riding
8 km, tennis, swimming pool

In the centre of the legendary Auvergne, this majestic château shelters the descendants of General Lafayette who perpetuate the art of stylish reception with elegance. The apartments with sumptuous decorations and memorabilia collections are the guarantors of the noble class.

Visa • Master Card

Road map p. 619

A72 exit Thiers. D7 dir. Vollore-Ville

Clermont-Aulnat: 50 km

106, avenue d'en Carbouner 66160 Le Boulou
Tel.: 33 (0) 4.68.83.15.88 – Fax: 33 (0) 4.68.83.26.62

chartreuses@chateauxhotels.com
Famille BLANQUIER

9 rooms: 55 € / 93 €
1 flat: 168 € / 183 €
Breakfast: 10 €
1/2 board: 52 € / 69,5 €
Table d'hôtes (sur rés.): 20 €

In a green landscape facing the Pyrénées, ten miles from the beaches, this 17th century traditional Catalonian house offers a friendly atmosphere and good living. Tranquil rooms, terraces, garden, authentic local Mediterranean cuisine - the ingredients that give our region all its appeal.

hotel annual closing
01/01 > 31/01 ● 04/11 > 31/01
restaurant annual closing
01/01 > 31/01 ● 04/11 > 31/01
equipments
telephone, T.V. Satellite, minibar
environment
architecture 17e, park 0.3 ha, garden, terrace 200 m², view, total calm
leisure, relaxation
tennis 0.2 km, golf course 25 km, horse-riding 7 km, thermal baths, sauna, jacuzzi

Visa ● Diners ● MASTER CARD

Road map p. 619

A9 exit Le Boulou, D618, 3 km turn right dir. les Chartreuses du Boulou

Rivesaltes-Perpignan: 25 km

Château de Courtalain

Courtalain

www.chateauxhotels.com/courtalain | reservation service: 33 (0) 1.40.07.00.20

Domaine de Courtalain 28290 Courtalain
Tel.: 33 (0) 2.37.98.80.25 – Fax: 33 (0) 2.37.98.84.64
courtalain@chateauxhotels.com
Comte de GONTAUT BIRON
24 rooms: 67 € / 106 €
1 suite: 183 €
Breakfast: 7 €
Menu(s): 35 €

hotel annual closing
01/12 > 01/03

equipments
telephone, T.V., baby-sitting

environment
architecture 18ᵉ, furniture 18ᵉ,
park 200 ha, garden, total
calm

leisure, relaxation
golf course 30 km, horse-riding
4 km

Get away from the bustle to this unspoilt country setting: a listed 15th-19th century historic monument on a 1000-acre property. Comfortable guest rooms in the converted outbildings, hospitality, fine food and gracious living.

Visa ● Diners ● MASTER CARD

Road map p. 619

A11 exit Brou dir. Arrou

Orly/Charles-de-Gaulle:
120 km

51700 Igny-Comblizy
Tel.: 33 (0) 3.26.57.10.84 – Fax: 33 (0) 3.26.57.82.80
jacquier@chateauxhotels.com
Robert & Christine GRANGER
6 rooms: 60 € / 90 €
Breakfast: 7 €
Table d'hôtes (sur rés.): 25 € / 40 €

Surrounded by the Champagne vineyards, an 18th century château hidden away in an idyllic setting of tranquil woodland. The tasteful decor of the guestrooms is matched only by the rich delights of the table. An elegant stopping place to enjoy forest walks. Golf nearby.

MASTER
CARD

Road map p. 619

A4 exit Dormans, D18 dir. Igny-Montmort

Open all year

equipments
T.V.

environment
architecture 18ª, park 13 ha, garden, view, vegetable garden, total calm

leisure, relaxation
heated pool/covered, tennis 7 km, golf course 8 km, horse-riding 14 km

Epernay: 25 km

I Nord Picardie

Château de La Grillère

Glénat

www.chateauxhotels.com/grillere | reservation service: 33 (0) 1.40.07.00.20

Le Bourg 15150 Glénat
Tel.: 33 (0) 4.71.62.28.14 – Fax: 33 (0) 4.71.62.28.70
grillere@chateauxhotels.com
Mme Claude BERGON
5 rooms: 100 € / 125 €
Breakfast: 8 €
Menu(s): 26 €

hotel annual closing
30/09 > 15/05

equipments
T.V.

environment
architecture 13/17e, park 2 ha, garden, terrace, view, total calm

leisure, relaxation
heated pool, tennis 9 km, golf course 15 km, horse-riding 3 km

The authenticity of this Louis XIV chateau is enough to seduce you, but its breath-taking view on the Monts du Cantal will thrill you even further. Spacious, personally decorated rooms. Dinner is composed of a choice of inventive and refined regional specialities. Nearby: Haute Auvergne golf course.

Visa • MASTER CARD

Road map p. 619

A20 exit Tulle. N120 Tulle-Aurillac or N122 Aurillac-Figeac then D7 and D32

Aurillac: 30 km

Le bourg 63340 Collanges
Tel.: 33 (0) 4.73.96.47.30 – Fax: 33 (0) 4.73.96.58.72
collanges@chateauxhotels.com
Pascale, Denis & Loïc FELUS
4 rooms: 61 € / 99 €
1 suite: 160 €
Table d'hôtes (sur rés.): 39 €

Following the path to Volcano, the castle is welcoming us, with wide open doors, like frozen in time by its ghosts and its angels. The wood in the fireplace sings... Always remembering the moments of laughter we shared, the sites we visited. Colourful bedrooms, classy living rooms.

Open all year
equipments
telephone
environment
architecture 15°, park 3 ha, garden, terrace 210 m², vegetable garden, total calm
leisure, relaxation
tennis 3 km, horse-riding 2 km

Visa

Road map p. 619

A75 exit St-Germain-Lembron or N9 dir. Ardes

Clermont-Ferrand: 45 km

Château de la Flocellière

La Flocellière

www.chateauxhotels.com/flocelliere | reservation service: 33 (0) 1.40.07.00.20

30, rue du Château 85700 La Flocellière
Tel.: 33 (0) 2.51.57.22.03 – Fax: 33 (0) 2.51.57.75.21

flocelliere@chateauxhotels.com
Vicomte & Vicomtesse Patrice VIGNIAL
6 rooms: 100 € / 130 €
Breakfast: 8 €
1/2 board: 110 € / 130 €
Table d'hôtes (sur rés.): 40 € / 54 €

Open all year
equipments
telephone, internet, T.V.
Satellite

environment
architecture 11/13/15°, park
15 ha, garden, view, vegetable
garden, total calm

leisure, relaxation
heated pool, tennis 0.5 km,
golf course 25 km, horse-riding
6 km, Puy du Fou" theme park
(7 km)"

In the midst of a fairly hilly Vendée - Loire Region, featured an old feudal fortress, set in grounds of some 15 acres which an expansive views of an idyllic landscape. Luxuriousness and refinement in rooms, lounges or reception halls. Excellent cuisine and Bordeaux and Loire wines.

Visa ● MASTER CARD

Road map p. 619

From Nantes exit Les Herbiers, dir.
Pouzanges - La Flocellière

Nantes Atlantique: 70 km

Les Monts 48210 La Malène
Tel.: 33 (0) 4.66.48.54.34 – Fax: 33 (0) 4.66.48.59.25
monts@chateauxhotels.com
Claudine LABOUREUR
3 rooms: 130 € / 145 €
2 suites: 153 €
Breakfast: 12 €

In Malène, above the Tarn gorges, this former XVIIIth century convent is an architectural jewel with three remarkably decorated rooms and suites. It offers perfect calm, an amazing view and the warm welcome of its relaxed hosts. A real charm.

hotel annual closing
10/01 > 01/03

equipments
telephone, internet, T.V., minibar, safe

environment
architecture 18e, park 217 ha, garden, terrace 12 m², view, total calm

leisure, relaxation
tennis 19 km, golf course 19 km, horse-riding 12 km

Visa ● MASTER CARD

Road map p. 619

North: A75 exit 40 Banassac la Canourgue - South: exit 43 Le Massegros

Rodez: 90 km

Château de Montbrun

Langeais | Saint-Michel-sur-Loire

www.chateauxhotels.com/montbrun | reservation service: 33 (0) 1.40.07.00.20

47, rte du Coteau Domaine de la Riboisière
37130 Saint-Michel-sur-Loire
Tel.: 33 (0) 2.47.96.57.13 – Fax: 33 (0) 2.47.96.01.28
montbrun@chateauxhotels.com
André PERES

6 rooms: 102 € / 132 €
1 suite: 157 €
Breakfast: 9 €
1/2 board: 92 € / 107 €
Table d'hôtes (sur rés.): 32 € / 48 €

Open all year
restaurant weekly closing
mon(lun), tue(lun), wen(lun),
thi(lun), fri(lun), sat(lun), sun(lun)

environment
architecture 19ᵉ, furniture 19ᵉ,
park 5 ha, garden, terrace
100 m², view, vegetable
garden

leisure, relaxation
heated pool, tennis 5 km, golf
course 25 km, horse-riding
5 km

Close to Tours, a family château with an outstanding view of the Loire and surrounding forests from the centenary wooded park. Rooms decorated with tapestries and antiques, sunny terrace, swimming pool in the grounds, refined traditional cuisine. A cosy spot in the Loire châteaux country.

Visa ● MASTER CARD

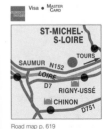

Road map p. 619

A10 exit Vouvray. dir. Saumur by
N152

 Tours: 30 km

1, chemin des Genêts 88160 Le Thillot

Tel.: 33 (0) 3.29.25.10.93 – Fax: 33 (0) 3.29.25.39.80

tanneurs@chateauxhotels.com

Marie-Antoinette DELLEA

5 rooms: 45,73 € / 76,22 €

2 suites: 106,71 € / 114,34 €

Breakfast: 7,62 €

Menu(s): 15,24 € / 22,87 €

A master's residence where Marie-Antoinette and Pierre Dellea reserve a warm welcome. The 2,5 acre French garden includes a Roman pond and rare medicinal plants. Comfortable and well decorated rooms. Home-made meals are served in the glass ceilinged, poolside dining room.

Open all year

equipments

T.V.

environment

architecture contemporaine, park 5 ha, garden, terrace 100 m², view, total calm

leisure, relaxation

covered pool, tennis 2 km, golf course 30 km, horse-riding 2 km, sauna

Visa ● MASTER CARD

Road map p. 619

N57 dir.Nancy-Mulhouse, N66 dir.Benelux-Bâle

✈ Bâle-Mulhouse: 50 km

La Bastide Rose
Le Thor
www.chateauxhotels.com/bastiderose | reservation service: 33 (0) 1.40.07.00.20

99, Chemin des Croupières 84250 Le Thor
Tel.: 33 (0) 4.90.02.14.33 – Fax: 33 (0) 4.90.02.19.38
bastiderose@chateauxhotels.com
Nicole SALINGER

5 rooms: 110 € / 145 €
1 flat: 230 € / 305 € - **2 suites:** 150 € / 260 €
Breakfast: 14 €
Menu(s): 17 € / 35 € - **1/2 board:** 96 € / 114 €
Table d'hôtes (sur rés.): 35 €

Open all year
equipments
telephone, internet, T.V., minibar, safe, baby-sitting
environment
architecture 17e, furniture 18e, park 2 ha, garden, terrace 50 m², view, total calm
leisure, relaxation
tennis 2 km, golf course 6 km, horse-riding 3 km, jacuzzi

An entire enchanting universe is sheltered behind the walls of this old Provençal house located between Lubéron and Comtat vènaissin: rare antiques, idyllic rooms, and quality cuisine. This is not a hotel but rather a house of a friend.

Visa ● MasterCard

Road map p. 619

A7 exit south of Avignon, D973, go trough Caumont, take D1 to Le Thor.

Provence-Alpes-Côte-d'Azur |

Avignon-Caumont: 15 km

600 Chemin de la ronze 69480 Morancé
Tel.: 33 (0) 4.37.46.10.10 – Fax: 33 (0) 4.37.46.10.11
chateaupin@chateauxhotels.com
Marine & Jean-François GONINDARD
2 rooms: 129,58 € / 144,83 €
3 suites: 144,83 € / 190,56 €
Breakfast: 7,62 €
Table d'hôtes (sur rés.): 32,01 € / 48.78 €

Serenity and gentleness personify this 13th century fortified house, overlooking the Saône Valley. The welcome is friendly, the old-style decoration intact, the four magnificent rooms and the cuisine delicious. A break in the journey or change of scenery that rhymes with amazement.

Open all year
equipments
telephone, internet, T.V.
Satellite, minibar, baby-sitting

environment
architecture 13^e, park 3 ha,
garden, terrace, view,
vegetable garden, total calm

leisure, relaxation
golf course 3 km, horse-riding
0.5 km, music salon

Visa ● MASTER CARD

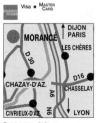

Road map p. 619

A6 exit Villefranche. N6 dir. Anse. D30
dir. Chazay/Civrieux

Lyon/St-Exupèry: 28 km

Château de Camon

Mirepoix I Camon

www.chateauxhotels.com/camon I reservation service: 33 (0) 1.40.07.00.20

09500 Camon
Tel.: 33 (0) 5.61.68.28.28 – Fax: 33 (0) 5.61.68.81.56
camon@chateauxhotels.com
Dominique du PONT
8 rooms: 106 € / 182 €
2 suites: 230 €
Table d'hôtes (sur rés.): 54 €

hotel annual closing
15/11 > 01/03
environment
architecture 16°, garden,
terrace, total calm

Impossible to not be filled with wonder before the luxurious-ness of the decoration of this former abbey located in one of the most beautiful villages of France. Everything here is a breath of serenity and enchantment. A favoured stopping place between Toulouse and Spain.

Visa ● Diners ● Master Card

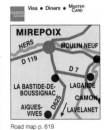

Road map p. 619

To Mirepoix, dir. "La Bastide de Boussignac" then Camon

 Toulouse: 100 km

www.chateauxhotels.com/bourdaisiere | reservation service: 33 (0) 1.40.07.00.20

25, rue de la Bourdaisière
37270 Montlouis-sur-Loire
Tel.: 33 (0) 2.47.45.16.31 – Fax: 33 (0) 2.47.45.09.11
bourdaisiere@chateauxhotels.com
Prince de BROGLIE – Martine de ROQUEFEUIL
17 rooms: 110 € / 199 €
3 flats: 145 € / 230 €
Breakfast: 12 €

Located at the heart of the Loire Valley, this 15th century château have been the home of some of history's most famous women, from François I's mistress to Gabrielle d'Estrées, Henri IV's favourite. Bedrooms are decorated in the style of these women. Tennis, outdoor heated pool.

Open all year

equipments
lift, telephone, internet, T.V., safe, baby-sitting

environment
architecture 16ᵉ, park 50 ha, garden, terrace 500 m², view, vegetable garden, total calm

leisure, relaxation
heated pool, golf course 15 km, horse-riding 0.8 km, archery

Visa • MASTER CARD

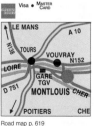

Road map p. 619

A10 exit Center of Tours-Amboise, D140

Tours/St-Symphorien: 15 km

Château de Fragne

Montluçon ı Verneix

www.chateauxhotels.com/fragne ı reservation service: 33 (0) 1.40.07.00.20

03190 Verneix
Tel.: 33 (0) 4.70.07.88.10 – Fax: 33 (0) 4.70.07.83.73
fragne@chateauxhotels.com
Mmes. de MONTAIGNAC

4 rooms: 95 €
1 suite: 145 €
Breakfast: 9 €
Table d'hôtes (sur rés.): 50 €

hotel annual closing
15/10 > 01/05
restaurant annual closing
01/10 > 01/06
environment
architecture 18ᵉ, park 20 ha,
garden, terrace 125 m²
leisure, relaxation
golf course 15 km, horse-riding
30 km

18th-century family château, in a region rich in Bourbon history. Cosy, peaceful atmosphere. Beautiful park. Near Tronçais forest for excellent stag hunting. 2 hours and a half from Paris. Large terrace looking onto the park where you can enjoy the sunsets, and dine in fine weather.

Visa • MASTER CARD

Road map p. 619
A71 exit Montluçon, D39 dir. Verneix

Clermont-Ferrand: 90 km

Château de la Ballue 593
Mont-Saint-Michel I Bazouges La Pérouse
www.chateauxhotels.com/ballue I reservation service: 33 (0) 1.40.07.00.20

35560 Bazouges La Pérouse
Tel.: 33 (0) 2.99.97.47.86 – Fax: 33 (0) 2.99.97.47.70
ballue@chateauxhotels.com
Alain SCHROTTER – Marie-France BARRERE
4 rooms: 144 € / 175 €
1 suite: 213 € / 244 €
Breakfast: 11 €

Idealy situated between St Malo & Mont-St-Michel, the perfect place for restoring body & soul in the gracious & restfull ambiance of its five rooms with canopy beds & en-suite bathroom, its C17th salons and baroque gardens. A place exceptional for its beauty, charm and for the lifestyle it epitomizes (Condé Nast Travel).

hotel annual closing
01/01 > 28/02

environment
architecture 17e, furniture 17e, park 3 ha, garden, view

leisure, relaxation
sauna, jacuzzi, guided tour of the château's baroque gardens, art contemporain

Visa ● MASTER CARD

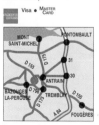

Road map p. 619

A84 La Gravelle, then N157 Vitré, D178, N155

Rennes Saint-Jacques: 55 km

Le Château

La Rochelle ı Moreilles

www.chateauxhotels.com/chateaumoreille ı reservation service: 33 (0) 1.40.07.00.20

85450 Moreilles
Tel.: 33 (0) 2.51.56.17.56 – Fax: 33 (0) 2.51.56.30.30
chateaumoreille@chateauxhotels.com
Danielle RENARD
3 rooms: 61 € / 85 €
3 suites: 100 € / 145 €
Breakfast: 9,5 €
Menu(s): 30 € - **1/2 board:** 70 € / 85 €

Open all year
reservation only between
01/10 and 31/03
equipments
telephone, T.V.
environment
architecture 17/19e, park,
terrace 120 m²
leisure, relaxation
tennis 6 km, golf course
25 km, horse-riding 8 km

For romantic souls who want to rediscover the charm and warmth of a large family home of yesterday, welcome to this former abbey 30 minutes from La Rochelle. Set out on foot or on horseback to discover the fabulous fauna and flora of this region. An oasis of well-being.

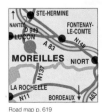

Road map p. 619
A83 exit 7 (10 mn)

 La Rochelle: 35 km

Chemin Marcel Provence
04360 Moustiers-Sainte-Marie
Tel.: 33 (0) 4.92.74.67.67 – Fax: 33 (0) 4.92.74.65.72
bouscatiere@chateauxhotels.com
Tonia PEYROT
5 rooms: 115 € / 175 €
Breakfast: 12 €

In the heart of the charming village of Moustiers Sainte-Marie this XVIIIth century house, clinging to the cliffside, offers a rare setting with a complete change of scenery. The hanging shaded garden of linden trees, the lounge-kitchen and the five rooms of astonishing freshness will quickly entice seduction.

Visa ● MASTER CARD

Road map p. 619

Motorway A8 (from Nice): exit Draguignan

hotel annual closing
01/01 > 22/02 ● 04/11 > 20/12

equipments
internet, T.V.

environment
architecture 18ᵉ, furniture 19ᵉ, garden, view

leisure, relaxation
tennis 4 km, horse-riding 2 km, swimming 3 km, climbing 10 km , paragliding 10 km

Marseille Provence: 80 km

Château Plessis Brézot

Nantes **I** Monnières

www.chateaushotels.com/plessisbrezot **I** reservation service: 33 (0) 1.40.07.00.20

44690 Monnières
Tel.: 33 (0) 2.40.54.63.24 – Fax: 33 (0) 2.40.54.66.07
plessisbrezot@chateaushotels.com
Annick CALONNE
5 rooms: 74 € / 104 €

Open all year
on request from 01/11 > 31/03

environment
architecture 16e, park 3 ha,
view, total calm

leisure, relaxation
covered pool, golf course
15 km, horse-riding 10 km

Tradition, modernity, skill - the motto of this magnificent 16th century house. Attractive rooms, wooded grounds and indoor pool all add to the atmosphere of serenity. The wine produced on the estate has repeatedly won distinctions in wine guides. Several restaurants nearby.

Road map p. 619

To Nantes N249 dir.Poitiers, then
N149 exit Le Pallet, then D7 dir.Monnières

Nantes: 18 km

château de Villemenant 58130 Guérigny
Tel.: 33 (0) 3.86.90.93.10 – Fax: 33 (0) 3.86.90.93.19
villemenant@chateauxhotels.com
David CHESNAIS
3 rooms: 74 € / 114 €
1 suite: 130 €
Breakfast: 9 €
Table d'hôtes (on request): 36 €

The beautiful Nivernais region is shelter for this gorgeous listed XIVth century château that couples all of the charm and nobleness of the past with modern comforts. The warm welcome of its hosts, the luxurious rooms and the excellent cuisine make this place a pause of quality where one feels good to stop (dog 8 €).

Open all year
equipments
telephone
environment
architecture 14e, park 3 ha, garden, view, total calm
leisure, relaxation
tennis 1.8 km, golf course 30 km, horse-riding 4 km, trails, car-racing 30 km, living room with piano

Road map p. 619

From Paris A6, A77 then N7 dir. Nevers. Exit Pougues-les-Eaux. D8 dir. Guérigny

Nevers: 20 km

Château de La Verrerie

Oizon **I** Aubigny-sur-Nère

www.chateauxhotels.com/verrerie | reservation service: 33 (0) 1.40.07.00.20

OIZON 18700 Aubigny-sur-Nère

Tel.: 33 (0) 2.48.81.51.60 – Fax: 33 (0) 2.48.58.21.25

verrerie@chateauxhotels.com

Comte Béraud de VOGÜE

11 rooms: 145 € / 395 €

1 suite: 297 €

Breakfast: 12 €

Menu(s): 17 € / 26 € - **Carte:** 35 €

1/2 board: 108 € / 217 €

hotel annual closing
01/01 > 30/01

restaurant annual closing
01/01 > 30/01

equipments
telephone, safe, baby-sitting

environment
architecture 16ᵉ, park 20 ha,
garden, terrace, view, total
calm

leisure, relaxation
golf course 30 km,
horse-riding, tennis, hiking,
biking

*A lovely Renaissance castle
nestled alongside a romantic
lake and surrounded by a
large forest, between the
Sancerre vineyards and the
Loire Valley castles, the Château offers large rooms filled
with antiques. Good menu selection in the authentic and
warm surroundings of a 17th
century cottage.*

Visa ● MASTER CARD

Road map p. 619

A6 dir. Lyon then A77 dir. Nevers exit
Gien - D940 dir. Gien/Bourges

 Orly: 152 km

79600 Saint-Loup-Lamaire
Tel.: 33 (0) 5.49.64.81.73 – Fax: 33 (0) 5.49.64.82.06
saintloup@chateauxhotels.com
Comte Charles-Henri de BARTILLAT

9 rooms: 130 € / 190 €
2 flats: 190 € / 230 €
Breakfast: 12,5 €
Table d'hôtes (sur rés.): 55 €

*One of France's finest castles
from Louis XIII's time, with its
listed gardens and 15th century tower keep. Everything
here is marked by a love of
beauty and authenticity. The
rooms are a harmonious
blend of past and present.
Fine table d'hôte. A wonderful
place for wedding.*

Open all year
equipments
baby-sitting
environment
architecture, park 50 ha,
garden, terrace 20 m², view,
total calm
leisure, relaxation
golf course 30 km, horse-riding
15 km, tennis 1 km,
swimming-pool 1 km,
windsurfing 1 km, nearby
Futuroscope and the Loire
Castels

Visa

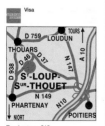

Road map p. 619

A10 exit 26 North of Châtellerault,
D725 dir. Airvault

Poitiers: 48 km

Le Prieuré Saint-Martial

Pézenas I Alignan-du-Vent

www.chateauxhotels.com/saintmartial I reservation service: 33 (0) 1.40.07.00.20

Saint-Martial 34290 Alignan-du-Vent
Tel.: 33 (0) 4.67.24.96.51 – Fax: 33 (0) 4.67.24.99.49
saintmartial@chateauxhotels.com
Véronique & Hubert de COLOMBE
8 flats: 125 € / 275 € - **8 suites:** 125 € / 275 €
Breakfast: 7,62 €

Open all year
equipments
telephone, T.V., baby-sitting
environment
architecture, park 3 ha,
garden, terrace 130 m², total
calm
leisure, relaxation
heated pool/covered, tennis
3 km, golf course 10 km,
horse-riding 4 km, sauna,
weekly packages

5 km from Pezenas, built on the site of a Roman villa (8th and 15th c. vestiges), this fine ensemble of 18th century houses offers the calm of wooded grounds, and spacious suites with garden or terrace. Here, where past and present are one, you are at home, prefectly independent. . A dream.

Visa ● **MASTER CARD**

Road map p. 619

A9 exit Agde-Pézenas, to Valros dir. Alignan

Béziers: 20 km

22400 Planguenoual
Tel.: 33 (0) 2.96.32.73.71 – Fax: 33 (0) 2.96.32.79.72
hazaie@chateauxhotels.com
Christine MARIVIN
4 rooms: 116 € / 183 €
1 flat: 183 € / 214 € - **1 suite:** 130 € / 145 €
Breakfast: 11 €

A 16th century residence with its own romantic park very close to beaches. Enormous, comfortable guestrooms, monumental granite fireplaces, family furniture, bathrooms with balneotherapy. Pleasant service, numerous activities nearby (golf, tennis, riding, sailing...) Ideal for exploring Brittany.

Open all year

equipments
telephone, internet, T.V., safe

environment
architecture 16e, park 3 ha, garden, terrace 80 m², vegetable garden, total calm, pond

leisure, relaxation
heated pool, tennis 4 km, golf course 9 km, horse-riding 4 km, balneo, jacuzzi, sea-fishing

Road map p. 619

N12 exit D81 Saint-René then dir. Le Val-André

Saint-Brieuc Armor: 20 km

Château du Launay

Ploerdut

www.chateauxhotels.com/launay | reservation service: 33 (0) 1.40.07.00.20

56160 Ploerdut
Tel.: 33 (0) 2.97.39.46.32 – Fax: 33 (0) 2.97.39.46.31
launay@chateauxhotels.com
Famille REDOLFI-STRIZZOT
10 rooms: 92 € / 115 €
Breakfast: 8 €
Menu(s): 23 € - **1/2 board:** 72 € / 83,5 €

hotel annual closing
01/01 > 28/03

equipments
telephone

environment
architecture 17ᵉ, park 20 ha, garden, vegetable garden, total calm

leisure, relaxation
heated pool, tennis 7 km, golf course 35 km, horse-riding 10 km, hammam, fitness center

Deep in the mysterious heartland of Brittany, Le Launay will enchant you with its charm and authenticity. An invigorating place to let the imagination roam, as you explore the land of the Druids, where the legends of Merlin and his ladylove still linger as though they lived only yesterday.

Visa ● MASTER CARD

Road map p. 619

N24 dir. Lorient, exit Pontivy

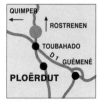

Lorient: 52 km

29710 Landudec
Tel.: 33 (0) 2.98.91.52.11 – Fax: 33 (0) 2.98.91.52.52
guilguiffin@chateauxhotels.com
Philippe DAVY
4 rooms: 115 € / 140 €
2 suites: 170 € / 200 €

Sumptuous XVIIIth century chateau in Brittany, classified historical monument. Rows of lounges level with the terrace. Elegant and very comfortable rooms. Endless walks in the lush forest. Near to historical sites of Quimper, Pont-Aven, Douarnenez. 10 minutes from beaches.

hotel annual closing
15/11 > 01/03: on reservation during that period.

equipments
safe

environment
architecture 18º, park 24 ha, garden, total calm

leisure, relaxation
tennis 15 km, golf course 25 km, horse-riding 15 km

Visa ● Diners ● MASTER CARD

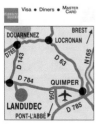

Road map p. 619

On D784 between Quimper and Audierne

 Quimper - Pluguffan: 10 km

Château de Garrevaques

Revel I Garrevaques

www.chateauxhotels.com/garrevaques I reservation service: 33 (0) 1.40.07.00.20

château de Garrevaques 81700 Garrevaques
Tel.: 33 (0) 5.63.75.04.54 – Fax: 33 (0) 5.63.70.26.44

garrevaques @ chateauxhotels.com
Marie-Christine COMBES
7 rooms: 115 € / 122 €
1 suite: 198 € / 214 €
1/2 board: 84 € / 92 €
Table d'hôtes (sur rés.): 28 € / 31 €

Open all year
equipments
baby-sitting

environment
architecture 19e, furniture 19e,
park 7 ha, garden, terrace
70 m², total calm

leisure, relaxation
golf course 20 km,
horse-riding, beauty salon,
balneo, gliding, microlight flying

A château restored in the XIXth century. XV generation will welcome you in the lounges with grisaille tapestries by Zuber. Billiards, flying club 800 metres away. Chauffeur and guide service. Theme holidays for groups of 8 people (minimum). On the menu, home made foie gras, regional products. Spanish and English spoken.

Visa ● Diners ● MASTER CARD

Road map p. 619

A61 exit Castelnaudary. A68 exit Verfeil-Castres

Toulouse/Carcassonne:
50 km

Chateau de Montgouverne 37210 Rochecorbon
Tel.: 33 (0) 2.47.52.84.59 – Fax: 33 (0) 2.47.52.84.61
montgouverne@chateauxhotels.com
Laurent GROSS
4 rooms: 95 € / 140 €
2 suites: 140 € / 170 €
Breakfast: 8 €

It is enough to get a glimpse of Montgouverne surrounded by the Vouvray vineyards to guess at a magic place. In this XVIIIth-century chateau, your hosts celebrate the pleasure of welcoming you. Charm, comfort, elegance plunge you into dreamland which you never want to leave.

Open all year
equipments
telephone, internet, T.V. Satellite
environment
architecture 18e, furniture 18e, garden, view
leisure, relaxation
heated pool, tennis 1 km, golf course 10 km, horse-riding 10 km

Visa ● Diners ● MASTER CARD

Road map p. 619

A10 exit 20 Tours-Ste-Radegonde or N152 dir. Vouvray

 Tours: 8 km

Château de Courtebotte

Saint-Emilion I Saint-Jean de Blaignac
www.chateauxhotels.com/courtebotte I reservation service: 33 (0) 1.40.07.00.20

33420 Saint-Jean de Blaignac
Tel.: 33 (0) 5.57.84.61.61 – Fax: 33 (0) 5.57.84.68.68
courtebotte@chateauxhotels.com
Michel MORTEYROL
4 rooms: 100 € / 180 €
2 suites: 180 €
1/2 board: 95 € / 135 €
Table d'hôtes (sur rés.): 45 €

Open all year
environment
park 6 ha, terrace 60 m², view,
total calm
leisure, relaxation
tennis 2 km, golf course
25 km, horse-riding 1 km

This splendid chateau built during the reign of Henry IV provides you with an unmatched view of the Dordogne. The castle's glory is reflected in the three impressive fireplaces of the period and in the rooms' stunning decor. Overlooking a river, this is a sumptuous and friendly place to stay.

Road map p. 619

From Libourne, dir. Bergerac, at Saint-Emilion, dir. La Réole (D670)

Sud Ouest I

 Bordeaux-Mérignac: 40 km

Route de Saint-Emilion 33330 Saint-Emilion
Tel.: 33 (0) 5.57.24.62.61 – Fax: 33 (0) 5.57.24.68.25
francmayne@chateauxhotels.com
Georgy FOURCROY
5 rooms: 138 € / 200 €
Breakfast: 10 €

The XVIth century Franc-Mayne château has a 17-acre vineyard, situated in the heart of the Saint-Emilion vintages. The fully restored interior consists of a ground floor featuring a great sitting room with a billiard room, a beautiful stone-walled dining room and a traditional kitchen with fireplace.

hotel annual closing
01/12 > 28/02
equipments
telephone
environment
architecture 16e, furniture 18e, park 7 ha, garden, view, total calm
leisure, relaxation
golf course 20 km, horse-riding 6 km, visits to wine cellars, wine-press and souterrains

Visa ● Diners ● MASTER CARD

Road map p. 619

A10 exit St-André de Cubzac-Libourne. N89 dir. Libourne

Bordeaux-Mérignac: 45 km

Château des Salles
Saint-Fort-sur-Gironde
www.chateauxhotels.com/dessalles | reservation service: 33 (0) 1.40.07.00.20

17240 Saint-Fort-sur-Gironde
Tel.: 33 (0) 5.46.49.95.10 – Fax: 33 (0) 5.46.49.02.81
dessalles@chateauxhotels.com
Sylvie COUILLAUD
5 rooms: 69 € / 100 €
Breakfast: 8,5 €
Menu(s): 28 € - **1/2 board:** 66,25 € / 73,75 €
Table d'hôtes (sur rés.): 28 €

hotel annual closing
30/09 > 01/04
equipments
telephone, T.V.
environment
architecture 15°, park 6 ha,
garden, vegetable garden
leisure, relaxation
tennis 1 km, golf course
30 km, thermal baths, beaches

Superb manor house in a charming clement setting in the heart of the Saintonge, in Pineau de Charentes and Cognac country. Cosy, family atmosphere, traditional fare, farm-fresh products. Near Bordelais, Médoc and Saint-Emilion vineyards, abundance of Romanesque art. German and English spoken.

Visa ● MASTER CARD

Road map p. 619

A10 exit 37 Mirambeau - D730
Bordeaux-Royan

Bordeaux: 80 km

Ouest Atlantique |

N560 83860 Nans-les-Pins
Tel.: 33 (0) 4.94.78.92.06 – Fax: 33 (0) 4.94.78.60.46
nans@chateauxhotels.com
M. & Mme. Johannes BAMBECK
5 rooms: 106,71 € / 137,20 €
3 suites: 152,45 € / 182,94 €
Menu(s): 35,06 € / 48,78 €
Breakfast: included

At the foot of the Sainte Baume hills, an elegant 19th century residence with an air of the south. Guests can relax and unwind in the cosy guestrooms, around the pool, in the grounds or on the terrace. The chef is proud of his kitchen garden and proposes inventive flavours of Provençal cuisine.

hotel annual closing
18/11 > 10/12
restaurant weekly closing
mon
01/04 > 31/08
mon, tue
01/09 > 31/03
equipments
telephone, T.V., safe, baby-sitting
environment
architecture 19e, park, garden, terrace 90 m², view
leisure, relaxation
golf course 1.5 km, horse-riding 5 km, jacuzzi

Visa • MASTER CARD

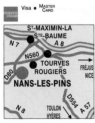

Road map p. 619

A8 "La Provençale" exit St-Maximin-la-Ste-Beaume, N560 dir. Auriol

Marignane: 43 km

Le Mas des Figues

Saint-Rémy-de-Provence

www.chateauxhotels.com/masfigues | reservation service: 33 (0) 1.40.07.00.20

Chemin d'Arles 13210 Saint-Rémy-de-Provence
Tel.: 33 (0) 4.32.60.00.98 – Fax: 33 (0) 4.75.60.85.21
masfigues@chateauxhotels.com
Philippe MICHELOT
6 rooms: 100 € / 200 €
Breakfast: 16 €
Table d'hôtes (sur rés.): 26 € / 30 €

hotel annual closing
01/11 > 31/03
restaurant annual closing
01/11 > 31/03
restaurant weekly closing
mon(lun), tue(lun), wen(lun),
thi(lun), fri(lun), sat(lun), sun(lun)
01/04 > 31/10
equipments
internet, T.V., minibar, safe
environment
architecture 17°, furniture 19°,
park 3 ha, terrace, view, total
calm, oliveraie

leisure, relaxation
heated pool, tennis 5 km, golf
course 10 km

*How could anyone not fall
under the spell of this ancient
Provencal country house
redolent with the scent of lavender! Home-made jams,
home-grown olive-oil, bees-
waxed furniture in bright spacious rooms painted in
Provencal hues, a terrace
shaded by a plane tree, a sing-
ing fountain: the South!*

Road map p. 619

5km west St-Rémy-de-Provence by
D99 et D27

Marseille: 60 km

Château de Crazannes

Saintes ı Crazannes

www.chateauxhotels.com/crazannes ı reservation service: 33 (0) 1.40.07.00.20

17350 Crazannes

Tel.: 33 (0) 6.80.65.40.96 – Fax: 33 (0) 5.46.91.34.46
crazannes@chateauxhotels.com
Hervé de ROCHEFORT
6 rooms: 75 € / 190 €
2 suites: 125 € / 200 €
Breakfast: 9 €

Near Cognac, 15th c. château listed as a historical monument, adorned with a fine Gothic facade. In the grounds, the Romanesque chapel, tower and water-filled moat mirror the comfort of the antique style guestrooms. The château, tower and inn can be rented by the week, service included.

hotel annual closing
15/11 > 01/04

environment
architecture 15°, furniture 18°, park 8 ha, garden, terrace 50 m², view, total calm

leisure, relaxation
heated pool, tennis 5 km, golf course 12 km, horse-riding 6 km, thalassotherapy, thermal baths

Visa ● Diners

Road map p. 619

460 km south west from Paris A10 exit N° 35, Saintes Centre, then N137 dir. Rochefort

Bordeaux: 120 km

Château de la Crée
Santenay-en-Bourgogne
www.chateauxhotels.com/cree | reservation service: 33 (0) 1.40.07.00.20

Les Hauts-de-Santenay
21590 Santenay-en-Bourgogne
Tel.: 33 (0) 3.80.20.62.66 – Fax: 33 (0) 3.80.20.66.50

cree@chateauxhotels.com
Rolande & Yves-Eric REMY-THEVENIN

4 rooms: 130 € / 184 €
1 suite: 250 € / 290 €
Breakfast: 11 €
Menu(s): 55,00 € / 120,00 €
1/2 board: 120 € / 180 €

Open all year

equipments
telephone, internet, T.V.,
baby-sitting, 2 bars

environment
architecture 18e, furniture 18e,
park 3.5 ha, garden, terrace
600 m², view, total calm

leisure, relaxation
golf course 15 km, horse-riding
1 km, thalassotherapy, balneo,
thermal baths, tennis, bicycle
hire at the hotel, hiking

*Near the Hospices de
Beaune, all the elegance of an
18th century manor renovated
for the delight of the eye and
the palate. Prestigious rooms,
splendid library, fascinating
memorabilia and fine local cuisine. Prestigious wines from
the estate, matured in the
beautiful old cellars.*

Visa ● Master Card

Road map p. 619

A6 exit Beaune south or Beaune north
, N74/N6 dir.Chagny then Santenay

Lyon/St-Exupèry: 100 km

Le Clos des Tourelles

Châlons-sur-Saône I Sennecey-le-Grand

www.chateauxhotels.com/tourelles I reservation service: 33 (0) 1.40.07.00.20

Château de la Tour 71240 Sennecey-le-Grand
Tel.: 33 (0) 3.85.44.83.95 – Fax: 33 (0) 3.85.44.90.18
tourelles@chateauxhotels.com
Christine ROUCHER – Laurence DERUDDER
6 rooms: 70 € / 100 €
1 flat: 140 € - **2 suites:** 145 €
Table d'hôtes (sur rés.): 23 €

In the grounds of a beautiful park, this chateau stunningly combines the 11th and 19th centuries. Enter a fairytale world of elegant, luminous rooms, delicious cuisine and fine house wines. A charming spot from which to discover Burgundy.

hotel annual closing
15/11 > 15/03
restaurant annual closing
15/11 > 15/03
equipments
telephone, internet, T.V., safe
environment
architecture 19e, park 17 ha, terrace

Visa ● MASTER CARD

Road map p. 619

A6 exit Tournus, dir. Châlons-sur-Saône 7 km

Satolas: 120 km

| Bourgogne Franche-Comté

Château de l'Aubrière

Tours I La Membrolle-sur-Choisille

www.chateauxhotels.com/aubriere I reservation service: 33 (0) 1.40.07.00.20

Route de Fondettes
37390 La Membrolle-sur-Choisille
Tel.: 33 (0) 2.47.51.50.35 – Fax: 33 (0) 2.47.51.34.69

aubriere@chateauxhotels.com
Comtesse Violaine de LUSSAC

9 rooms: 70 € / 120 €
4 suites: 135 € / 185 €
Breakfast: 9,15 €
Table d'hôtes (sur rés.): 38.15 €

hotel annual closing
01/01 > 28/03 • 30/09 > 28/02

equipments
telephone, T.V., minibar, safe

environment
architecture 19e, park 15 ha,
garden, view

leisure, relaxation
heated pool, tennis 0.1 km,
golf course 7 km, horse-riding
10 km, sauna, jacuzzi

*10 mm from old Tours, in a
38-acre park, a small 19th century Touraine chateau overlooking the Choisille valley.
Blue suite with a canopied
bed, 2 suites in the tower with
sky bed. Room with sauna,
water-jet bath, reception
rooms for seminars, wed-
dings, etc.*

Visa ● MASTER CARD

Road map p. 619

A10 exit Tours North, N138 dir. Le
Mans-Laval

Tours: 5 km

Rue du Château 30700 Saint-Maximin

Tel.: 33 (0) 4.66.03.44.16 – Fax: 33 (0) 4.66.03.42.98

saintmaximin@chateauxhotels.com

Jean-Marc PERRY

2 rooms: 95 € / 160 €
3 suites: 125 € / 265 €
Menu(s): 39 €

In the heart of French Toscany, near Uzès, this sumptuous house defies time. The XIIth century tower and XVIIth century arched roof offer shelter to the visitor, behind the warmth of golden stones and modern-day comfort. The olive trees are century-old and the beautiful jars come from Anduze. Superb.

Visa ● MASTER CARD

hotel annual closing
01/02 > 28/02

restaurant annual closing
01/02 > 28/02

restaurant weekly closing
mon, tue, wen(lun), thi(lun), fri(lun), sat(lun), sun(lun)
01/04 > 31/10
mon, tue, wen, thi, fri(lun), sat(lun), sun
01/11 > 28/02

equipments
safe

environment
architecture 17e, garden, terrace 30 m², view, total calm

leisure, relaxation
heated pool, golf course 2 km, horse-riding 5 km, hammam, fitness

Road map p. 619

A9 exit Avignon-Remoulins. D981 dir. Uzès

✈ Nîmes-Garons: 50 km

┃ Midi

🅿 〰

Château de Busset
Vichy I Busset
www.chateauxhotels.com/busset I reservation service: 33 (0) 1.40.07.00.20

Le Bourg 03270 Busset
Tel.: 33 (0) 4.70.59.13.97 – Fax: 33 (0) 4.70.59.29.78
busset@chateauxhotels.com
Beat Martin DUTLI
9 rooms: 73,18 € / 134,16 €
Breakfast: 9,15 €

Open all year
environment
architecture 10ᵉ, park 7 ha,
garden, terrace 60 m², view,
total calm

leisure, relaxation
tennis 0.5 km, golf course
12 km, horse-riding 4 km

A gracious welcome awaits you at this splendid listed castle, a masterpiece of Medieval and Renaissance architecture, surrounded by French and Italian gardens. Royal rooms, including one where king-to-be Henry IV stayed. Life in a castle, just as you would dream of it.

Road map p. 619

A72 exit Gannat or A71 exit Thiers ,
D906 dir. Thiers/Vichy

 Clermont-Ferrand: 40 km

Château de Jallanges

Vouvray

www.chateauxhotels.com/jallanges | reservation service: 33 (0) 1.40.07.00.20

Vernou-sur-Brenne 37210 Vouvray
Tel.: 33 (0) 2.47.52.06.66 – Fax: 33 (0) 2.47.52.11.18
jallanges@chateauxhotels.com
Stéphane FERRY-BALIN
5 rooms: 110 € / 255 €
2 flats: 150 € / 270 € - **2 suites:** 135 € / 215 €
Breakfast: 9,15 €
Menu(s): 45,73 €
Table d'hôtes (sur rés.): 45.73 €

A 15th c. classified monument in the Loire Valley, set in an 86-acre Renaissance-style park, bears witness to centuries of beautiful architecture and gracious living French-style. Live the castle life, from the splendidly furnished drawing-rooms to the exquisite guestrooms looking out over the centenary trees.

Visa • MASTER CARD

Open all year

equipments
internet, T.V., minibar, baby-sitting

environment
architecture 15^e, park 20 ha, garden, terrace, view, total calm

leisure, relaxation
heated pool, tennis 3 km, golf course 10 km, horse-riding 10 km

Road map p. 619

A10 exit Vouvray N° 20, N152 dir. Vouvray-Vernou

Tours Nord: 10 km

| Centre Maine Val-de-Loire

Carte routière
Plan de découpage

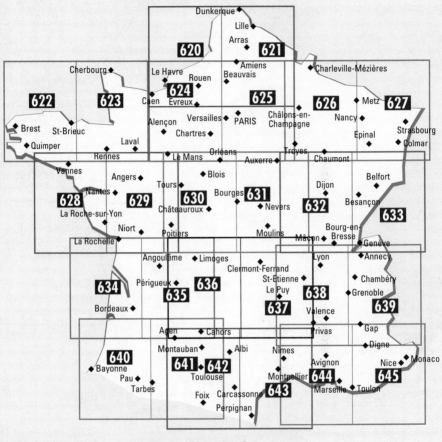

Echelle de la carte

0   10   20   30   40 km.

Blay Foldex
1200221775

Cartes - Plans - Guides
40 - 48, rue des Meuniers
93108 MONTREUIL CEDEX (FRANCE)
Tél.: 01 49 88 92 10 - Fax : 01 49 88 92 09
w w w . b l a y f o l d e x . c o m

Malgré tout le soin apporté à la réalisation de cette carte, nous devons décliner
toute responsabilité à la suite de modification ou d'imperfection.

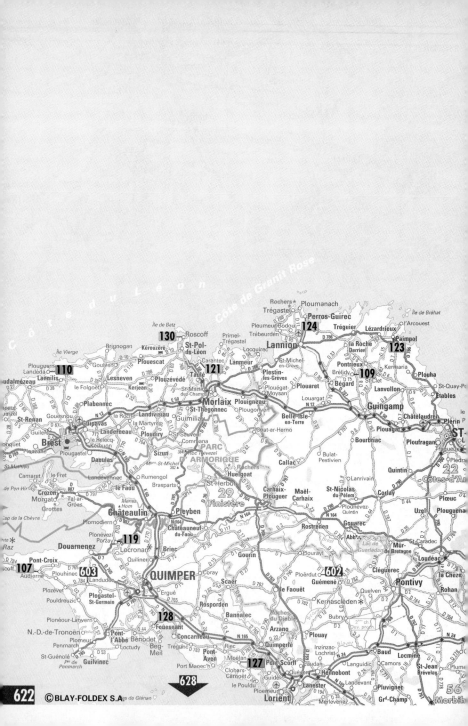

©BLAY-FOLDEX S.A

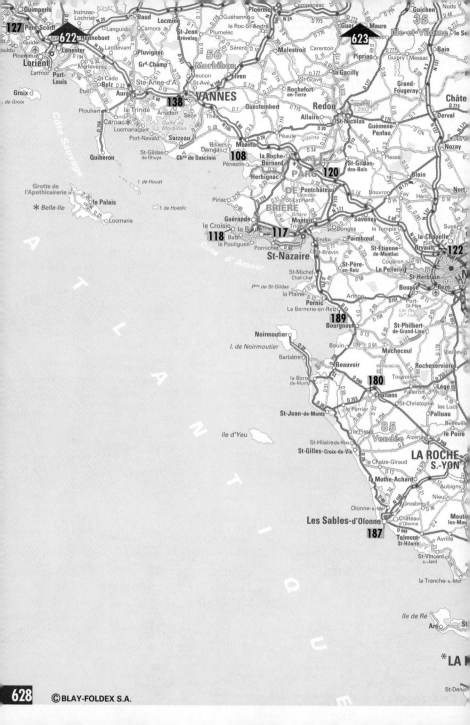

©BLAY-FOLDEX S.A.

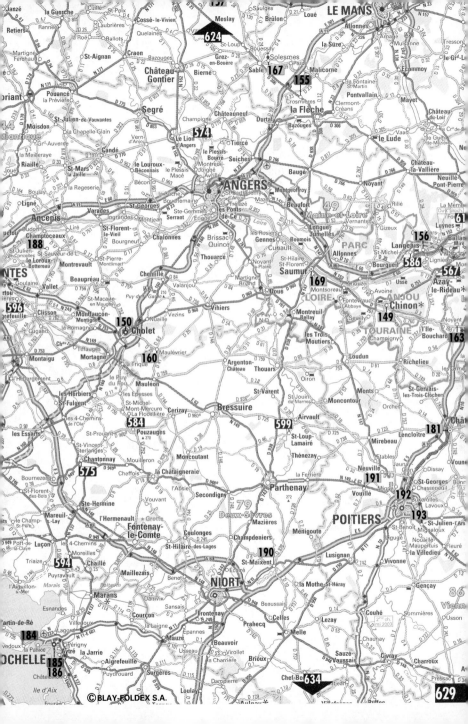

© BLAY-FOLDEX S.A.

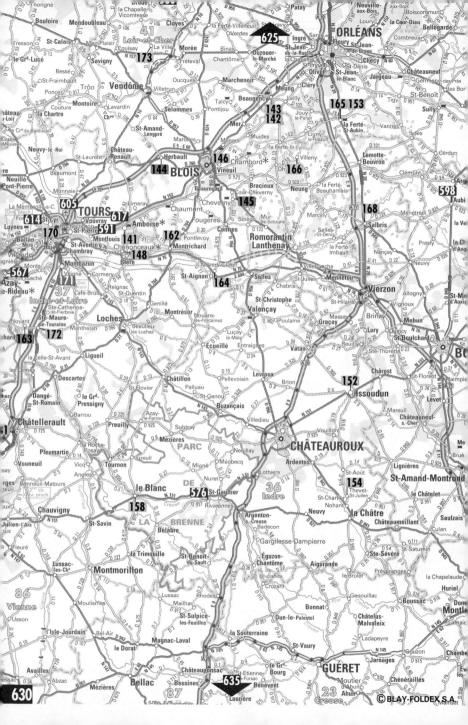

634 ©BLAY-FOLDEX S.A.

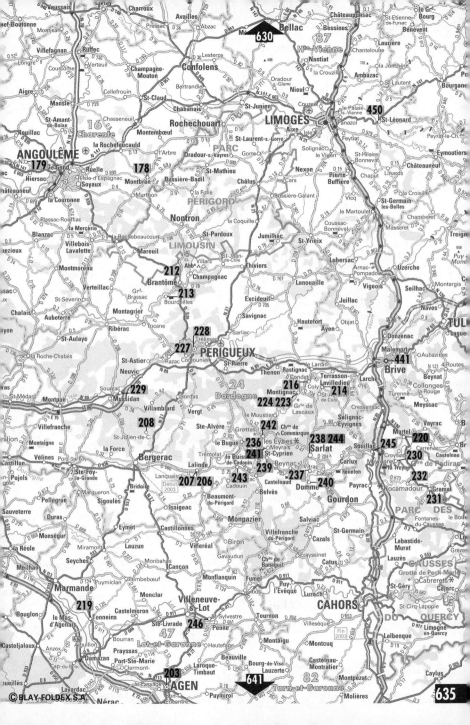

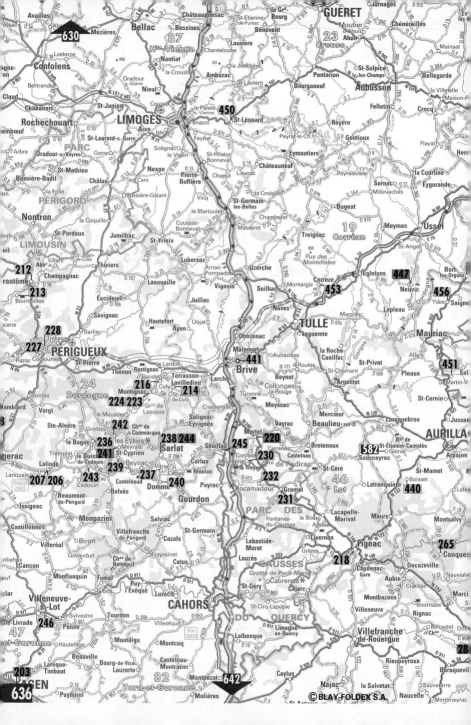

M É D I T E

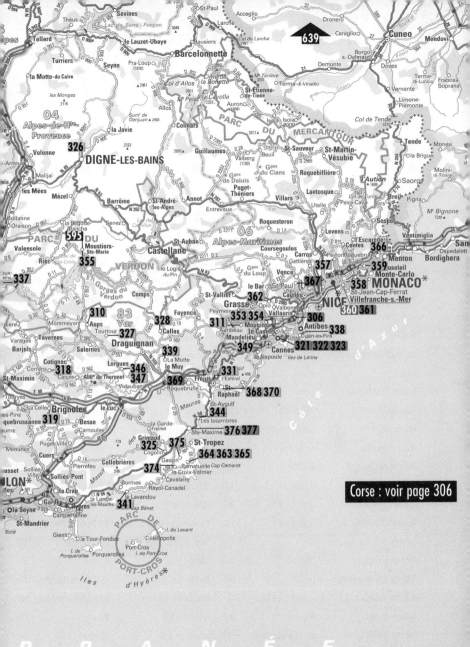

Corse : voir page 306

NB : only restaurant

NB : only restaurant

NB : only restaurant

NB : only restaurant

NB : only restaurant

Travel around Europe with the partners of Châteaux & Hôtels de France

The European Federation of Historic Lodgings brings together twelve European hotel chains whose establishments form part of their countries' historic and architectural heritage.

You can now travel in Europe and be certain to enjoy the same high standards in 9 countries: Austria, France, Great Britain, Ireland, Italy, Norway, Portugal, Spain and Sweden. A guide to the European Federation of Historic Lodgings and to each of its member chains is available from the head office of Châteaux & Hôtels de France

HOSTERIAS REALES

Set off on a discovery to places filled with history. Choose from 5 hotel-style establishments including 2 former monasteries – an excellent way to discover Spain.

HOSTERIAS/HOSPEDERIAS REALES
HOSPEDERIA REAL EL BUSCON DE QUEVEDO
C/Frailes, 1 - 13320 Vva. De Los infantes
(Ciudad Real)
Tel : 0034 92 63 61 788 - Fax : 0034 92 63 61 797
www.paralelo40.org/buscon
buscon@paralelo40.org

Châteaux & Hôtels de France

Chateaux, abbeys, manors, former mills... The 532 Châteaux & Hôtels de France are part of the cultural and architectural heritage which reflect the historic traditions of France and her regions.

Châteaux & Hôtels de France
12, rue Auber - 75009 Paris
Tél : 33 1 40 07 00 20 - Fax : 33 1 40 07 00 30
www.chateauxhotels.com
resa@chateauxhotels.com

SCHLOSSHOTELS HERRENHÄUSER

Faithful to the Austrian reputation for cultural diversity, these 36 private establishments which make up this association, each express a particular lifestyle and heritage from their prestigious past.

Schlosshotels & Herrenhäuser
A-5020 Salzburg, Moosstrasse 60
Call number and toll free:
+43/662/83 06 81 41
fax: +43/662/83 06 81 61
E.mail: office@schlosshotels.co.at
www.schlosshotels.co.at

ESTANCIAS DE ESPANA

This organisation brings together 51 establishements which were previously monasteries, palaces, chateaux or mills. They offer places of character for your stay in Spain.

ESTANCIAS DE ESPAÑA
MENÉNDEZ PIDAL, 31
28036 MADRID
Phone: 34 91 345 4141 - Fax: 34 91 345 5174
E-mail: info@estancias.com
web: www.estancias.com

PRIDE OF BRITAIN HOTELS

38 manors, chateaux and master's residence have been brought together to form the heart of this private association. They represent the pride of Great Britain and are there to help you discover this country which has always cultivated its variety.

IRELAND'S BLUE BOOK

An exclusive listing of 38 Irland's finest owner run Country manor Houses, Castles and Restaurants with accommodation. For the discerning traveller to the Emerald Isle..

PRIDE OF BRITAIN HOTELS
Cowage Farm/Foxley
Wiltshire
SN16 0JH
England

Reservations (from Europe):
+44 870 609 3012
(from USA): 1-800 98 PRIDE
web: www.prideofbritainhotels.com
e-mail: info@prideofbritainhotels.com

IRELAND'S BLUE BOOK
Ardbraccan Glebe Navan Co. Meath
Ireland
Tel: +353 (0)46-23416 - Fax: +353 (0)46-233292
www.irelandsbluebook.com
E mail: mail@irelandsbluebook.com

ABITARE LA STORIA

All across Italy, whether in the country or the city, you can revel in the luxury of these sumptuous residences converted into hotels and restaurants.

HOTE IS HERITAGE LISBOA

The 3 former palaces of Heritage are living witnesses of Lisbon's history and culture. Family tradition and tasteful surroundings give an incomparable insight into the city and the spirit of Portugal.

Abitare La Storia
Via V. Veneto, 183
00187 Roma - ITALIE
Téléphone: +39 06-42 01 21 38 -Fax: +39 06-42 02 79 80
www.abitarelastoria.it
e-mail: mailbox@abitarelastoria.it

HOTEIS HERITAGE LISBOA
Tv.Salitre, 5 - 1269-066 Lisboa - Portuga
Tel: + 351 213 218 200
Fax: +351 213 471 630
heritage.hotels@heritage.pt
www.heritage.pt

POUSADAS DE PORTUGAL

Created in the 1940s, the Pousadas are former regional stopover points for travellers, descended from those used in the Middle Ages. They are currently 44 Pousadas which all constitute an important part of the Portuguese national heritage.

POUSADAS DE PORTUGAL
Avenida Sta. Joana Princesa, 10
1749-090 Lisboa
Tel: 0035 1 21 844 2001
Fax: 0035 1 21 844 2085
www.pousadas.pt
guest@pousadas.pt

COUNTRYSIDE HOTELS

A warm Swedish welcome awaits you in 35 prestigious châteaux, manor houses and inns, many featuring top-ranking gourmet restaurants.

Box 69, SE- 830 13 Åre, Sweden
+46- 647 - 506 80
+46- 647- 519 20
info@countrysidehotels.se
www.countrysidehotels.se

DE HISTORISKE HOTEL

The Historical Hotels in Scandinavia comprises 32 well-run and long established hotels and restaurants built between 1380 and 1939, all of which have their own character and style. This is a unique opportunity for visitors to experience the beauty of Norwegian nature with its extreme contrasts, combined with a stay at a hotel steeped in tradition.
The Historical Hotels, winner of the Norwegian Tourist Boards "Best taste of Norway" 2001 award.

De Historiske Hotel

De Historiske Hotel
P.O.Box 1940 Nordnes
N-5817 Bergen
Norway
Office : Strandgaten 223
Phone : + 47 5531 6760 - Fax : + 47 5531 9105
E-mail : dhhlise@bbe.no / dhh@atm.no
www.dhhscandinavia.com

WELSH RAREBITS

Visit the Welsh country in the Welsh rarebits way. The unique selection of 43 hotels chosen for their caracter and charming service. You will have choice between farmhouse hotels or cosy country hideaways.

WELSH RAREBITS

Welsh Rarebits
Princes Square
Montgomery Powys
Wales. U.K.
SY15 6PZ
Tel: +44 1686 668030 - Fax: +44 1686 668029
e-mail: info@rarebits.co.uk
website: www.welsh.rarebits.co.uk

Where to find the guide ?

The guide is available free of charge.
* At each of the 532 establishments in the chain
* At the head office of Châteaux & Hôtels de France: 12 rue Auber, 75009 Paris, France
* At French tourist offices (Maison de la France) around the world
* At the Paris Tourist Office, avenue des Champs-Elysées, and at over 250 tourist offices in French towns and cities

Guide 2002 Châteaux & Hôtels de France

Guide edited by **Vega Gestion** SIRET 38225685700055 12, rue Auber 75009 Paris - 630000 copies published in France by **Maury Imprimeur SA.** Graphic design **Studio 421®**. Road maps and town guides printed by **Studio 421®**. Unauthorised copying prohibited. All rights reserved.

ISSN 1255-6157, **ISBN** 2-95120-399-3

This guide describes our distinguished collection of chateaux and residences. The owners of each property remain solely responsible for the services and information provided. The rates quoted in this quoted in this guide were correct at the time of going to press and are subject to change without notice.

24 rue Feydeau 75002 Paris

PHOTOS TAKEN BY

Adhoc (150) ; Agence Maltier (192) ; Agnès Rodier / Stéphane de Bourgies (155) ; Alain Gouillardon (163) ; Alain Hochet (449) ; Argaud (613) ; Atoll Photographie - Mr Iltis (525) ; Auber (596) ; Bernard Charlon (185) ; Bielsa (61) ; C. Legay / C.D.T. Moselle (517) ; Caroline De Otero (221) ; Christian Vallee (108, 167) ; Christophe Ena (590) ; Concept Image (79) ; Davault (164) ; Deroude (469) ; Didier Morel (82) ; Didier Villain (49) ; Diwezha et B. Le Glatin (127) ; Eliophot (45, 88, 107, 112, 115, 131, 172, 173, 487, 508, 514, 516, 518, 519, 520, 528, 530, 181, 190, 204, 223, 422, 423, 424, 425, 446; 451, 470) ; Etienne Hemermann (427) ; Eurociel / Gérard Corret (483) ; F. Burlot (467) ; Frédéric Durout (504) ; Frédéric Baucereau / Joël Demase (577) ; G Bligny (612) ; Gérard Glomeau (474, 491) ; Guillaume de Laubier (229) ; Henri Gaud (598) ; Hubert Taillard – GPO (121) ; Irène Soissons (582) ; J. P. Barrat (218) ; J. Tiercin (550) ; J.M. Garredard (421) ; J.P. Marty (586) ; Jack Photo (206) ; Jac'Phot (220, 224, 230) ; Jacques Bourboulon (50) ; Jean Claude Marlaud (117) ; Jean-Claude Amiel (59) ; Jean-Jacques Humphrey /Vichy Tourisme Promotion (616) ; Jérôme Mondière (457) ; Josiane Piffaut (472) ; L. Rouland / Jac'Phot (238) ; L. Rouland / P. Vandaele (236) ; Lavielle (233) ; Marie Peterson (134) ; Michel Bozzani (597) ; Michel Jolyot (552) ; Michel Ogier / J.F. Leroux (111) ; Mr Bernuy (471) ; Mr Berny (480) ; Mr Gondrand (450) ; Mr Haltier (191) ; Mr Prouzeau (594) ; Mr Quefelou (109) ; Mr Souchard / Mr Weiss (197) ; ONO-EPS / ROY / Studio Photos du Lys (540) ; Pascal Muradian (489) ; Patrick Bertrand (182) ; Philippe Mazère (194) ; Photo Bayle (442) ; Photo Caribou (579) ; Photo Passion Fontainebleau (68) ; Photos Ancel (523) ; Pierre Jacquemin (589) ; Publiphil / Busch (137) ; Quadrin et Juan (179) ; Sam Bellet (549) ; Société Archant (119) ; Société Infra (527) ; Stéphane Ferry-Balin (617) ; Studio Laroque (81) ; Vincent Bourdon (44) ; Marie Claire Copyright/Marie-Pierre Morel (77)/Armanet alexis (247)/Alexandre Bailache (175) ; Photononstop/Daniel Thierry (65) ; Photononstop/Serge Deschamp (389) ; Gettyimages/Stone/Patrick Ingrand (39) ; Gettyimages/Stone/David Eperson (301) ; Gettyimages/Stone/Bruno de Hoghues(381) ; Gettyimages/Stone(139,459, 25, 27, 33 et 37)) ; zefa visuelmédia (29) ; phovoir (105, 199, 437, 499 et 533).

Stamp of the establishment offering this guide